Al-Junūn:
Mental Illness in the Islamic World

Al-Junūn:
Mental Illness in the Islamic World

Edited by

Ihsan Al-Issa

INTERNATIONAL UNIVERSITIES PRESS, INC.
Madison   Connecticut

Library of Congress Cataloging-in-Publication Data

Al-Junun : mental illness in the Islamic world / edited by Ihsan Al
-Issa.
    p.   cm.
    Includes bibliographical references and index.
    ISBN 0-8236-3337-3
    1. Psychiatry—Islamic countries.   2. Mental illness—Islamic
countries.   3. Muslims—Mental health.   I. Al-Issa, Ihsan.
RC451.I74J86   1999
362.2′0917′671—dc21   99-41683
                         CIP

Manufactured in the United States of America

In memory of my father Abdulla Ibin Issa Ibin Ali Ibin Sha'ban Ibin Abdulla Ibin Ahmad Al-Sūbaie who symbolized for me the Islamic humanitarian ideals and the search for knowledge.

Table of Contents

Contributors

Tayseer Ahmad, Ph.D., is a clinical psychologist in the department of psychiatry, King Hussain Medical Center, Amman, Jordan. He is a consulting editor of the *Arab Journal of Psychiatry*.

Jawahir Al-Abdul-Jabbar, Ph.D., is a clinical psychologist at the department of neurosciences, King Faisal Specialist Hospital and Research Center, Riyadh, Saudi Arabia. Her major research interests are in psychotherapy in the Arab culture and gender roles in Saudi Arabia.

M. Alhamad Abdulrazzak, M. Med. Psych., BS Psych, J. B. Psych., is an assistant professor at the College of Medicine, King Saud University, and consultant psychiatrist at King Khalid University Hospital. His current research is in the areas of liaison referral to psychiatry, validation of a menstrual symptom questionnaire, the treatment of depression, and a Risperdal multicenter drug trial study.

Ihsan Al-Issa, Ph.D., F. B. Psych. S., is the General Secretary of the International Arab Psychological Association. His present research interest is in the indigenization of Arab psychology and the study of the concept of the self in Arab Islamic communities.

Mona Al-Sawaf, M.D., is the chief of psychiatry at King Fahad Hospital, Jedda, Saudi Arabia. Her major interest is in media psychiatry and medical education. She is a member of the WHO Multicenter International Team for the Study of Postnatal Psychiatric Disorder.

Abdullah Sultan Al-Subaie, MD, FRCP (C), is an associate professor of psychiatry, College of Medicine, King Saud University and the chairperson of the Saudi Board in Psychiatry. His current research is in the areas of the epidemiology of eating disorders and childhood disorders, nicotine dependence and its relationship to anxiety and depression, ECT practices, and the effects of psychiatric treatments in Saudi Arabia.

Mohammad-K. Atef-Vahid, Ph.D., is an assistant professor of clinical psychology, a member of the Scientific Board of Iran University of Medical Sciences, and a consultant editor of *Andeesh-Va Raftar,* the Iranian Journal for Psychiatry and Clinical Psychology.

M. Zain Azhar, M.D., M.Psych. Med., is an associate professor of psychiatry and consultant psychotherapist at the University of Science Hospital, Malaysia. He is the president of Malaysian Psychological Medical Association and editorial member of the *Malaysia Journal of Medical Sciences,* the *Malaysian Journal of Psychiatry,* and *Malaysian Psychiatry.* His current research is concerned with the application of Islamic cognitive therapy to anxiety and psychotic patients.

Seyed Akbar Bayanzadeh, Ph.D., is an assistant professor and on the editorial board of *Andeesh-Va-Raftar.* He is a member of the scientific board of Iran University of Medical Sciences and acting director of Tehran Psychiatric Institute.

Jafar Bolhari, M.D., is an associate professor and director of the Tehran Psychiatric Institute and the WHO Mental Health Collaborative Center. He is a member of the scientific board of Iran University Medical Sciences and Health Services and the editor-in-chief of *Andeesh-Va-Raftar.*

Kutaiba Chaleby, M.D., was formerly Head of Section of Psychiatry, Department of Neurosciences, King Faisal Specialist Hospital and Research Center, Riyadh, Saudi Arabia. He is now at Sci-Waymart Forensic Treatment Center, Waymart, Pennsylvania. His major research interest is in Islamic Forensic Psychiatry and Psychotherapy in the Arab culture.

Mohamed Fakhr El-Islam, FRCP, FRC Psych., is emeritus professor of psychiatry at Cairo University and Secretary of the World Psychiatric Association, Section of Transcultural Psychiatry. His research covers a wide range of psychiatric problems including the transcultural application of social psychiatry to Arabian communities. In addition to his pioneering transcultural research, he was a major figure in the establishment of both the mental health services for the State of Qatar and the Department of Psychiatry at the University of Kuwait.

Fereydoon Mehrabi, M.D., is an associate professor of psychiatry and Head of the Department of Psychiatry at Iran University of Medical Sciences and Mental Health. He is a member of the scientific board of Iran University of Medical Sciences and Health Services, and a member of the editorial board of *Andeesh-Va-Raftar.*

Malik Hussain Mubbashar, MB, FRCP (LON), FRCP (EDIN), FRCP Psych. (LON), FCPS (Psych.) DPM, is professor and director of the Institute of Psychiatry and WHO Collaborating Center. He is also a National Coordinator of Mental Health Program for Pakistan and a member of WHO expert advisory panel for Mental Health and Substance Abuse.

Davoud Shahmohammadi, M.D., is an assistant professor of psychiatry and Head of the Research Department at Tehran Psychiatric Institute. He is a member of the Scientific Board of Medical Sciences and Health Services.

Adnan Y. Takriti, M.D., FRC Psych., DPM, is the editor-in-chief of the *Arab Journal of Psychiatry* which is published by the Arab Federation of Psychiatrists in Amman-Jordan. His major research interest is in anxiety disorders and behavior cognitive therapy.

Seyed-Ahmad Vaezi, M.D., is an associate professor of Psychiatry and director of the office of Islamic Studies of Mental Health at Tehran Psychiatric Institute. He is a member of the Scientific Board of Iranian University of Medical Sciences and Health Services and the director in chief of the Quarterly Journal of *Andeesh-Va-Raftar.*

S. L. Varma, M.B.B.S., M.D., is an associate professor of psychiatry at the University of Science Hospital, Malaysia. He is currently carrying out research in social and community psychiatry.

Preface

There are about 1 billion Muslims in the world including over 15 million living in the West. However, the study of mental illness in Islamic societies has rarely been taken seriously by Western scholars. During the colonial era, the study of Muslim culture was carried out by non-Muslims in order to satisfy their intellectual curiosity for the exotic rather than to understand the Muslim religion. Casual observations are often generalized to all Muslims. However, in recent years many Muslim scholars who studied in the West have carried out research on mental illness in Muslim countries and the present volume reports some of their achievements.

The first three chapters lay the groundwork for the remaining parts of the volume. Chapter 1 on religion and psychopathology deals with methodological and research issues investigated by mental health researchers mainly within the Judeo-Christian context. A growing area of Islamic psychiatry is expected to face many similar methodological and research problems. Another rich source of information for contemporary researchers in Muslim countries is the history of medieval Islamic psychiatry (chapter 2) whose concepts of mental illness are still prevalent among the majority of the Muslim population. Chapter 3 on Islamic forensic psychiatry discusses how Islam has dealt with the insane. Although Islamic law has its own unique conception of the person and of abnormal conduct, it seems to share many ideas with Western forensic psychiatry.

The second section of the volume deals with mental illness and the development of psychiatric services in seven Muslim countries. The last chapter in the second section reviews studies on anxiety disorders in Islamic societies. The authors are mainly first or second generation psychiatrists or psychologists brought up in an Islamic society but trained in Western countries, who follow the biomedical model in psychiatry; yet, their chapters reveal an awareness of the influence of cultural factors on psychopathology. Although Islam started in a nomadic tribal society, it has shown adaptability to accommodate people from different backgrounds. However, in each Muslim country there are unique forces that bring diversity under the banner of Islamic unifying beliefs. Thus, although the reader finds similarities among Islamic communities, generalization about Muslims from Algiers or Cairo to a village in Saudi Arabia is rather hazardous. Similarly, Muslims in the diaspora discussed in section III share many mental health problems with other Muslims. However, they also have to deal with problems of adaptation in a Western Christian society.

Although many chapters in the volume discuss treatment, section IV is entirely devoted to psychotherapy as well as to sexuality and the treatment of sexual dysfunction of Muslim patients. The processes and goals of psychotherapy for Muslims and the adaptation of Western techniques are of interest to professionals in Muslim countries as well as in Europe and North America. Finally, the epilogue is an overview and a discussion of research problems and findings about mental illness in Muslim societies. Even though Iran is represented in this volume, it is unfortunate that it was difficult to obtain information on the effects of war on many other Muslim countries such as Bosnia, Iraq, Lebanon, Kuwait and Palestine.

This volume raises the basic question of how to integrate the Qur'anic teaching and the Prophet model of tradition and behavior, which represent Islamic ideals, with the present rapid cultural change and Westernization. The traditional Muslim society whose principles are based on symmetry, balance, and stability, is now threatened by materialistic indulgence and sudden change, which are confusing and anxiety arousing. Not unlike Muslim populations, Islamic psychiatry is in search of its own identity and is attempting to assert itself in the face of Western intellectual domination. Psychiatric problems, regardless of the cultural context, have always mirrored the underlying stresses of society, and readers interested in the study of cultural diversity may find interesting cross-cultural contrasts: while phobia is associated with females in the West, it is more prevalent among males in some Muslim countries; the obsessive–compulsive symptoms of devout Muslims are related to religious rituals while Christian priests in the West are tortured by obsessive–compulsive blasphemous thoughts; sexual dysfunction of virgin Muslim women is related to a vicariously learned fear of penetration on the wedding night in contrast to the sexual anxieties of Western women as a result of actual traumatic sexual experience. This volume will provide the reader with many more fascinating illustrations and contrasts in transcultural psychiatry.

A little about the title of the volume: for most Muslims, *al-junūn* (being possessed by the *jinni* or spirit) *is* madness and the term *mental illness* is related to Western medicine and more often used in a professional context rather than during everyday life. *Al-junūn* also reflects popular attitudes of Muslim societies toward madness since the *majnūn* (the madman) is not only the hospitalized patient but also anyone (a son, a daughter, a brother, a sister, a friend or a coworker) who deviates from cultural norms or manifests unacceptable behavior. The label captures the meaning of the popular "wise fool" in Islamic societies discussed in chapter 2 as well as the madman in a mental institution. Although *al-junūn* brings a stigma with it, the broad use of the term as compared with "mental illness" reflects the tolerance of madness in the traditional Islamic societies.

Finally, the material presented in this volume on the relationship between psychopathology and religion in general or Muslim religion in particular reflects a broad interdisciplinary approach to psychopathology and should be of interest not only to researchers and practitioners in the area of mental health (psychiatry, psychology, and social work) but also to experts in other areas such as anthropology, history, religious studies, sociology and political science. It is hoped that in the multicultural global village, this volume will increase our knowledge and understanding of the Muslim religion and Muslims wherever they are.

I.

General Issues

1.

Religion and Psychopathology

Ihsan Al-Issa

Both physical and mental healing have been an integral part of religion throughout the history of humanity (Alexander and Selesnick, 1966). Until the beginning of the eighteenth century, medicine was dominated by theology and British physicians needed a bishop's license to practice. It was only by 1800 that the situation was reversed when doctors authorized the clergy to minister in the asylums (Foskett, 1996). Although religion is part of human culture, it has occupied a marginal position in the mainstream of modern psychiatry and clinical psychology. Religion is rarely referred to in recent textbooks of psychiatry, except in the context of religious delusions (Gelder, Gath, and Mayou, 1989). The relationship between religion and psychiatry or clinical psychology has been also controversial. Religion was equated with neuroses and irrationality by well-known figures such as Freud (1927) and Ellis (1980). Freud associated religious beliefs and practices with the repression of instincts, intrapsychic conflicts, and obsessional neurosis. Early in this century, James (1902) also noted that leaders of religious groups:

> [O]ften have led a discordant inner life, and had melancholy during a part of their career. They have . . . been liable to obsessions and fixed ideas; and frequently they have fallen into

3

trances, heard voices, seen visions, and presented all sorts of peculiarities which are ordinarily classed as pathological. Often, moreover, these pathological features in their career have helped to give them their religious authority and influence [p. 8].

In contrast, others have suggested that religion is positively related to mental health (Jung, 1938; Allport, 1950; Mowrer, 1960). This chapter reviews the studies which attempted to relate religion to psychological adjustment and mental illness. First, we deal with studies of religion and mental illness in general and the methodological problems associated with this research area. Second, we discuss research relating religion to anxiety, obsessive–compulsive disorder, depression, guilt and suicide, psychosis, and delinquency, criminality, and drug abuse. Finally, we describe specific techniques used in religious psychotherapy.

EARLY REVIEWS OF RELIGION AND PSYCHOPATHOLOGY

In the second half of the twentieth century several reviews have assessed the relationship between religion and psychopathology. Argyle and Beit-Hallahmi (1958) reported a positive relationship between formal religion and personal adjustment. Religion was found to play a role in the control of impulsive behavior such as suicide and alcohol consumption. The better mental health of the religious was attributed to the availability of social support, companionship, and the presence of a sense of identity and belonging. In a review by Sanua (1969), the evidence was inconsistent as "most studies show no relationship between religiousness and mental health, while others point out that the religious person may at times show greater anxiety and at times less anxiety" (p. 1206). He also found no evidence that religion serves to deter deviancy and social pathology: "the evidence regarding the relationship between social pathology and religion points out that the latter may not necessarily fulfill the function ascribed to it—namely, that of an integrating force in society and contributor to the mental health of the members of that society" (p. 1207). Dittes (1969) attributed to religion negative effects such as personal and intellectual inadequacy, hypersuggestibility, and the use of unadaptive defense mechanisms. Stark (1971) reported that research with psychiatric outpatients shows that they were more likely than "normals" to be of no religious affiliation and to view religion as unimportant, or less likely to belong to a church congregation. This supported his hypothesis "that mental illness and religious commitment are negatively related" (p. 169).

Later reviews emphasized methodological problems that might explain the inconsistent relationship between religiosity and mental health. Lea (1982) pointed out that the study samples tend to be drawn from students and religious individuals, with no control of demographic factors. Batson and Ventis (1982) demonstrated that the relationship between religion and mental health depends on the definition of mental health. Religion tends to have a positive effect on mental health when the latter is defined in psychiatric terms as the absence of illness. However, it is associated with negative mental health when it is defined according to humanistic criteria such as personal competence and control, and self acceptance or self-actualization. Bergin (1983) found in a meta-analysis of 24 studies from 1951 to 1979 that positive and negative results may be due to the different definitions of religion used. He concluded that "positive effects of some kinds of religiosity are being balanced by negative effects of other kinds, which yield unimpressive or ambiguous average effects" (p. 180). Gartner, Larson, and Allen (1991) found that the relationship between religion and 21 measures of mental health are mixed. "Soft" measures of mental health such as paper and pencil tests produce a negative relationship; while hard measures such as suicide rates, objective measures of drug and alcohol use, and rates of delinquency produce a positive relationship. Others found that behavioral measures of mental health tend to be more positively related to religion than intrapsychic measures of mental health (Bergin,

1983; Donahue, 1985). Moreover, measures of religious behavior and religious participation are more positively related to mental health than attitude scales (Gartner et al., 1991).

METHODOLOGICAL ISSUES

The Multidimensionality of Religion and Mental Health

Religion is a multidimensional concept that may be expressed in different ways. Definitions of religion used in research tend to emphasize certain aspects of religion such as the cognitive or ritualistic (Lenski, 1963), symbolic or motivational (Geertz, 1966), and existential aspects (Allport, 1950; Bellah, 1971). Because of the multidimensionality of religion, a broad concept of religion may not be useful unless it is operationally defined. Using a global concept of religion such as comparing Catholics with Protestants or Muslims with Christians completely ignores the multidimensional nature of religion. Similarly, religiosity may be measured in terms of the intensity of religious beliefs (the cognitive dimension) or frequency of church attendance and degree of participation in church-related activities (rituals) but ignores other dimensions. Church attendance is a poor measure of religiosity since people attend church for reasons other than religious ones such as socializing or conforming to social norms. Church attendance is also affected by health status and the ability to get to church. Thus, physical health should be controlled when church attendance and mental health are investigated. In his review of the literature on religion and mental health among the elderly, Koenig (1992) cited 21 studies showing that church attendance is related to lower symptom levels and better adjustment, happiness, and well-being. However, he noted that because there is a very strong relationship between good physical health and psychological well-being, church attendance may relate to well-being only because of its relationship with physical health (Levin and Markides, 1986). Church attendance may simply serve as an index of physical health and by itself has nothing to do with mental health. A follow-up study of 8 years revealed that chronically ill persons attended church less frequently (Comstock and Partridge, 1972). It should also be noted that the nature of some mental illnesses may reduce church attendance. For example, social phobics and agoraphobics may not go to church because of the nature of their disorder.

One of the most influential dimensions of religiosity is the intrinsic–extrinsic dimension of religion suggested by Allport and Ross (1967). Intrinsic religion is an end in itself in a person's life, whereas extrinsic religion is a means to reach certain worldly goals and adapt to social conventions. Batson and Ventis (1982) added another religious orientation dimension called "quest" which represents a mature type of religiosity that questions traditional orthodox religion. Allen and Spilka (1967) suggested "committed" and "consensual" forms of religion which are related to intrinsic and extrinsic religion respectively. Both committed and intrinsic religions are associated with better health. Intrinsic religiosity has been found to correlate negatively with depression (Watson, Morris, and Hood, 1988a,b, 1990), trait anxiety (Baker and Gorsuch, 1982), obsessive–compulsive symptoms (Dixon, Alexander, and Anderson, 1990), and drug use (P. L. Benson, 1992).

Age, Stress, and Religiosity

The age of subjects may affect the relationship between religiosity and psychopathology. Most studies used adolescents and college students in relating psychopathology to religion (Koenig, Ford, George, Blazer, and Meador, 1993). Since religious beliefs increase with age (Princeton Religious Research Center, 1985), the possibility is raised that people may turn to religion as a source of comfort when dealing with stresses of adulthood and later life. Older people, for example, are more vulnerable to certain life events (loss, poor health) and may turn to religion for comfort. That people may turn to religion during stress was demonstrated by Osarchuk and Tatz (1973). They experimentally induced death anxiety in subjects, monitoring their religious beliefs; as the fear intensified, belief in an afterlife likewise increased; that is, stress had increased religiosity.

The beneficial effects of religion may be masked by the tendency of people to turn to religion when they are under stress. In support of this view, a study by Koenig, George, Blazer, and Pritchett (1993) found that persons actively engaged in prayer or Bible study were those from lower-status economic and racial groups with significant stressors and few resources to turn to. The masking effect of stress on the benefits of religion may explain reported findings that private religious activities such as TV viewing, radio listening, prayer, and Bible reading tended to have either no beneficial effects or even adverse effects on mental health (Koenig, Ford, George et al., 1993).

Stark (1968) had shown that the frequency and importance of prayer increased with age, suggesting that as people get older, they turn to religion as a coping mechanism to deal with stressors. In a longitudinal study, Markides, Levin, and Ray (1987) found that a positive relationship between prayer and life satisfaction decreased over time among older subjects, suggesting an increase in prayer among elders in poorer physical or psychological health. Turning to religion and prayer in times of distress (religious coping) may reduce existing relationship between religion and mental health (i.e., distressed persons become more religious). However, the relationship between religiosity as measured by church attendance and well-being referred to in the last section (Koenig, 1992), tends to persist even when physical health was controlled (Idler, 1987; Koenig, Kvale, and Ferrel, 1988). Moreover, involvement in church-related activities is more likely to be associated with positive mental health and well-being than participation in social activities without religious orientation (Pihlbald and Adams, 1972; Edwards and Klemmack, 1973; Cutler, 1976).

Furthermore, psychopathology which is precipitated by stressors may interfere with the ability to experience and express religion. Stark (1971) compared a group of outpatients in a mental health clinic with controls on religious commitment. He found that nonreligion as measured by considering religion as not important at all or by other indices of religiosity, was significantly more prevalent among patients. It was concluded that comparing the mental health of the religious with those who are less religious or irreligious may amount to comparing people with varying degrees of psychological disturbance. Thus, the effects of psychological disturbance on religiosity should also be considered.

RELIGION AND MENTAL ILLNESS

Anxiety

In an early review by Sanua (1969), it was concluded that religiosity is inconsistently associated with anxiety. In more recent reviews (Gartner et al., 1991; Pressman, Lyons, Larson, and Gartner, 1992) the authors reached a similar conclusion showing that the evidence is inconsistent. In the Gartner et al. review four studies reported that anxiety is positively related to religion (Wilson and Miller, 1968; Spellman, Baskett, and Byrne, 1971; Hassan and Khalique, 1981; Gupta, 1983), three studies found negative relationship (Williams and Cole, 1968; Morris, 1982; Hertsgaard and Light, 1984), and three studies found no relationship (L. B. Brown, 1962; Heitzelman and Fehr, 1976; Epstein, Tamir, and Natan, 1985).

The review by Pressman et al. (1992) indicates that the relationship between religious commitment and anxiety reveals the same inconsistency. Six studies found a positive relationship (Young and Daniels, 1980; Richardson, Berman, and Piwowarski, 1983; Smith, Nehemkis, and Charter, 1983; Tobacyk, 1983; Aday, 1984–1985; Westman and Canter, 1985); three studies found negative relationship (Beg and Zilli, 1982; Florian, Kravetz, and Frankel, 1984; Dodd and Mills, 1985); and five studies found no relationship (Muchnik and Rosenheim, 1982; Mahabeer and Bhana, 1984; Rosenheim and Muchnik, 1984; Kunzendorff, 1985; Dahawn and Sripat, 1986). Pressman et al. (1992) also reported two studies showing a curvilinear relationship between religious commitment and death anxiety in which the moderately religious are the most anxious and the very religious and nonreligious were the least anxious (McMordie, 1981; Downey, 1984).

In using three age groups (age 18–39; age 40–59; and age 60–97) and the data from the NIMH Epidemiological Catchment Area Survey (Blazer, Hughes, and George, 1987), Koenig, Ford, George et al. (1993) found that religiosity does not have a consistent, unidirectional effect. The socially oriented dimension of church attendance tends to be negatively related to anxiety disorders. As pointed out earlier in this chapter, this relationship may be the result of the nature of some of these disorders (social phobia and agoraphobia) which may prevent the sufferer from attending church. On the other hand, religious group activities such as going to church may provide the individual with social support and may function as a form of social integration (the feeling that one is part of a larger community that helps to protect against feelings of alienation and powerlessness). Koenig, Ford, George et al. (1993) suggested that the benefits of religious participation go beyond social contacts. "Church attendance may reaffirm religious beliefs and world-view in a way that enhances cognitive—as well as social—integration and further reinforces a sense of belonging, world coherence, predictability and safety" (p. 336).

Religious affiliation was significantly related to anxiety disorders in the study by Koenig, Ford, George et al. (1993). Persons with no religious affiliation had the highest rates of disorders, followed closely by individuals affiliated with fundamentalist Pentecostal religious groups. Individuals from mainline Protestant denominations and those considering themselves "born again," on the other hand, had the lowest rates of anxiety disorder. The higher rates of anxiety disorders among the nonaffiliates may be interpreted in terms of alienation and lack of social integration.

Consistent with higher rates of anxiety disorder among Pentecostals (Koenig, Ford, George et al., 1993) other investigators demonstrated higher rates of mental disorder in nonmainline Protestants (MacDonald and Luckett, 1983). Meador, Koenig, Turnbull, Blazer, Hughes, and George (1992) also found that Pentecostals, especially those in young age groups, showed higher rates of major depressive disorder. It is possible that individuals in general, and particularly younger adults, are drawn into fundamentalist denominations because of preexisting problems with anxiety. Alternatively, as with prayer and Bible reading, persons with low socioeconomic status and from minority racial groups who may face stressors may also reveal more intense religious devotion because of the lack of other resources. These interacting factors show that the relationship between religious affiliation and anxiety is rather complex and that further research is needed.

The definition of religiousness in different studies may explain inconsistent findings in this research area. DeFigueirdo and Lemkan (1978), for example, found that somatic symptoms of anxiety were positively associated with public religious participation but they were negatively related to private religiousness. Bergin, Masters, and Richards (1987) also found that intrinsic rather than extrinsic religiousness is related to low anxiety level.

In a study of the relationship between religiosity and neuroticism (neuroticism is highly related to anxiety), Francis, Pearson, Carter, and Kay (1981) administered the Junior Eysenck Personality Inventory along with the Francis scale of Attitude towards Christianity to a sample of 1088 15- and 16-year-olds within state-maintained schools. There was a significant positive correlation between neuroticism and religiosity. Females obtained higher scores than males on the index of religiosity. This finding is consistent with much research concerned with sex differences in religiosity (Ekehammar and Sidanius, 1982). At the same time, the females also recorded higher scores on the index of neuroticism. This, too, is consistent with much research concerned with sex differences in neuroticism (Jorm, 1987). When sex differences were partialed out, the apparent significant correlation between neuroticism and religiosity disappeared, indicating that the observed relationship was entirely an artifact of sex differences. This result emphasizes the importance of controlling for sex differences in the relationships between dimensions of personality and religion, and it may account for some of the discrepant findings in earlier studies.

Death anxiety is a major area of concern for most religions.

Common observation would suggest that the threat of punishment (Hell) and the promise of reward (Heaven) are expected to arouse conflicts in the individual and increase death anxiety. Templer and Dotson (1970) administered the Templer Death Anxiety scale (Templer, 1970) and a religious inventory to undergraduate students, but found no significant relationship between death anxiety and religion. However, in another study in which the subjects were deeply involved in religion, Templer (1972) found a negative relationship; those persons who had strong attachment to their belief system and attended religious functions more frequently, had lower levels of death anxiety as compared with others. A similar negative relationship between death anxiety and religiosity was found in the study of highly religious Saudi Arabian students in the United States (Long and Elghanemi, 1987). Other studies either confirmed the negative relationship (Young and Daniels, 1980; Minean and Brush, 1980–1981; Aday, 1984–1985), or found little relationship between religiosity and death anxiety (Lonetto and Templer, 1986). McMordie (1981) reported a curvilinear relationship with persons of intermediate religious participation having higher death anxiety than both persons high and low on the religious dimensions. However, more recent work reveals that the spiritual or faith aspects of religion rather than religious practice are associated with low death anxiety (Rasmussen and Johnson, 1994). Little research has been carried out on the relationship between religiousness and death anxiety in psychiatric patients. A mixed group of psychiatric patients studied by Templer and Ruff (1975) revealed no significant relationship between death anxiety and religious beliefs and practices. The exception, however, was that patients tended to have higher death anxiety who think that the most important aspect of religion is that it offers the possibility of life after death.

Obsessive–Compulsive Disorder (OCD)

Exaggeration of normal religious rituals may become pathological if it is not accepted by the individual and his group. For example, an exaggerated form of confession verging on the psychopathological, was found with a patient tormented by the anxiety of committing "mortal sins" and who went for confession twice daily (Vergote, 1988). Vergote labeled this kind of extreme guilt as the "religious neurosis of culpability." Greenberg and Witztum (1992) suggested that a confession which has to be repeated frequently by Catholics is often a source of obsessive–compulsive disturbance. Ignatius of Loyola, the father of the Jesuit order, and Martin Luther, a devout Catholic monk before founding Protestant Christianity, are cited by Greenberg and Witztum (1992) for the long hours they spent ruminating over transgressions and recounting them in detail in confession. However, it is doubtful whether such behavior was considered abnormal by their followers. In contrast to the Catholic emphasis on confession, the emphasis on prayer in Protestant Christianity may result in blasphemy and swearing aloud in church. In this case, pathology is in contrast with rather than an exaggeration of normal religious behavior as in the Catholic case of obsessive–compulsive disorder.

Concern with purity and contamination in the Jewish dietary laws may take an exaggerated form of obsessive–compulsive behavior. Greenberg and Witztum (1992) give the example of "Strictly religious Jewish female patients with obsessive–compulsive disorder [who] commonly show symptoms involving washing of the hands and food utensils, and compulsive checking before and during menstrual immersion [ritual bathing]. Male patients often display excessive perianal washing before prayers, as well as compulsive and repetitive praying in response to self-doubt concerning the adequacy of their devotion" (p. 308).

Obsessive–compulsive disorder was considered rare in certain Western communities and non-Western cultures, and researchers may assume that it may be masked by rigid and ritualistic behavior accepted by the group. J. W. Eaton and Weil (1970), for example, described OCD among the Hutterites:

> It was our impression that neurotic Hutterites react to most stresses with signs of depression rather than with anxiety symptoms or obsessive or paranoid tendencies as neurotic patients

often do in the American culture. This rareness of obsessive and compulsive behavior may have something to do with the relative rigidity of the Hutterite culture. Persons who would seem to be compulsive in a loosely structured social system would be more normal in a Hutterite colony, where life is highly regulated by tradition. The Hutterite culture provides such persons with socially approved outlets for compulsiveness. They need only to be orthodox! Some Hutterites were regarded by their community as fanatical in their orthodoxy, but in no case seen by our staff did the psychiatrist think that a diagnosis of compulsive neurotic reaction would be justified [p. 452].

Other cross-cultural examples of OCD which are believed to be masked by religious rituals came from Islamic countries and India (Al-Issa and Oudji, 1998). One culture-specific obsessive–compulsive syndrome among practicing Muslims is *waswās*, which literally refers to whispered promptings of the devil (Pfeiffer, 1982). It relates to ritual cleanliness and to doubting about the validity of the ritual procedures during prayer. The faithful suffering from *waswās* find it hard to terminate the ablution because they are afraid that they are not yet clean enough to carry out their prayer in an acceptable manner. Starting the prayer immediately after the ablution ritual, the faithful will repeat the introductory invocations as well as the raising of the arms more times than is called for, because they are distracted from focusing on God. Finally, at the end of the prayer, the faithful may have doubts about whether they might perhaps have forgotten some words, and so they will start all over again from the beginning. This syndrome, however, is not considered an illness that requires treatment; it is simply a temptation of the devil that distracts the faithful from carrying out their daily religious duties. The meticulousness of the victim in religious matters deserves respect rather than ridicule by the community. Another example from India is purity mania (*Suci Bhay*) which is based on Hinduism (Chakraborty and Banerji, 1975). A typical example of purity mania is an elderly woman who always carries a bottle of Ganges water under her arm which she uses to dispense "purity," by sprinkling water around her.

Islamic prayer rituals may be reflected in the symptoms of OCD. In Saudi Arabia, Mahgoub and Abdel-Hafeiz (1991) found that body-washing and fear of contamination related to religious themes were frequent among patients. A study in Egypt by Okasha, Saad, Khalil, El-Dawla, and Yahia (1994) reported that the most common obsessive symptoms were related to religious themes and contamination (60% each), while rituals (68%) were the most common compulsions. Religious and sexual themes were the most prevalent among patients. In another study in Qatar, obsessive thoughts of harming oneself or others were attributed to impulses induced by the devil among female patients (El-Islam, 1994). These religious themes seem to be more frequent among Muslim OCD patients than among Hindu patients studied by Akhtar, Wig, Varma, Pershad, and Verma (1975), and are almost absent among Western patients.

Depression, Guilt and Suicide

In a review of the relationship between religion and depression, Stack (1992) reported that while some studies found no relationship (Spendlove, West, and Stanish, 1984; Stack, 1985) others found that religion provides protection against depression (Brown and Lowe, 1951; Mayo, Puryear, and Richek, 1969; Hertsgaard and Light, 1984; Hathaway and Pargament, 1990). Martin and Stack (1983), using a national random sample, found a negative relationship between religion and depression in the United States. However, religion played only a minor role in explaining the variance in depression. For example, educational level is five times more closely associated with the variance in depression than either church attendance or a belief in afterlife. Stack (1992) concluded in his review that the overall evidence favors a negative relationship between depression and religion. He suggested that religion may provide social support, foster a sense of optimism, and may alter the potential negative perceptions of suffering or even viewing suffering in a positive way.

In a study of elderly patients with broken hips, Pressman, Lyons, Larson, and Strain (1990) found both religious beliefs and practices are significantly associated with lower levels of depressive symptoms and better ambulation status following discharge from hospital. Brown and Harris (1982) also found that churchgoing is related to lower depression in a rural setting in Scotland. Churchgoing in the small Scottish islands is considered as an index of social integration and to be closest to the traditional way of life of the islander.

In one study prayer was ranked seventh in effectiveness among 25 possible coping behaviors mediating between life events and depression in a sample of 176 patients attending a general practice clinic (Parker and Brown, 1982). In another study (Koenig, Siegler, Meador, and George, 1990) religious coping behaviors such as church attendance, prayer, reading religious literature, trust or faith in God, tend to buffer against stresses of hospitalization and physical illness. Religious copers had less major depression or depressive symptoms and were less likely to develop the illness over time. Overall, religious beliefs and practices tend to reduce vulnerability to depression.

It has often been suggested that religion, and particularly Christian faith traditions, are conducive to guilt, shame, and sin and therefore foster lower self-esteem and depression (Hood, 1992). However, religious guilt for real sin may be distinguished from irrational guilt which is associated with mental illness. Religious guilt is linked with sin and the lack of perceived forgiveness in the subject's mind (Nayani and Bhugra, 1996). Nayani and Bhugra suggested that the notion of sin which used to imply impurity had been transformed into that of guilt indicating the emergence of the individual agent responsible for the misdeed.

However, religious guilt may present itself in mental illness as a complicating factor linked with religiosity and specific religious values (Cox, 1996). For example, Fernando (1966, 1967) reported that Jewish patients reported less guilt than Catholics and Protestants, suggesting that different religious faiths may differentially make people vulnerable to self-blame and guilt feelings.

It is difficult to study the relationship between religion, depression, and guilt feeling since the manifestation of the latter tends to be confounded by sociocultural factors. Murphy

(1978) demonstrated that in the West, guilt appeared only about the end of the seventeenth century in the clinical description of depression. In the 1960s, Beck (1973) found that guilt feeling was present in 80 percent of cases of moderate and severe depression. However, it has been suggested by Hamilton (1982) that guilt is less prevalent now than before. Krahl (1995) reported a study showing changes in guilt feelings over time. Case histories of 480 depressive patients in Germany, admitted to the Psychiatric University Hospital in Munich between 1910 and 1963, were compared. It was found that guilt feelings, which ranked first amongst symptoms in 1910, had dropped from 62 to 41 percent by 1963. Guilt feelings about religious, ethical, or sexual offenses and criminal acts all became significantly less. This finding is consistent with less involvement in religious matters and more liberal views about sexuality in the general population. The recent decrease in guilt feelings is consistent with reports that social pathology and personality disorder are on the increase (Saugstad, 1989; Paris, 1991).

In contrast to the early Beck (1973) study which found a relationship between the degree of guilt and the severity of depression, Prosen, Clark, Harrow, and Fawcett (1983) found no such a relationship. In psychiatric patients, it was also reported that sin does not play a major role in depression as compared with other mental illnesses (Kroll and Sheehan, 1989; Sheehan and Kroll, 1990). Kroll and Sheehan reported that patients with a diagnosis of major depression were low in their rate of believing that they had sinned during the past week. This goes against the expectation that such patients would manifest excessive self-blame and guilt. In the second study, by Sheehan and Kroll (1990), it was shown that a significantly higher percentage of patients with personality disorder than other patients endorsed the item "I am in hospital now because I have sinned." No depressed patients and 10 percent of schizophrenic patients agreed with this statement. Similarly, only 6 percent of the depressed patients agreed that they would not get better if they did not do penance for their sins compared with 40 percent for both the schizophrenic and the personality disorder patients. These data are consistent with the observation that the report of guilt feeling is decreasing among depressive patients, except that the distinction between sin and pathological guilt should be kept in mind (Nayani and Bhugra, 1996).

Low self-esteem is a major vulnerability factor in depression (Brown and Harris, 1978). A review by Hood (1992) revealed an inconsistent relationship between self-esteem and religion. However, self-esteem was found to be positively related to intrinsic religiousness and negatively related to extrinsic religiousness. Intrinsic religion tended to be related to a positive, loving concept of God, and extrinsic religion with a negative, punitive concept of God (Spilka, Hood, and Gorsuch, 1985). Overall, the evidence indicates that religion is conducive to high self-esteem which may reduce vulnerability to depression.

Religious integration, which is defined in terms of religious affiliation, is expected to increase social integration and lower the rate of suicide (Durkheim, 1897). Catholics are considered higher on religious integration than Protestants and are expected to have lower rates of suicide. The relationship between Catholicism and suicide seems to depend on many factors such as modernization (Pope and Danigelis, 1891) and divorce rate (Stack, 1981). Durkheim's prediction of higher rate of suicide among Catholics has been refuted by studies in the United States (Bainbridge and Stark, 1982; Bankston, Allen, and Cunningham, 1983). Indeed, the Bankston, Allen, and Cunningham study has shown that Catholicism may actually increase the incidence of suicide. Other studies reviewed by Stack (1992) show that factors such as the percentage of Catholics or Protestants, sex ratio, educational diversity, and population size influence the relationship between Catholicism and suicide.

Church membership as an index of religious commitment was negatively related to suicide (Stark, Doyle, and Rushing, 1983), but such relationship disappeared when geographic mobility was taken into consideration. Pescosolido (1990) suggested that a region with a concentration of a particular denomination provides networking and social support for members of that faith and will result in lower rates of suicide. For example, he found that the rate of suicide is high among Southern Jews since they lack the social networks they enjoy in

New England. Similarly, Catholics have high rate of suicide in the South as compared with the Northeast which is a strongly Catholic region. After consideration of the various factors that are involved in the relationship between religion and suicide, Stack (1992) concluded that the evidence only slightly supports the notion that religious commitment lowers suicide rate.

Psychosis

Religion is expected to influence the contents of psychotic symptoms. Historically, this influence has been fading away in Western countries, which may be due to the decline in religiousness. While hospitals in the nineteenth century were full of "Gods," "Saints," "Christs," and "Virgin Marys" (Hurd, 1888), Rokeach (1964) in the late 1950s had difficulty in finding "Christs" for his study in one mental hospital in the United States. Rokeach finally succeeded in locating three Christs scattered in different hospitals. Nowadays, "Gods," "Christs," "Saints," and "Virgin Marys" are rare or even nonexistent on psychiatric wards.

It is often difficult to distinguish between "religiously driven" behavior such as speaking in tongues (glossolalia) and visions on the one hand, and schizophrenic "crazy talk" and hallucinations on the other (Loewenthal, 1995). Glossolalia, for example, is widely practiced by members of Pentacostal and charismatic Christian churches, but such behavior may have nothing to do with mental illness. Nevertheless, such normal behavior within the religious context may be exaggerated by some overzealous church members making the distinction between religious verbalization and psychotic "crazy talk" extremely difficult (see cases reported by Littlewood and Lipsedge, 1989). Yet, religious and psychotic behavior may be qualitatively different from each other. As Loewenthal (1995) pointed out:

> Glossolalia lasts for only a few minutes. Glossolalia always occurs in the context of a religious ceremony and although the sounds

are incomprehensible, the symbolic meaning is clear to all participants. In schizophrenic speech disorder, the individual words
in the discourse are recognizable, but the links between them
cannot be followed. The speech disorder of schizophrenia continues for days, weeks or longer. Unlike glossolalia, although
the individual words are comprehensible, the overall meaning
[of the speech of the schizophrenic] is obscure [p. 168].

Similarly, religiously sanctioned hallucinations such as visions, which were prevalent in medieval Europe, tended to be
stylized and meaningful to the individual and his group (Al-
Issa, 1995). It was observed that studies during this century
found that more than one-third of the population had experienced seeing visions and hearing voices (Al-Issa, 1995) and
these individuals tended to be slightly better adjusted and more
mentally healthy than the general population (Hay, 1982).
However, hallucinating individuals tend to keep their experiences secret and never tell others about them for fear of being
considered mentally ill. Barker (1996) argued that since Western society does not provide individuals with an explanation
for these experiences, or with a social context in which they
can safely admit to having them, people may find refuge in
new religions and cults. Of course, the unusual experiences of
members of new religions or cults may be related to mental
illness, but it was found that mentally ill members often had
a history of mental illness before they joined (Barker, 1984;
Richardson, van der Lans, and Derks, 1986; Bilu, 1995). For
example, Bilu pointed out that religious penitents (born again
Jews) in Israel tend to be at high risk for schizophrenia and
affective disorders; but for the majority of them, these psychiatric difficulties preceded the religious transformation.

Although religiousness may color the symptoms of psychosis, evidence relating religion or religious attitudes to psychosis
is conflicting (Francis, 1996). Studies with children (Francis
and Pearson, 1985; Francis, Lankshear, and Pearson, 1989;
Francis and Montgomery, 1992) and adults (Francis, 1991)
found a negative relationship between psychoticism and religion. Other studies, however, failed to find such a relationship
(Nias, 1973; Watson, Morris, Foster, and Hood, 1986; Caird,

1987; Egan, 1989; Johnson, Danko, Darvill, Bochner, Bowers, Huang, Park, Pecjak, Rahim, and Pennington, 1989).

Delinquency, Criminality, and Drug Abuse

It is expected that religion would provide social control and thus reduce risk-taking behavior such as crime and drug use and abuse. However, an early study revealed that youngsters who believed in supernatural sanctions or attended church were as likely to be delinquent as other children (Hirschi and Stark, 1969). Later studies, however, indicated a negative relationship between religiousness and delinquency (Higgins and Albrecht, 1977; Peek, Curry, and Chalfant, 1985). These contradictory results may be explained in terms of the social context in which the study was carried out (Stark, Kent, and Doyle, 1982). A negative correlation between religion and delinquency tends to be found in communities where the majority are religious and where there is a high rate of church membership. In communities where only a minority are religious, religion has no power to deter delinquency among individually religious young people. For example, studies have consistently found that where organized religion is relatively strong, churchgoing and believing individuals were far less likely to steal than their irreligious counterparts. A person's religious faith apparently is ineffective unless community pressure makes a connection between beliefs and behavior (see Bainbridge, 1992). Bainbridge (1992) pointed out that in areas with strong organized religion, lack of religious belief affiliation is simply one more kind of deviance from the norm, thus correlating with other kinds of deviance. By contrast, in areas of weak organized religion, irreligiosity is not considered deviant at all, and thus should not correlate with deviance. However, religion seems to deter crimes related to hedonistic behavior such as illegal drug use, heavy alcohol drinking, and promiscuous sexuality even in areas which are weak in organized religion, in contrast to the larceny type of delinquency (Middleton and Putney, 1962; Burkett and White, 1974; Wuthnow, 1978; Hadaway, Elifson, and Petersen, 1984; see also Bainbridge, 1992).

In adult crime, there is consistent negative relationship between religiousness and reported official crime rates in the United States (Bainbridge, 1992). However, violent crime (homicide, rape, robbery, and assault) had a much weaker relationship with church membership than did property crimes (burglary, larceny, and auto theft). It has been suggested that religion may be better at deterring consciously committed crimes that belong to sustained periods of deviant behavior (property) and less effective at deterring impulsively violent acts like murder and assault (Bainbridge, 1992). However, this explanation was questioned by Bainbridge who pointed out that it is difficult to categorize certain crimes into one type or another, such as robbery, which belongs to the categories of both property and violent crime. Bainbridge suggested that other factors may interact with religion in affecting the rate of crime, such as geographical mobility (which is related to church membership), percent of families in poverty, and percent of the divorced.

There is almost consistent evidence that religiousness and substance use are negatively related to each other (Benson, 1992). This relationship was reported for both sexes (Jessor, Jessor, and Finney, 1973; Gottlieb and Green, 1984; Adlaf and Smart, 1985; Donahue, 1987; Benson and Donahue, 1989), racial groups (Donahue, 1987; Benson and Donahue, 1989), and regardless of the way religion was defined; for example, church membership, church attendance, and religious salience or importance for the individual (Benson, 1992). Control of other factors such as age, region, education, income, peer drug use, relationship with parents, school performance, and attitude of parents and friends does not change such a negative relationship (Benson, 1992).

The most frequently investigated substances were alcohol and marijuana use. Of 38 studies covered in a review by Benson (1992) 29 indicated a negative relationship with alcohol, and 26 with marijuana. Investigations of tobacco use and illicit drug use other than marijuana also show a negative relationship with religion. Wuthnow (1978) compared the rates of being "high on drugs" for five religious orientations. The nonreligious reported higher rates than those with conservative, liberal, or nominal religious orientations. Those who accept nonconventional religious ideas such as Eastern religions or the occult reported even higher rates than the nonreligious.

Overall, the evidence seems to show that religiousness is related to the onset of drug use. While almost all studies investigated the role of religion in preventing the onset of drug use, the issues of regular use or problem use and addiction were neglected (Bainbridge, 1992).

RELIGION AND PSYCHOTHERAPY

It has been suggested that psychotherapy is a moral enterprise and psychotherapists are described as forming a "secular priesthood" (London, 1986; Jones, 1994). In the therapeutic relationship, clients do not usually separate psychological from moral phenomena. For some clients, expressing emotions such as anger may be considered as both a psychological and a moral issue. Therapists' values and morality are also involved in the therapeutic relationship. Similarly, theories of psychotherapy are value-laden with assumptions about human life and what is good (adaptive, realistic, rational) and bad (abnormal, pathological, etc.) for the patient (Worthington, Kurusu, and McCullough, 1996).

In North America, Lukoff, Francis, and Turner (1992) found that over 80 percent of the population believed in a God or a spiritual force, even though they might not practice any specific religion. Mental health professionals were less likely to hold a religious belief or practice a religion. The distance between the religious belief of a practitioner and their patients could create a "religiosity gap" (Cox, 1996) that may interfere with the therapeutic relationship. The religiousness of the therapist is particularly important with highly religious clients who prefer therapists of similar religious values to themselves (Worthington, 1988). This has been supported in the study of both Orthodox Jewish clients (Wikler, 1989) and Protestant Christian college students (Keating and Fretz, 1990). A discrepancy between the beliefs of the therapist and clients may interfere with successful therapy in which the clients are expected to adopt the values of their therapists (Worthington et al., 1996). (The therapist represents the values of society [Christianity, democracy, individualism] and psychological adjustment is defined according to these values.)

Some investigations found that therapists tend to be biased in evaluating religious clients (Lewis and Lewis, 1985; Houts and Graham, 1986; Gartner, Harmatz, Hohmann, Larson, and Gartner, 1990), while others did not confirm these results (Kivley, 1986; Reed, 1992). In evaluating the methodology of these investigations, Worthington et al. (1996) concluded that the evidence seems to support the bias of therapists in diagnosing clients. In one study, Gartner, Harmatz, Hohmann, Larson, and Gartner (1990) surveyed 363 clinical psychologists in order to investigate diagnostic bias. Clinicians rated two case histories that were identical except for two variables. In one, the patient was described as a member of an extreme political or religious group of either the right or left wing (e.g., John Birch Society, Fundamentalist Christian, American Socialist Party, or Atheists International); in the other, no mention was made of group membership. Gartner et al. supported the hypothesis that clinicians would be influenced by patient ideology. Patients who belonged to extreme groups were judged as promoting less clinician empathy, having more pathology, having more internal and external stress, and being less mature than were patients with the same symptoms but with no mention of membership in the extreme group. Worthington et al. (1996) commented that: "Despite the suggestion that some therapists may show bias in clinical judgment, the present body of research is inconclusive. Research to date has been analogue, and all studies have been relatively remote from true clinical situations. For firm conclusions to be drawn, researchers must conduct and report field studies of actual patients and therapists" (p. 467).

Among people who sought help for personal problems between 1956 and 1976, 39 percent saw clergy. This number has been virtually unchanged since the mid-1950s (Worthington et al., 1996). The severity of problems seen by clergy is similar to those seen by mental health professionals. Larson, Hohmann,

Kessler, and Meador (1988) examined data on 18,495 people (from the Epidemiological Catchment Area [ECA] study: Eaton, Holzer, Von Korff, Anthony, Helzer, George, Burnham, Boyd, Kessler, and Locke, 1984; Regier, Myers, Kramer, Robins, Blazer, Hingh, Eaton, and Locke, 1984; Eaton and Kessler, 1985), who sought help from both a mental health specialist and pastor. Those who sought help from both mental health specialist and pastor were more likely to have been diagnosed as having major affective disorders or panic disorders than were other clients. Most people sought help from clergy as often as mental health specialists for serious problems except that they were more likely to seek help from mental health specialists for substance abuse problems (Worthington et al., 1996). Cooperation between pastors and secular professionals tend to be one-sided in the referral of cases. Pastors refer difficult cases to secular professionals but they reported almost no referrals from mental health professionals to them (Worthington et al., 1996).

Christensen and Jacobson (1994) reviewed research on the effectiveness of paraprofessional counseling relative to professional counseling. They found no difference between the two types of counseling. Most studies used clients who were mildly or moderately disturbed. Religious lay counseling has been found to improve self-concept and has the same rates of success as psychotherapy (Harris, 1985; Walters, 1987). However, the general quality of studies evaluating the effectiveness of religious lay counseling has been criticized (Worthington et al., 1996).

Religious Therapeutic Techniques

The most frequently used techniques by Christian counselors are prayer, promoting forgiveness, teaching biblical concepts, and to a lesser extent Christian meditation (Worthington, Dupont, Berry, and Duncan, 1988; Ball and Goodyear, 1991; Jones, Watson, and Wolfram, 1992; Richards and Potts, 1995). The effectiveness of *prayer* has been investigated more often in the area of physical than mental health (Finney and Malony, 1985; Duckro and Magaletta, 1994; McCullough, 1995). One well-designed study was reported by Byrd (1988). Patients admitted to a coronary unit were assigned to one of two groups. The prayer group received daily prayer by three to seven Christians praying outside the hospital (intercessory prayer). Patients did not know they were being prayed for. Those who prayed knew the patient's first name, diagnosis, and general condition, and they received periodic updates on the patient's condition. In the no-prayer group, patients were not assigned to people for daily prayer. Physicians did not know which patients were in which group, nor did the researcher of the study, who collected and analyzed the patient outcome data. For days in the critical care unit, days in the hospital, number of medications at discharge, development of new symptoms, and rated outcomes, patients who were prayed for did substantially better than did patients who were not prayed for. This single study, despite its careful design, could have produced its findings simply by chance and its replication is needed.

The relaxation response with all its physiological benefits has been elicited through prayer (Benson, 1987). Different types of prayer may have different effects (Poloma and Pendleton, 1991). Meditative prayer is devotional and usually engaged in as a form of worship. Petitional prayer is aimed at alleviating a particular suffering, one's own suffering, or the suffering of another (intercessory prayer). Ritual prayer is repetitive and may have either calming effects or negative psychological and physical effects (depending on the person and situation). Colloquial prayer is like a conversation with God, in which the person may seek guidance or forgiveness or simply talk with God about positive or negative experiences.

Similar to prayer, *forgiveness* has been frequently used by both secular and religious counselors (Jones, Watson, and Wolfram, 1992; Worthington et al., 1996). Hebl and Enright (1993) studied a treatment to promote forgiveness ($n = 13$) comparing an eight-session structured group with a discussion group unrelated to forgiveness ($n = 11$). The participants were older women selected from a Christian church who sought to forgive an offender for a specific offense. Participants in the forgiveness group had lower indices of depression and trait anxiety than did participants in the control group. *Granting* forgiveness seems important in fostering smooth interpersonal relationships and positive mental health. However, empirical studies of *seeking* forgiveness have been reported only in the social psychological literature (Cody and McLaughlin, 1988; Bassett, Hill, Pogel, and Lee, 1990; Weiner, Graham, Peter, and Zmuidinas, 1991).

Many studies have been carried out in the 1960s and 1970s on Hindu or Buddhist-based *meditation* (Smith, 1975). However, it was reported that since the early 1980s research interest in meditation has significantly decreased. Alexander, Langer, Newman, and Chandler (1989) investigated meditation in a home for older people. Half of the subjects were assigned to daily meditation, and half were not. After three years, a fourth of the no-treatment group but none of the meditation group had died. In the area of psychopathology a study by Carlson, Bacaseta, and Simanton (1988) found that the effects of devotional meditation and progressive relaxation are equal. Most of what can be accomplished therapeutically with meditation can be accomplished with relaxation training, which is generally easier and avoids the religious connotations of meditation. Meditation has been used in a variety of situations such as general stress and tension, general anxiety, test anxiety, drug abuse, alcohol abuse, and sleep problems (Carrington, 1982, 1984; Shapiro and Walsh, 1984; Kabat-Zinn, Massion, Kristeller, Peterson, Fletcher, Pbert, Linderking, and Santorelli, 1992) as well as in prevention (see review by de Silva, 1996). It has also significant physiological effects such as reduction of oxygen consumption; lowered heart rate, breathing rate, and blood pressure; reduction in serum lactic acid levels; increased skin resistance; and change in blood flow (Benson, 1975; Woolfolk, 1975).

There have been attempts to integrate religiousness into general theoretical approaches such as the religious adaptation of the cognitive–behavioral, psychodynamic, existential–humanistic, and health psychology programs, that is, *integrative therapy* (Payne, Bergin, and Loftus, 1992). Propst, Ostrom, Watkins, Dean, and Mashburn (1992), for example, compared nonreligious cognitive–behavioral therapy with religious cognitive–behavioral therapy and pastoral counseling treatment in the treatment of depression with religious clients. For depression, by the end of treatment, religious cognitive–behavioral therapy reduced depression more than a waiting list. Nonreligious cognitive–behavioral therapy and pastoral counseling treatment did not. Other studies investigated the effectiveness of modified rational–emotive therapy (Johnson and Ridley, 1992; Johnson, De Vries, Ridley, Pettorini, and Peterson, 1994). Christian marital therapy has been proposed (see Worthington for review, 1994) but little research has been carried out on its effectiveness with religious clients (Worthington et al., 1996).

SUMMARY

Early reviews show inconsistent relationship between religion and psychopathology, raising methodological issues in this research area. Both the definition of mental health and religion tend to determine whether such a relationship is positive or negative. In particular, the multidimensionality of religion has to be taken into consideration in the interpretation of data. One of the most influential dimensions of religiousness is the intrinsic–extrinsic dimension. It is also shown that age, stress, and religiousness interact in an interesting way. Both religiousness and stress increase with age and thus confound the relationship between religion and psychological or physical distress. The question whether psychopathology and psychological distress may interfere with religiosity is also raised.

The relationship between religiousness and anxiety tends to be inconsistent depending on the dimension of religiousness being studied. Both religious affiliation and intrinsic religiousness are negatively associated with anxiety. Neuroticism was positively related to religion, but when the effect of sex was partialed out (women tended to be high on both religiousness and neuroticism) the significant relationship disappeared. The relationship between death anxiety and religiousness is inconsistent, except that the spiritual aspects of religion rather than religious practice is associated with low death anxiety. Religious rituals may mask or color the manifestation of obsessive–compulsive disorder.

Although many studies of the relationship between religiousness and depression are inconsistent, the overall evidence suggests that religion may serve as an antidote against depression. A distinction is made between irrational pathological guilt and sin. The latter which is related to religion does not seem to be prevalent among depressed patients. Religious commitment seems to be slightly related to lower rates of suicide. Religious beliefs influence the contents of both delusions and hallucinations. However, a distinction is made between visual hallucinations and religious visions. The evidence relating religion or religious attitudes to psychosis is conflicting. While the relationship between religion and delinquency is complicated by many factors, religion has a consistently negative relationship to reported adult criminal behavior but such a relationship is stronger for property than impulsive crime. There is an almost consistent evidence of a negative relationship between religiousness and substance use involving alcohol and tobacco, and marijuana and other illicit drugs.

Religious orientation and moral values tend to affect psychotherapy, particularly the clinical judgment of the therapist. Paraprofessional counseling seems to be as effective as professional counseling. Prayer, forgiveness, meditation, and integrative therapy (religious cognitive–behavioral therapy) are used as psychotherapeutic techniques based on religion.

REFERENCES

Aday, R. H. (1984–1985), Belief in afterlife and death anxiety: Correlates and comparisons. *Omega J. Death & Dying*, 15:67–75.

Adlaf, E. M., & Smart, R. G. (1985), Drug use and religious affiliation, feelings, and behavior. *Brit. J. Addict.*, 80:163–171.

Akhtar, S., Wig, N. N., Varma, V. K., Pershad, D., & Verma, S. K. (1975), A phenomenological analysis of symptoms in obsessive-compulsive neurosis. *Brit. J. Psychiatry*, 127:342–348.

Alcock, J. E. (1992), Religion and rationality. In: *Religion and Mental Health*, ed. J. F. Schumaker. New York: Oxford University Press, pp. 122–131.

Alexander, C. N., Langer, E. J., Newman, R. I., & Chandler, H. M. (1989), Transcendental meditation, mindfulness, and longevity: An experimental study with the elderly. *J. Personal. & Soc. Psychol.*, 57:950–964.

Alexander, F. G., & Selesnick, S. T. (1966), *The History of Psychiatry*. New York: Harper & Row.

Allen, R. O., & Spilka, B. (1967), Committed and consensual religion: A specification of religion-prejudice relationships. *J. Scientific Study of Religion*, 6:191–206.

Allport, G. W. (1950), *The Individual and His Religion*. New York: Macmillan.

———— Ross, J. M. (1967), Personal religious orientation and prejudice. *J. Personal. & Soc. Psychol.*, 5:432–443.

Argyle, M., & Beit-Hallahmi, B. (1958), *The Social Psychology of Religion*. London: Routledge & Kegan Paul.

Bainbridge, W. S. (1992), Crime, delinquency and religion. In: *Religion and Mental Health*, ed. J. F. Schumaker. New York: Oxford University Press, pp. 199–210.

———— Stark, R. (1982), Suicide, homicide and religion. *Annual Review of the Social Sciences of Religion*, 5. The Hague, Netherlands: Mouton.

Baker, M., & Gorsuch, R. (1982), Trait anxiety and intrinsic–extrinsic religiousness. *J. Scient. Study of Relig.*, 21:119–122.

Ball, R. A., & Goodyear, R. K. (1991), Self-reported professional practices of Christian psychotherapists. *J. Psychol. & Christianity*, 10:144–153.

Bankston, W. B., Allen, H. D., & Cunningham, D. S. (1983), Religion and suicide: A research note on sociology's "one law." *Soc. Forces*, 62:521–528.

Barker, E. (1984), *Of Gods and Men: New Religious Movements in the West*. Macon, GA: Mercer University Press.

———— (1996), New religions and mental health. In: *Psychiatry and Religion*, ed. D. Bhugra. London: Routledge, pp. 125–137.

Bassett, R. L., Hill, P. C., Pogel, M. C., & Lee, M. (1990), Comparing psychological guilt and Godly sorrow: Do Christians recognize the difference? *J. Psychol. & Theol.*, 18:244–254.

Batson, C. D., & Ventis, W. L. (1982), *The Religious Experience*. New York: Oxford University Press.

Beck, A. T. (1973), *The Diagnosis and Management of Depression*. Philadelphia: University of Pennsylvania Press.

Beg, M. A., & Zilli, A. S. (1982), A study of the relationship of death anxiety and religious faith to age differentials. *Psychologia,* 25:121–125.

Bellah, R. N. (1971), The historical background of unbelief. In: *The Culture of Unbelief,* ed. R. Caporale & A. Grumelli. Berkeley: University of California Press, pp. 39–52.

Benson, H. (1975), *The Relaxation Response.* New York: Morrow.

———— (1987), *Your Maximum Mind.* New York: Times Books.

Benson, P. L. (1992), Religion and substance use. In: *Religion and Mental Health,* ed. J. F. Schumaker. New York: Oxford University Press, pp. 211–220.

———— Donahue, M. J. (1989), Ten year trends in at-risk behavior: A national study of black adolescents. *J. Adol. Res.,* 4:125–139.

Bergin, A. E. (1983), Religiosity and mental health: A critical reevaluation and meta-analysis. *Prof. Psychol.: Res. & Pract.,* 14:170–184.

———— Masters, K. S., & Richards, P. S. (1987), Religiousness and mental health reconsidered: A study of an intrinsically religious sample. *J. Counsel. Psychol.,* 34:197–204.

Bilu, Y. (1995), Culture and mental illness among Jews in Israel. In: *Culture and Mental Illness: An International Perspective,* ed. I. Al-Issa. Baltimore: University Park Press, pp. 129–146.

Blazer, D. G., Hughes, D. C., & George, L. K. (1987), The epidemiology of depression in an elderly community population. *The Gerontologist,* 27:281–287.

Brown, D. G., & Lowe, W. L. (1951), Religious beliefs and personality characteristics of college students. *J. Soc. Psychol.,* 33:103–129.

Brown, G. W., & Harris, T. (1982), Social class and affective disorder. In: *Culture and Psychopathology,* ed. I. Al-Issa. Baltimore: University Park Press.

———— ———— (1978), *Social Origins of Depression: A Study of Psychiatric Disorder in Women.* London: Tavistock Publications.

Brown, L. B. (1962), A study of religious belief. *Brit. J. Psychol.,* 53:259–272.

Burkett, S. R., & White, M. (1974), Hellfire and delinquency: Another look. *J. Scient. Study of Relig.,* 13:455–462.

Byrd, R. C. (1988), Positive therapeutic effects of intercessory prayer in a coronary care unit population. *S. Med. J.,* 81:826–829.

Caird, D. (1987), Religiosity and personality: Are mystics introverted, neurotic, or psychotic? *Brit. J. Soc. Psychol.,* 26:345–346.

Carlson, C. R., Bacaseta, P. E., & Simanton, D. A. (1988), A controlled evaluation of devotional meditation and progressive relaxation. *J. Psychol. & Theol.,* 16:362–368.

Carrington, P. (1982), Meditation techniques in clinical practice. In: *The Newer Therapies: A Source Book,* ed. L. E. Abt & I. R. Stuarts. New York: Van Nostrand.

—— (1984), Modern forms of meditation. In: *Principles and Practices of Stress Management,* ed. R. L. Woodfaldk & M. Lehrer. New York: Guilford.

Chakraborty, A., & Banerji, G. (1975), Ritual: A culture-specific neurosis, and obsessional states in Bengali culture. *Ind. J. Psychiatry,* 17:211–216.

Christensen, A., & Jacobson, N. S. (1994), Who (or what) can do psychotherapy: The status and challenge of nonprofessional therapies. *Psycholog. Sci.,* 5:8–14.

Cody, M. J., & McLaughlin, M. L. (1988), Accounts on trial: Oral arguments in traffic court. In: *Analyzing Everyday Explanations,* ed. C. Antaki. London: Sage, pp. 113–126.

Comstock, G. W., & Partridge, K. B. (1972), Church attendance and health. *J. Chron. Dis.,* 172:665–672.

Cox, J. L. (1996), Psychiatry and religion: A general psychiatrist's perspective. In: *Psychiatry and Religion,* ed. D. Bhugra. London: Routledge, pp. 157–166.

Cutler, S. J. (1976), Membership in different types of voluntary associations and psychological well-being. *The Gerontologist,* 16:335–339.

Dahawn, N., & Sripat, K. (1986), Fear of death and religiosity as related to need for affiliation. *Psycholog. Studies,* 31:35–38.

DeFigueirdo, J. M., & Lemkan, P. V. (1978), The prevalence of psychosomatic symptoms in a rapidly changing bilingual culture: An exploratory study. *Soc. Psychiatry,* 13:125–133.

De Silva, P. (1996), Buddhist psychology and implications for treatment. In: *Psychiatry and Religion,* ed. D. Bhurgra. London: Routledge, pp. 112–124.

Dittes, J. E. (1969), The psychology of religion. In: *The Handbook of Social Psychology,* ed. G. Lindzey & E. Aronson. Reading, MA: Addison-Wesley, pp. 602–659.

Dixon, W., Alexander, J., & Anderson, W. (1990), The relationship between intrinsic and extrinsic religious orientation and obsessions and compulsions. Paper presented at the 62nd Annual Meeting of the Midwestern Psychological Association, Chicago, Illinois, May.

Dodd, D. K., & Mills, L. L. (1985), FADIS: A measure of the fear of accidental death and injury. *Psycholog. Rec.,* 35:269–275.

Donahue, M. J. (1985), Intrinsic and extrinsic religiousness: Review and meta-analysis. *J. Personal. & Soc. Psychol.,* 48:400–419.

———— (1987), Religion and drug use: 1976–1985. Paper presented at the annual meeting of the Society for the Scientific Study of Religion, Louisville, Kentucky.

Downey, A. M. (1984), Relationship of religiosity to death anxiety of middle-aged males. *Psycholog. Rep.*, 54:811–822.

Duckro, P. N., & Magaletta, P. R. (1994), The effect of prayer on physical health: Experimental evidence. *J. Relig. & Health*, 33:211–219.

Durkheim, E. (1897), *Suicide.* New York: Free Press, 1966.

Eaton, J. W., & Weil, R. J. (1970), The mental health of the Hutterites: In: *Cross-Cultural Studies of Behavior*, ed. I. Al-Issa & W. Dennis. New York: Holt, Rinehart & Winston, pp. 445–454.

Eaton, W. W., & Kessler, L. G., Eds. (1985), *Epidemiologic Field Methods in Psychiatry: The NIMH Epidemiologic Catchment Area Program.* New York: Academic Press.

———— Holzer, C. E., Von Korff, M., Anthony, J. C., Helzer, J. E., George, L., Burnham, A., Boyd, J. H., Kessler, L. G., & Locke, B. Z. (1984), The design of the Epidemiologic Catchment Area surveys: The control and measurement of error. *Arch. Gen. Psychiatry*, 41:942–948.

Edwards, J. N., & Klemmack, D. L. (1973), Correlates of life satisfaction: A reexamination. *J. Gerontol.*, 28:497–502.

Egan, V. (1989), Links between personality, ability and attitudes in a low-IQ sample. *Personal. & Individ. Diff.*, 10:997–1001.

Ekehammar, B., & Sidanius, J. (1982), Sex differences in sociopolitical attitudes: A replication and extension. *Brit. J. Soc. Psychol.*, 21:249–257.

Ellis, A. (1980), Psychotherapy and atheistic values: A response to A. E. Bergin's "Psychotherapy and religious values." *J. Consult. & Clin. Psychol.*, 48:635–639.

Epstein, L., Tamir, A., & Natan, T. (1985), Emotional health state of adolescents. *Internat. J. Adol. Med. & Health*, 1:13–22.

Fernando, S. (1966), Depressive illness in Jews and non-Jews. *Brit. J. Psychol.*, 12:991–996.

———— (1967), Cultural differences in hostility of depressive patients. *Brit. J. Psychiatry*, 113:607–617.

Finney, J. R., & Malony, H. N. (1985), Empirical studies of Christian prayer: A review of the literature. *J. Psychol. & Theol.*, 13:104–115.

Florian, V., Kravetz, S., & Frankel, J. (1984), Aspects of fear of personal death, levels of awareness and religious commitment. *J. Res. Personal.*, 18:289–304.

Foskett, J. (1996), Christianity and psychiatry. In: *Psychiatry and Religion: Context, Consensus and Controversies*, ed. D. Bhugra. London: Routledge, pp. 51–64.

Francis, L. (1996), Religion, neuroticism and psychoticism. In: *Psychiatry and Religion*, ed. D. Bhugra. London: Routledge, pp. 149–160.

Francis, L. J. (1991), Personality and attitude towards religion among adult churchgoers in England. *Psycholog. Rep.*, 69:791–794.

———— Lankshear, D. W., & Pearson, P. R. (1989), The relationship between religiosity and the short form JEPQ (JEPQ-S) indices of E, N, L and P among eleven year olds. *Personal. & Individ. Diff.*, 10:763–769.

———— Montgomery, A. (1992), Personality and attitudes towards religion among 11–16 year old girls in a single sex Catholic school. *Brit. J. Relig. Ed.*, 14:114–119.

———— Pearson, P. R. (1985), Psychoticism and religiosity among 15 year olds. *Personal. & Individ. Diff.*, 6:397–398.

———— ———— Carter, M., & Kay, W. K. (1981), The relationship between neuroticism and religiosity among English 15- and 16-year-olds. *J. Soc. Psychol.*, 114:99–102.

Freud, S. (1927), The future of an illusion. *Standard Edition*, 21:1–56. London: Hogarth Press, 1961.

Gartner, J., Harmatz, M., Hohmann, A., Larson, D. & Gartner, A. F. (1990), The effect of patient and clinician ideology on clinical judgment: A study of ideological countertransference. *Psychotherapy*, 27:98–106.

———— Larson, D. B., & Allen, G. D. (1991), Religious commitment and mental health: A review of the empirical literature. *J. Psychol. & Theol.*, 19:6–25.

Geertz, C. (1966), Religion as a cultural system. In: *Anthropological Approaches to the Study of Religion*, ed. M. Banton. New York: Praeger, pp. 1–46.

Gelder, M., Gath, D., & Mayou, R. (1989), *Oxford Textbook of Psychiatry*. Oxford: Oxford University Press.

Gottlieb, N. H., & Green, L. W. (1984), Life events, social network, life-style, and health: An analysis of the 1979 national survey of personal health practices and consequences. *Health Ed. Quart.*, 11:91–105.

Greenberg, D., & Witztum, E. (1992), Content and prevalence of psychopathology in world religions. In: *Religion and Mental Health*, ed. J. F. Schumaker. New York: Oxford University Press, pp. 300–314.

Gupta, A. (1983), Mental health and religion. *Asian J. Psychol. &* *Ed.,* 11:8–13.

Hadaway, C. K., Elifson, K. W., & Petersen, D. M. (1984), Religious involvement and drug use among urban adolescents. *J. Scient. Study of Relig.,* 23:109–128.

Hamilton, M. (1982), Symptoms and assessment of depression. In: *Handbook of Affective Disorders,* ed. E. Paykel. London: Churchill Livingstone, pp. 3–23.

Harris, J. (1985), Non-professionals as effective helpers for pastoral counselors. *J. Pastoral Care,* 39:165–172.

Hassan, M. K., & Khalique, A. (1981), Religiosity and its correlates in college students. *J. Psycholog. Res.,* 25:129–136.

Hathaway, W. L., & Pargament, K. I. (1990), Intrinsic religiousness, religious coping, and psychosocial competence. *J. Scient. Study of Relig.,* 29:423–441.

Hay, D. (1982), *Exploring Inner Space: Scientists and Religious Experience.* Harmondsworth, U.K.: Penguin.

Hebl, J., & Enright, R. D. (1993), Forgiveness as a psychotherapeutic goal with elderly females. *Psychotherapy,* 30:658–667.

Heitzelman, M. E., & Fehr, L. A. (1976), Relationship between religious orthodoxy and three personality variables. *Psycholog. Rep.,* 38:756–758.

Hertsgaard, D., & Light, H. (1984), Anxiety, depression and hostility in rural women. *Psycholog. Rep.,* 55:673–674.

Higgins, P. C., & Albrecht, G. L. (1977), Hellfire and delinquency revisited. *Soc. Forces,* 55:952–958.

Hirschi, T., & Stark, R. (1969), Hellfire and delinquency. *Soc. Problems,* 17:202–213.

Hood, R. W., Jr. (1992), Sin and guilt in faith traditions: Issues for self-esteem. In: *Religion and Mental Health,* ed. J. J. Schumaker. New York: Oxford University Press, pp. 110–121.

Houts, A. C., & Graham, K. (1986), Can religion make you crazy? Impact of client and therapist religious values on clinical judgments. *J. Consult. & Clin. Psychol.,* 54:267–271.

Hurd, H. M. (1888), The religious delusions of the insane. *Amer. J. Insanity,* April:1–17.

Idler, E. L. (1987), Religious involvement and health of the elderly: Some hypotheses and an initial test. *Soc. Forces,* 66:226–238.

El-Islam, M. F. (1994), Cultural aspects of morbid fear in Qatari women. *Soc. Psychiatry & Psychiatric Epidemiol.,* 29:137–140.

Al-Issa, I. (1995), The illusion of reality or the reality of illusions. Hallucinations and culture. *Brit. J. Psychiatry,* 166:368–373.

————— Oudji, S. (1998), Culture and anxiety. In: *Cultural Clinical Psychology Theory: Research and Practice*, ed. S. S. Kazarian & D. R. Evans. New York: Oxford University Press, pp. 127–151.

James, W. (1902), *The Varieties of Religious Experience*. New York: Longmans, Green.

Jessor, R., Jessor, S. L., & Finney, J. (1973), A social psychology of marijuana use: Longitudinal studies of high school and college youth. *J. Personal. & Soc. Psychol.*, 26:1–15.

Johnson, R. C., Danko, G. P., Darvill, T. J., Bochner, S., Bowers, J. K., Huang, Y-H., Park, J. Y., Pecjak, V., Rahim, A. R. A., & Pennington, D. (1989), Cross-cultural assessment of altruism and its correlates. *Personal. & Individ. Diff.*, 10:855–868.

Johnson, W. B., & Ridley, C. R. (1992), Brief Christian and non-Christian rational emotive therapy with depressed Christian clients: An exploratory study. *Counsel. & Values*, 36:220–228.

————— DeVries, R., Ridley, C. R., Pettorini, D., & Peterson, D. R. (1994), The comparative efficacy of Christian and secular rational-emotive therapy with Christian clients. *J. Psychol. & Theol.*, 22:130–140.

Jones, S. L. (1994), A constructive relationship for religion with the science and profession of psychology. Perhaps the boldest model yet. *Amer. Psychologist*, 49:184–199.

————— Watson, E. J., & Wolfram, T. J. (1992), Results of the Rech Conference survey on religious faith and professional psychology. *J. Psychol. & Theol.*, 20:147–158.

Jorm, A. F. (1987), Sex differences in neuroticism: A quantitative synthesis of published research. *Austral. & NZ J. Psychiatry*, 21:501–506.

Jung, C. G. (1938), *Psychology and Religion*. New Haven, CT: Yale University Press.

Kabat-Zinn, J., Massion, A. O., Kristeller, J., Peterson, L. G., Fletcher, K., Pbert, L., Linderking, C. O., & Santorelli, S. R. (1992), Effectiveness of a meditation-based stress reduction program in the treatment of anxiety disorders. *Amer. J. Psychiatry*, 149:936–943.

Keating, A. M., & Fretz, B. R. (1990), Christians' anticipations about counselors in response to counselor descriptions. *J. Counsel. Psychol.*, 37:293–296.

Kivley, L. R. (1986), Therapist attitude toward including religious issues in therapy. *J. Psychol. & Christianity*, 5:37–45.

Koenig, H. G. (1992), Religion and mental health in later life. In: *Religion and Mental Health*, ed. J. F. Schumaker. New York: Oxford University Press, pp. 177–188.

——— Ford, S. M., George, L. K., Blazer, D. G., & Meador, K. G. (1993), Religion and anxiety disorder: An examination and comparison of association in young, middle-aged, and elderly adults. *J. Anx. Disord.*, 7:321–342.

——— George, L. K., Blazer, D. G., & Pritchett, J. (1993), The relationship between religion and anxiety in a sample of community-dwelling older adults. *J. Geriat. Psychiatry*, 26:65–93.

——— Kvale, J. N., & Ferrel, C. (1988), Religion and well-being in later life. *The Gerontologist*, 28:18–28.

——— Siegler, I. C., Meador, K. G., & George, L. K. (1990), Religious coping and personality in later life. *Internat. J. Geriat. Psychiatry*, 5:123–131.

Krähl, W. (1995), Social and cultural factors in German psychiatry. In: *Handbook of Culture and Mental Illness: An International Perspective*, ed. I. Al-Issa. Madison, CT: International Universities Press, pp. 249–268.

Kroll, J., & Sheehan, W. (1989), Religious beliefs and practices among 52 psychiatric inpatients in Minnesota. *Amer. J. Psychiatry*, 146:67–72.

Kunzendorff, R. (1985), Repressed fear of inexistence and its hypnotic recovery in religious students. *Omega J. Death & Dying*, 16:23–33.

Larson, D. B., Hohmann, A. A., Kessler, L. G., & Meador, K. G. (1988), The couch and the cloth: The need for linkage. *Hosp. & Commun. Psychiatry*, 39:1064–1069.

Lea, G. (1982), Religion, mental health, and clinical issues. *J. Relig. & Health*, 21:336–351.

Lenski, G. (1963), *The Religious Factor*. Garden City, NY: Anchor Books.

Levin, J. S., & Markides, K. S. (1986), Religious attendance and subjective health. *J. Scient. Study of Relig.*, 25:31–40.

Lewis, K. N., & Lewis, D. A. (1985), Impact of religious affiliation on therapists' judgment of patients. *J. Consult. & Clin. Psychol.*, 53:926–932.

Littlewood, R., & Lipsedge, M. (1989), *Aliens and Alienists: Ethnic Minorities and Psychiatry*, 2nd ed. London: Unwin Hyman.

Loewenthal, K. M. (1995), *Mental Health and Religion*. London: Chapman & Hall.

London, P. (1986), *The Modes and Morals of Psychotherapy*, 2nd ed. Washington, DC: Hemisphere.

Lonetto, R., & Templer, D. I. (1986), *Death Anxiety*. New York: Hemisphere.

Long, D. L., & Elghanemi, S. (1987), Religious correlates of fear of death among Saudi Arabians. *Death Studies*, 11:89–98.

Lovekin, A., & Malony, H. N. (1977), Religious glossolalia: A longitudinal study of personality changes. *J. Scient. Study of Relig.*, 16:383–393.

Lukoff, D., Francis, L., & Turner R. (1992), Towards a more culturally sensitive DSM-IV. Psychoreligious and psycho-spiritual problems. *J. Nerv. & Ment. Dis.*, 180:673–682.

MacDonald, C. B., & Luckett, J. B. (1983), Religious affiliation and psychiatric diagnoses. *J. Scient. Study of Relig.*, 22:15–37.

Mahabeer, M., & Bhana, K. (1984), The relationship between religion, religiosity and death anxiety among Indian adolescents. *SA J. Psychol.*, 14:7–9.

Mahgoub, O. M., & Abdel-Hafeiz, H. B. (1991), Pattern of obsessive–compulsive disorder in Eastern Saudi Arabia. *Brit. J. Psychiatry*, 158:840–842.

Markides, K. S., Levin, J. S., & Ray, L. A. (1987), Religion, aging, and life satisfaction: An eight-year three-wave longitudinal study. *The Gerontologist*, 27:660–665.

Martin, J., & Stack, S. (1983), The effect of religiosity on alienation. *Sociolog. Focus*, 16:65–76.

Mayo, C. C., Puryear, H. B., & Richek, H. G. (1969), MMPI correlates of religiousness in late adolescent college students. *J. Nerv. & Ment. Dis.*, 149:381–385.

McCullough, M. E. (1995), The effects of prayer: Conceptual issues, research review, and research agenda. *J. Psychol. & Theol.*, 23:15–29.

McMordie, W. R. (1981), Religiosity and fear of death: Strength of belief system. *Psycholog. Rep.*, 49:921–922.

Meador, K. G., Koenig, H. G., Turnbull, J., Blazer, D. B., Hughes, D. C., & George, L. K. (1992), Religious affiliation and major depression. *Hosp. & Commun. Psychiatry*, 43:1204–1208.

Middleton, R., & Putney, S. (1962), Religion, normative standards, and behavior. *Sociometry*, 25:141–152.

Minean, J. O., & Brush, L. R. (1980–1981), The correlations of attitudes toward suicide with death anxiety, religiosity, and personal closeness. *Omega*, 11:317–324.

Morris, P. A. (1982), The effect of pilgrimage on anxiety, depression and religious attitude. *Psycholog. Med.*, 12:291–294.

Mowrer, O. H. (1960), Some constructive features of the concept of sin. *J. Counsel. Psychol.*, 7:185–188.

Muchnik, B., & Rosenheim, E. (1982), Fear of death, defense style, and religiosity among Israeli Jews. *Israeli J. Psychiatry & Rel. Sci.*, 19:157–164.

Murphy, H. B. M. (1978), The advent of guilt feeling as a common depressive symptom: A historical comparison on two continents. *Psychiatry*, 41:229–242.

Nayani, T., & Bhugra, D. (1996), Guilt, religion and ritual. In: *Psychiatry and Religion*, ed. D. Bhugra. London: Routledge, pp. 198–213.

Nias, D. K. B. (1973), Attitudes to the Common Market: A case study in conservatism. In: *The Psychology of Conservatism*, ed. G. D. Wilson. London: Academic Press, pp. 239–255.

Okasha, A., Saad, A., Khalil, A. H., El-Dawla, A. S., & Yahia, N. (1994), Phenomenology of obsessive-compulsive disorder: A transcultural study. *Comprehen. Psychiatry*, 35:191–197.

Osarchuk, M., & Tatz, S. (1973), Effect of induced fear of death on belief in afterlife. *J. Personal. & Soc. Psychol.*, 27:256–260.

Paris, J. (1991), Personality disorders, parasuicide and culture. *Transcult. Psychiatric Res. Rev.*, 28:25–39.

Parker, G. B., & Brown, L. B. (1982), Coping behaviors that mediate between life events and depression. *Arch. Gen. Psychiatry*, 39:1386–1391.

Payne, I. R., Bergin, A. E., & Loftus, P. E. (1992), A review of attempts to integrate spiritual and standard psychotherapy techniques. *J. Psychother. Integ.*, 2:171–192.

Peek, C. W., Curry, E. W., & Chalfant, H. P. (1985), Religiosity and delinquency over time. *Soc. Sci. Quart.*, 66:120–131.

Pescosolido, B. (1990), The social context of religious integration and suicide: Pursuing the network explanation. *Sociolog. Quart.*, 31:337–357.

Pfeiffer, W. (1982), Culture-bound syndromes. In: *Culture and Psychopathology*, ed. I. Al-Issa. Baltimore: University Park Press, pp. 201–218.

Pihlblad, C. T., & Adams, D. L. (1972), Widowhood, social participation and life satisfaction. *Internat. J. Aging & Hum. Develop.*, 3:323–330.

Poloma, M. M., & Pendleton, B. F. (1991), The effects of prayer and prayer experiences on measures of general well-being. *J. Psychol. & Theol.*, 19:71–83.

Pope, W., & Danigelis, N. (1981), Sociology's one law. *Soc. Forces*, 60:495–516.

Pressman, P., Lyons, J. S., Larson, D. B., & Gartner, I. (1992), Religion, anxiety and fear of death. In: *Religion and Mental Health*, ed. J. F. Schumaker. New York: Oxford University Press, pp. 98–109.

———— ———— ———— Strain, J. J. (1990), Religious belief, depression, and ambulation status in elderly women with broken hips. *Amer. J. Psychiatry*, 147:758–760.

Princeton Religion Research Center (1985), *Religion in America.* Princeton, NJ: The Gallup Poll.

Propst, L. R., Ostrom, R., Watkins, P., Dean, T., & Mashburn, D. (1992), Comparative efficacy of religious and nonreligious cognitive–behavioral therapy for the treatment of clinical depression in religious individuals. *J. Consult. & Clin. Psychol.*, 60:94–103.

Prosen, M., Clark, D. C., Harrow, M., & Fawcett, J. (1983), Guilt and conscience in major depressive disorders. *Amer. J. Psychiatry*, 140:839–844.

Rasmussen, C. H., & Johnson, M. E. (1994), Spirituality and religiosity: Relative relationship to death anxiety. *Omega*, 29:313–318.

Reed, P. R. (1992), Psychologists' views of a patient's religiousness. *Psycholog. Rep.*, 70:1031–1036.

Regier, D. A., Myers, J. K., Kramer, M., Robins, L. N., Blazer, D. G., Hough, R. L., Eaton, W. W., & Locke, B. Z. (1984), The NIMH Epidemiologic Catchment Area program: Historical context, major objectives, and study population characteristics. *Arch. Gen. Psychiatry*, 41:934–941.

Richards, P. S., & Potts, R. W. (1995), Using spiritual interventions in psychotherapy: Practices, successes, failures, and ethical concerns of Mormon psychotherapists. *Prof. Psychol.: Res. & Pract.*, 26:163–170.

Richardson, J. T., van der Lans, J., & Derks, F. (1986), Leaving and labelling: Voluntary and coerced disaffiliation from religious social movements. *Res. Soc. Movements, Conflicts & Change*, 9:97–126.

Richardson, V., Berman, S., & Piwowarski, M. (1983), Projective assessment of the relationships between the salience of death, religion, and age among adults in America. *J. Gen. Psychol.*, 109:149–156.

Rokeach, M. (1964), *The Three Christs of Ypsilanti.* New York: Alfred A. Knopf.

Rosenheim, E., & Muchnik, B. (1984), Death concerns in differential levels of consciousness as functions of defense strategy and religious belief. *Omega J. Death & Dying*, 15:15–24.

Sanua, V. D. (1969), Religion, mental health, and personality: A review of empirical studies. *Amer. J. Psychiatry*, 125:1203–1213.

Saugstad, L. F. (1989), Social class, marriage, and fertility in schizophrenia. *Schizophr. Bull.*, 15:9–43.

Shapiro, D. H., & Walsh, R. N., Eds. (1984), *Meditation: Classic and Contemporary Perspectives.* New York: Aldine.

Sheehan, W., & Kroll, J. (1990), Psychiatric patients' belief in general health factors and sin as causes of illness. *Amer. J. Psychiatry,* 147:112–113.

Smith, D. K., Nehemkis, A. M., & Charter, R. A. (1983), Fear of death, death attitudes and religious conviction in the terminally ill. *Internat. J. Psychiatry in Med.,* 13:221–232.

Smith, J. C. (1975), Meditation as psychotherapy: A review of the literature. *Psycholog. Bull.,* 82:558–564.

Spellman, C. M., Baskett, G. D., & Byrne, D. (1971), Manifest anxiety as a contributing factor in religious conversion. *J. Consult. & Clini. Psychol.,* 36:245–247.

Spendlove, D. C., West, D. W., & Stanish, W. M. (1984), Risk factors in the prevalence of depression in Morman women. *Soc. Sci. & Med.,* 18:491–495.

Spilka, B., Hood, R. W., Jr., & Gorsuch, R. L. (1985), *The Psychology of Religion: An Empirical Approach.* Englewood Cliffs, NJ: Prentice-Hall.

Stack, S. (1981), Suicide and religion: A comparative analysis. *Sociolog. Focus,* 14:207–220.

——— (1985), Religion and anomia: Regional vs national specifications. *J. Soc. Psychol.,* 125:133–134.

——— (1992), Religiosity, depression, and suicide. In: *Religion and Mental Health,* ed. J. F. Schumaker. New York: Oxford University Press, pp. 87–97.

Stark, R. (1968), Age and faith: A changing outlook at an old process. *Sociol. Anal.,* 29:1–10.

——— (1971), Psychopathology and religious commitment. *Rev. Relig. Res.,* 12:165–176.

——— Doyle, D. P., & Rushing, L. (1983), Beyond Durkheim: Religion and suicide. *J. Scient. Study of Relig.,* 22:120–131.

——— Kent, L., & Doyle, D. P. (1982), Religion and delinquency: The ecology of a "lost" relationship. *J. Res. Crime & Delinqu.,* 19:4–24.

Templer, D. I. (1970), The construction and validation of a death anxiety scale. *J. Gen. Psychol.,* 82:165–177.

——— (1972), Death anxiety in religiously involved persons. *Psycholog. Rep.,* 31:361–362.

——— Dotson, E. (1970), Religious correlates of death anxiety. *Psycholog. Rep.,* 26:895–897.

——— Ruff, C. F. (1975), The relationship between death anxiety and religion in psychiatric patients. *J. Thanatol.,* 3:165–168.

Tobacyk, J. (1983), Death threat, death concerns, and paranormal belief. *Death Ed.,* 7:115–124.

Vergote, A. (1988), *Guilt and Desire: Religious Attitudes and Their Pathological Derivatives*. New Haven, CT: Yale University Press.

Walters, R. P. (1987), A survey of client satisfaction in a lay counseling program. *J. Psychol. & Christianity*, 6:62–69.

Watson, P. J., Morris, R. J., Foster, J. E., & Hood, R. W. (1986), Religiosity and social desirability. *J. Scient. Study Relig.*, 25:215–232.

—— —— Hood, R. W. (1988a), Sin and self-functioning, Part 1: Grace, guilt, and self-consciousness. *J. Psychol. & Theol.*, 16:254–268.

—— —— —— (1988b), Sin and self-functioning, Part 2: Grace, guilt, and psychological adjustment. *J. Psychol. & Theol.*, 16:270–281.

—— —— —— (1990), Intrinsicness, self-actualization, and the ideological surround. *J. Psychol. & Theol.*, 18:40–53.

Weiner, B., Graham, S., Peter, O., & Zmuidinas, M. (1991), Public confession and forgiveness. *J. Personality*, 59:263–312.

Westman, A. S., & Canter, F. M. (1985), Fear of death and the concept of extended self. *Psycholog. Rep.*, 56:419–425.

Wikler, M. (1989), The religion of the therapist: Its meaning to Orthodox Jewish clients. *Hillside J. Clin. Psychiatry*, 11:131–146.

Williams, R. L., & Cole, S. (1968), Religiosity, generalized anxiety, and apprehension concerning death. *J. Soc. Psycholog*, 75:111–117.

Wilson, W., & Miller, H. L. (1968), Fear, anxiety, and religiousness. *J. Scient. Study of Relig.*, 7:111.

Woolfolk, R. L. (1975), Psychophysiological correlates of meditation. *Arch. Gen. Psychiatry*, 32:1326–1333.

Worthington, E. L., Jr. (1988), Understanding the values of religious clients: A model and its application to counseling. *J. Counsel. Psychol.*, 35:166–174.

—— Ed. (1994), Christian marriage counseling [Special issue]. *J. Psychol. & Christianity*, 13(2).

—— Dupont, P. D., Berry, J. T., & Duncan, L. A. (1988), Christian therapists' and clients' perceptions of religious psychotherapy in private and agency settings. *J. Psychol. & Theol.*, 16:282–293.

—— Kurusu, T. A., & McCullough, M. E. (1996), Empirical research on religion and psychotherapeutic processes and outcomes: A 10 year review and research prospective. *Psycholog. Bull.*, 119:448–487.

Wuthnow, R. (1978), *Experimentation in American Religion*. Berkeley: University of California Press.

Young, M., & Daniels, S. (1980), Born again status as a factor in death anxiety. *Psycholog. Rep.*, 47:367–370.

2.

Mental Illness in Medieval Islamic Society

Ihsan Al-Issa

Your companion
is not majnun [possessed]

                                    Sura 81: verse 22

While modern psychiatry and psychology in the Islamic countries is Western oriented, the roots of Islamic ethnopsychiatry
and ethnopsychology go back to the heights of Islamic civilization during the medieval period between the seventh and the
twelfth centuries. With the exception of the seminal volume by
Dols (1992), historians of medicine have shown little interest
in the history of Islamic psychiatry and often treated it as secondary to Arabian medicine[1] (Browne, 1921; Campbell, 1926).
Basic sources for an understanding of abnormality as well as
attitudes toward the mentally ill in Islamic society are the holy
book, the Qur'an and the prophet tradition *(hadith)*. However,

---

[1] The term *Arabian medicine* rather than *Islamic medicine* is used by historians
because the language of scholarship during the medieval era was Arabic, just as Latin
was the linguistic medium in Europe. The term *Arabian* does not necessarily imply
an Arab since other ethnic groups took part in the development of medicine for
which Arabic was the lingua franca. Similarly, the term *Islamic* does not exclude the
contribution of physicians from other religions.

the expansion of the Muslim empire brought influences from outside the Arabian penninsula and thus Islamic beliefs were fertilized by ideas, myths, folklore, and values from the newly expanded Muslim territories. Therefore, many ideas reported in this chapter on Islamic psychiatry may have nothing to do with basic Islamic dogma and beliefs.

Textbooks of Arabian medicine (e.g., Campbell, 1926) and the history of psychiatry (e.g., Alexander and Selesnick, 1966) often acknowledge the contribution of Muslim physicians during the medieval era in preserving the classic Greek medical heritage. However, this chapter will show that ancient medical theories were reformulated and modified to be adapted not only to the population in Arabia, but also to suit various cultural backgrounds in the vast medieval Islamic territories. In addition to the Hippocratic and Galenic humoral theories, Islamic society provided a wide range of concepts of mental illness as alternatives to the medical perspective. The contribution of Islamic culture is also reflected in a variety of approaches to the treatment of mental illness which goes beyond those derived from the Greek humoral theory. Thus, in addition to the reformulation of Greek theories by medieval Islamic physicians, this chapter will deal with popular theories of mental illness and its treatment.

THE MEDICAL APPROACH TO MADNESS

Galen's medical system had considerable influence on Islamic medicine. His medical works were first translated into Syriac and then into Arabic. The translation of Greek medical texts, including Galen's, was begun about A.D. 500 by Sergios of Ras Al-Ain (d. 536). In the eighth and ninth centuries, Johannitius or Hunayn Ibn Ishaq (d. 873) carried over the Greek works from Syriac into Arabic, the language of Islamic learning (Campbell, 1926). The humoral theory, the basic concept of Galen's theory of medicine, was derived from Hippocratic writings. The theory is based on the concept of the four elements of nature (air, earth, fire, and water) corresponding to blood, black bile, yellow bile, and phlegm, which are produced in the human body. Each humor is made of two qualities: blood is moist and hot, black bile is dry and cold, yellow bile is hot and dry, and phlegm is cold and moist. Humoral imbalance results in illness and the doctor has to manipulate the humors by their qualities to restore a humoral balance that is conducive to health. Health was based on the equilibrium or symmetry of temperaments (i 'tidal al-mizaj) in the physical as well as the psychological domains.

The reformulation of Greek medical theories, particularly the work of Galen, is reflected in the work of the physician Al-Razi (d. 932). He combined clinical experience in the Islamic hospital with his familiarity with Greek theories and Indian authors to produce his well-known medical encyclopedia called Kitáb al-Hawi or Continens. Although his major source of information was Galen, he cited a large number of other authorities such as Hippocrates, Plato, Rufus of Ephesus, Ishaq ibn Hunayn, and Jurjis ibn Jibril ibn Bakhtishu as well as others.

In Al-Hawi, Al-Razi devoted a whole chapter to melancholia. Symptoms of melancholia listed by Al-Razi such as sorrow, sadness, fear, irritation, misanthropy, love of seclusion, and dissatisfaction with the self and others, are reminiscent of the symptoms of depression. Consistent with his medical orientation, he recommended drugs for removing black bile, soporifics for the insomniacs, and narcotics for calming agitated patients.

The concept of lycanthropy (qutrub), which is often described by historians of psychiatry as the delusion that one is a wolf, is considered by Al-Razi and other Islamic physicians as a syndrome characterized by mental confusion that caused the sufferer to wander aimlessly. The patient secludes himself/herself in a graveyard, and cannot settle down in one place for more than an hour. The patient is described as ḥarban (fugitive) to emphasize social withdrawal and isolation from societies. The illness inflicts people more often in February. A qutrub originally means a fly which constantly and tirelessly hovers over the water, erratically hitting its surface. The term was used by Al-Razi to emphasize the lack of purpose of the patient.

Other symptoms of the lycanthrope or *qutrub* were yellow complexion, hollow eyes, dry mouth (thirst), sadness, and sorrow. The term *qutrub* may represent a new syndrome with its symptoms rather than the lycanthrope described by Western historians of psychiatry (cf. Dols, 1992).

The creativity of Al-Razi and other Muslim physicians is well demonstrated in their departure from the humoral theory. For example, Al-Razi believed that one type of melancholia is due to concern over small matters (i.e., obsessions) rather than to disturbance of humors. He suggested a "cognitive–behavioral" approach which deals with patients' obsessions with the past combined with encouraging the patient to carry out pleasurable activities (cf. Lewinson and Graf, 1973). Among Muslim physicians Al-Razi was the first to use the term *psychotherapy (Al-Ilaj Annafsani)* emphasizing the importance of the doctor always suggesting good health and encouraging the patient since changes of the soul precede those of the body (Ammar, 1987).

Following the work of Al-Razi, mental illness was extensively discussed in the works of Al-Majusi, Ishaq ibn Imran, and Ibn Sina. Al-Majusi (d. 982) wrote *Kitab al-Malaki* or *Kámil as-Sin'a a t-tibbiya,* a medical textbook consisting of both theoretical and practical parts. In the theoretical part, the effects of psychological events on health are discussed, such as the individual's environment, activity, rest, and nourishment. He attributed many illnesses to emotions; for example, anger, fear, anxiety, and passionate love may have negative health effects. Emotions are explained physiologically. Anger, for example, is the boiling of the blood in the heart, but with self-control, reason *('aql)* and patience, a person may resist emotions and illness. Happiness and gaiety can reduce grief and anxiety and thus restore health.

The second half of the *Kitab al-Malaki* dealt with the treatment of different illnesses such as lethargy, headache *(sada')* and vertigo, epilepsy, melancholia, lycanthropy, and love sickness. Melancholia is classified on etiological basis: cerebral, hypochondriacal, or *maraqiya* (ascending), and somatic. Treatment may consist of bleeding the patients, a drink made of poppy *(khashkhash),* and a special diet.

Ishaq Ibn 'Imran (d. A.D. 908) was a well-known physician who wrote a monograph on melancholia. His treatise was transmitted to medieval Europe through the Latin translation by Costantine Africanus (d. A.D. 1087). Like his predecessors, he distinguished between three types of melancholia; he indicated some common symptoms among them such as fear, sadness, delusions, and hallucinations. He supported the Hippocratic ideas against the view of epilepsy as a "sacred disease" caused by divine punishment. It was called "prophetic disease" *(al-marad al-kahina)* by people because of their ignorance of its causation which they attributed to the *jinn.* Doctors, on the other hand, called it the "great illness," "falling sickness" *(sar'),* or possession *(junun).* As for the treatment of mental illness, Al-Majusi suggested using persuasion together with music and potions. He listed 29 detailed recipes including pills, powders, electuaries, suppositories, laxatives, baths, oils, enemas, as well as others.

Ibn Sina's (d. A.D. 1073) *Qanun* has been more influential than Al-Majusi's book or Ibn 'Imran's monograph because of its comprehensiveness and its great influence on both medieval and Renaissance medicine in Europe as well as on Islamic medicine. It is difficult to give a full sense of the monumental encyclopedic work of Ibn Sina in this chapter, and we attempt to give a few examples of his exposition of symptoms, etiology, and treatment of mental illness.

Relevant to psychiatry is the discussion of phrenitis *(qaranitis),* its symptoms and treatment, as well as other brain inflammations such as severe delirium *(sabari),* lethargy or cold *sirsam (sirsam barid),* and sleepiness or apathy *(subat).* He distinguished phrenitis as hot *sirsam* from lethargy, cold *sirsam.* The symptoms are delirium *(hadhayan)* and mental confusion *(ikhti-lat)* with serious fever. Ibn Sina used the term *sirsam* (in Persian *sar* means head and *sam* means inflammation) as a general term to include fevers, burnt humors at the mouth of the stomach which rise to the brain, or inflammation in the brain and its membranes. *Sabari,* an excessive madness *(junun mufrit),* a new syndrome first reported by Ibn Sina, is caused by yellow bile. In *sabari,* the individual becomes disturbed *(mudturib)* and muddled *(mushawwash).* The illness is characterized by sleep disturbance, persistent insomnia, and increased agitation, hyperventilation, and forgetfulness. Although the symptoms of *sabari* may differ greatly from one case to another, it is treated by increasing moisture as well as restraining the patient by binding the limbs. Indeed, *sabari* is derived from the Arabic root *sabara* which can mean "to restrain." Other disturbances described by Ibn Sina are mental confusion and raving, frivolity *(ru'una)* and stupidity *(humq)*. In another chapter he dealt with mania *(maniya)* and rabies *(da' al-kalab)* (Dols, 1992).

Ibn Sina's description of melancholia is representative of symptoms of psychopathology in Islamic medieval society. The initial symptoms of melancholia are evil thoughts, fear without reason (phobia), quickness of anger, loneliness, trembling, dizziness. The fears tend to be irrational or even delusional, such as fear that the heavens are falling or the earth is about to swallow up the patient. Some patients may have fear of the *jinn*, or imagine things that are nonexistent (hallucinations) or imagine that they are kings, animals, devils, birds, or artisan tools (delusions). Those with morose temperament *(mizaj)* which arises from black bile may show concern with death, self-hate, obsession, and delusion.

Different etiologies are suggested for melancholia depending on whether it originates in the brain, the stomach, or other parts of the body. Ibn Sina believed that some foods or drinks result in black bile in the body and should be avoided by melancholics. Psychological factors such as excessive fear or grief are also considered as etiological factors in melancholia. A holistic approach is used by Ibn Sina in the treatment of melancholia, including psychological and physical manipulations. The patient is cheered up and seated in a temperate environment with moist air, scented with aromatic herbs, in addition to the provision of good food. Legumes, dried meat, lentils, cabbage, thick drinks, salted and acrid foods should be avoided. Fat and sweet food is beneficial. Harmful cold and dry temperament causing melancholia should be counteracted by cheering up the patient and using remedies such as musk, theriac (*tiryaq* is a general term used for narcotics in the Middle East), and mithridate.

Another syndrome described by Ibn Sina is love madness (*'ishq'*), which is described as a delusionary *(waswāsi)* illness with symptoms similar to melancholia. In the treatment of the lovesick, the patient should be evacuated if the condition was caused by a burnt humor. Then the body should be moistened and well nourished while the mind of the patient should be diverted from the love object. One way of diverting the patient is to arrange for a substitute for the loved person, particularly an experienced older woman. This procedure is quite similar to the Masters and Johnson (1970) treatment in which they provide specially trained female partner surrogates, except that in the Masters and Johnson sex therapy, the female surrogate aims at increasing the client's sexual arousal while Ibn Sina's older women aim at increasing the aversion of the client toward all women including the loved object. Sincere advice or a rebuke of the patient by the doctor is also recommended. The lovesick may be consoled by entertainment and/or be occupied with other activities such as hunting and games.

Muslim physicians such as Al-Razi, Al-Majusi, Ibn Imran, Ibn Sina, as well as others, had firmly established a medical model for understanding abnormal behavior and its treatment. They had described distinctive syndromes that had specific symptoms, etiologies, and treatment. The Greek syndromes were extended and new ones were added, resulting in a wider range of medicalized human behavior. Indeed, the study of insanity had become a branch of medicine with its own special syndromes and symptoms, as seen in the following excerpt from Ali ibn Rabban Al-Tabari's (d. 855) book *Firdaws al-hikma fi t-tibb:*

> I will mention in this chapter thirteen kinds of mental illnesses. Among them is epilepsy [*as-sar*]. . . . The people call it also the "prophetic illness" [*al-marad al-kahina*] because many of these sick people can tell the future and astonishing things appear to them. [Other illnesses include] despair [*al-wahsha*], madness [*al-waswasa*], delirium [*al-hadhayan*], damages to the imagination and intelligence [*fasad al-khayal wa l-'aql*], forgetfulness [*nisyan*], brutality in the open countryside with the wild animals

[al-tawahhush fi l-barari], insomnia [al-suhr], lethargy [al-subat], roaring in the head [al-dawi], vertigo [al-duwar], and swelling [waram]. In addition, I will mention six kinds of headache [as-suda'] [Dols, 1992, p. 115].

POPULAR APPROACHES TO MADNESS

In medieval Islamic society, the reformulation of Galenic medical theories existed side by side with popular concepts of madness. The public had defined a wide range of madness not as an illness, but as a condition that does not need treatment. The romantic fool, the holy fool, and the wise fool in Islamic society are mad men and women who show public ambivalence about madness, since they represent a social ideal of passionate chaste love, piety, and intelligence that is admired and envied in Islamic society (Dols, 1992). Indeed, some of these fools have become part of Islamic popular culture and remain part of public imagery up to the present time. These cultural types suggest that Islamic society had conceived a broader concept of madness, had shown less separation between sanity and madness, and was more tolerant of deviant behavior.

The Romantic Fool

Ishq' or excessive passionate love is considered as a form of madness in both medical and religious contexts as well as in popular culture in medieval Islamic society. Ibn Sina's treatise on love (Risala fi l-'ishq) is an example of the medical perspective which was referred to earlier in this chapter. Sacred love refers to the love of God by the holy fool or the mystic who holds religious ideals but whose love of God borders on the abnormal. Profane love or the love of another human being which may cause love sickness will be dealt with here.

The Arabic word 'Ishq' or excessive love is often associated with pain and unhappiness and this can be seen in Arabic songs and poetry (Giffen, 1971). Thus, medieval monographs on profane love contain poetry and stories depicting the circumstances and negative consequences of love. For example, an anthology by Al-Sarraj (d. A.D. 1106) entitled *Masari'al-'ushaq*, is a series of illustrations of the tragic consequences of passionate love. Indeed, the word *masari'* is the plural of *masra'* which is derived from a verb literally meaning "to throw down to the ground," but it is also used as in "falling down in an epileptic fit," "to go mad," or "to be killed in a battle." Similarly, an Islamic fundamentalist and moralist view of passionate love is expressed by Ibn Al-Jawzi (d. A.D. 1200) in his book *Dhamm al-hawa* in which he attributed incest, murder, suicide, madness and other disastrous consequences to passionate love (Giffen, 1971).

Passionate love is also considered by popular authors as a psychological stress that could aggravate physical illness. In his book, *al-Aghani,* Abu l-Faraj Al-Isbahani related the case of ja 'far ibn al-Mansur, who claimed to love a female *jinn.* As a result of his excessive passion for this imaginary woman, his epilepsy was aggravated and he suffered several epileptic attacks a day until he died. Such a dismal picture of passionate love in medieval Islamic society was seen in other early civilizations (Mace and Mace, 1980; Kakar and Ross, 1986). For most of Western history until the eighteenth century Enlightenment, love was not expected to end well; consider, for example, the fate of Romeo and Juliet or Ophelia and Hamlet (Hatfield and Rapson, 1996).

One of the best examples of the relationship between madness and romantic chaste love in popular Islamic literature is that of Qays, nicknamed *Majnun,* whose love for Layla drove him crazy. Apart from Qays' obsession with his beloved, his behavior reflected deviation from Arab cultural norms (Dols, 1992). A man was not expected to express his love publicly since it not only brought disgrace and dishonor to the woman and her family, but was against the tradition in which the families, as represented by the fathers, usually announced the marriage. Qays' aimless wandering out into the desert barefoot and bareheaded in rags was a violation of Muslim dress decorum. *Majnun* is depicted by Nizami in A.D. 1188 as a "psychotic" who blankly stared out into space, hallucinated (a hidden voice called out the name of Layla to him), and was followed and tormented by children in the streets. On the other hand, the belief that Qays was possessed by the *jinn* could help to explain not only his madness, but also his exceptional gift and inspiration for poetry.

In contrast to *Majnun,* Zulaykha's love for Yusuf (Joseph) elaborated by Jami (d. 1492) and cited in Dols (1992), from the story of Yusuf in the twelfth chapter of the Qur'an, had resulted in a different type of madness. Zulaykha was not disoriented as *Majnun,* and for the most part she behaved in a sane and rational manner. In fact, her story is full of plots and intrigues to win the love of Yusuf. During her "manic" attacks, however, she wailed and cried, rent her clothes, scratched her face with her hands, and tore out her hair. She also became agitated, crying and laughing. She expressed suicidal thoughts, threatening to kill herself to arouse Yusuf's compassion. A mood disorder seems to characterize Zulaykha more than *Majnun.* Other descriptions of the behavior of romantic fools can be found in *The Book of the Thousand and One Nights,* such as in the story of Kamar Al-Zaman and Budur.

Current textbooks on sex and love, which discuss the relationship between passionate love and mental illnesses such as anxiety, seem to support the medieval concept of the romantic fool (Hatfield and Rapson, 1996). Hatfield and Rapson cite the British novelist Winterson (1987) on the "symptoms" of love which are quite similar to those of anxiety: "Lovers are not at their best when it matters. Mouths dry up, palms sweat, conversation flags and all the time the heart is threatening to fly from the body once and for all. Lovers have been known to have heart attacks. Lovers drink too much from nervousness and cannot perform. They eat too little and faint during their fervently wished consummation" (p. 66). However, the direction of causality between passionate love and anxiety is not clear. Passionate love may cause anxiety. On the other hand, Hatfield, Brinton, and Cornelius (1989) found that anxiety increases vulnerability to passionate love.

The Wise Fool

The wise fool is an eccentric individual who only appears to be mad, but is clever at criticizing, warning, or making fun of others with a moral message (Dols, 1992). *The Book of the Wise Fools (Kitab 'Uqala al-majanin)* by Al-Naysaburi (d. 1016) is mainly devoted to this group of "abnormal" individuals who were integrated into Muslim society. He suggested that we cannot separate sanity from insanity. Since the world is created by God in opposites (youth vs. old age, strength vs. weakness, etc.), human life is a mixture of health and illness, reason and madness; and therefore the sane are never free from madness.

A sample of a list of the subtypes of madness reported by Al-Naysaburi may give some idea about the classification of madness in Islamic society. The classification of some mad people reported by him is based on etiology: the *ma'tuh* is someone who was born *majnun;* the *mamrur* is a man who was mad because of an excess of bile in his body; the *mamsus* is someone whom the *jinn* had attacked; and the *'ashiq* is an individual who is overwhelmed by love. Other classification was based on behavior and symptoms: the *akraq* is a person who is stupid and unable to manage his own affairs; the *mukhabbal, makhbul,* or *makhtabil* is confused, disturbed, or muddled; the *mahwus* is the religious visionary or the deluded; the *ahwaj* is reckless and foolhardy; and the *mustahtir* is heedless and thoughtless. However, the major part of the *Book of the Wise Fools* gives accounts of over a hundred wise fools. These fools come from different walks of life and included males, females, and slaves as well as different age groups, races, and professions. They provide good examples of the behavior of disturbed people and how society perceived them and reacted to them. Many of these wise fools had little concern with their appearance and may appear naked in public disregarding social convention. This outrageous behavior may be contrasted with their poetic gifts and their clever critique of society and its values. Many of them may have severe psychological disturbances and may end in hospitals. However, their disturbance tends to be attributed to spiritual factors, particularly divine love rather than to physical factors. Some of the wise fools may show psychotic symptoms. For example, Falit was an idiot *(ma'tūh)* who lived in Kufa and who believed that he was the caliph.

   Sadik is another idiot who lived wildly in the ruined buildings, graveyards, and forests. Other wise fools were mystics whose expression of love of God was mistaken for madness. One example is given in a tale in which Malek Ibn Dinar saw boys stoning a madman in Basra. The boys said that the madman claimed to see his Lord all the time. Malik stopped the boys and asked the madman what was the matter. The madman asked Malek, "What do they claim?" Malik replied, "They say you constantly see your Lord." The madman cried and recited lines of poetry saying that although his eyes cannot see Him, he can see Him with his heart. Using "seeing" in a metaphorical sense seems to have been misinterpreted as a hallucination by the boys. However, despite what appears to be the manifestations of psychopathology in the behavior of the wise fools, other facets of their personality seem to have had represented some ideals which were admired by the general public. Dols (1992) summed up the qualities of these wise fools in the personality of Buhlul: "The majority of the tales show Buhlul as a God-fearing admonisher and teacher. Aside from the stereotype of the village idiot, Buhlul was, in turn, a deeply religious man who had turned away from all worldly cares, trusting only in God; a skilled preacher who measured himself by the severest rules and did not hesitate about addressing his exhortations to the highest authority; an unconventional social critic. Almost all the facts of the other wise fools in Al-Naysaburi's collection are combined in Buhlul" (p. 358).

   Ibn Al-Jawzi (d. A.D. 1170) in his book *Akhbar al-Hamqua wal mughafalin (News of the Stupid and the Imbeciles)* also dealt with the wise fools. He differentiated between Al-Hamaq (stupidity) and Al-junun (madness). In Al-Hamaq, there is something wrong with the behavior which is a means to obtain a certain goal even though the goal itself seems to be sound. On the other hand, Al-Junun is characterized by a defect in both behavior and its goals. One of the Mughafalīn cited by Ibn Al-Jawzi is of an *Amir* (ruler) who tried to catch his bird that flew away by ordering that the gates of the city be locked. One of the Mughafalīn discussed by Ibn Al-Jawzi, and who is still alive in the imagination and folklore of Arab Muslims, is Juha (Mulla Nasrudin in Iran and Turkey). The following two pleasantries which are current in Muslim countries show indeed that he demonstrates apparent "stupidity" in his behavior (pleasantry no. 1) as well as a deep understanding of the diversity of human reactions and an awareness of the relativity of social norms (pleasantry no. 2).

1. Juha ran naked to an appointment in a nearby town. People asked what happened to him. "I was in such a hurry to get dressed that I forgot my clothes" (Shah, 1971).
2. Juha rode his donkey with his son walking behind him. "What a cruel father; he rides the donkey and leaves his son to walk," people said. He now asked his son to ride the donkey and he walked behind him. "What an impolite son; he rides the donkey, leaving his father walking," people said. When both of them rode the donkey, people said, "What a cruel man. He rides the donkey with his son, having no pity on the donkey." Both Juha and his son now walked behind the donkey. "Look at these two imbeciles (mughafeleen) who do not use their donkey for riding," people said. Finally, Juha and his son carried the donkey. "Look at these mad (majanin) who are carrying their donkey," people said (Al-Najjar, 1978).

THE ISLAMIC MENTAL HOSPITAL: THE *BIMARISTAN*

One important contribution of Islamic medicine is the care of the mentally ill in a hospital, which is called *bimaristan* (a place for the sick in Persian) or *maristan.* The first Islamic hospital was established in Baghdad in the early ninth century and was supported by the Caliph Harun Al-Rashid (d. 809) and his vizier Yahya ibn Barmak. Another early hospital was founded in Cairo in A.D. 872–873 by Ahmad ibn Tulun, the Abbasid governor of Egypt (Dols, 1992).

The hospitalization of the mentally ill was partly the result of the medicalization of a wide range of behavior by doctors, as well as the financial and moral support of rulers who regarded the hospital as a channel for fulfilling their religious obligations of charity to the poor and the needy (Dols, 1992). In contrast to the hospital in the West which started as a religious institution, the Islamic hospital was a secular establishment where mental illness was attributed to organic pathology. A variety of physical treatments were given to patients including baths, fermentations, compresses, bandaging, massage, bloodletting, cupping, and cautery. Medications included sedatives and stimulants. Antidepressants which were called *mufarreh al-nafs* (gladdening of the spirit) were used to reduce sadness. Bürgel (1974) described a famous drug during the medieval Islamic era was called *mufarrih al-nafs* (gladdening of the soul) and was expected to change grief and sadness into joy. There were simple and compound versions of the drug (certain kinds of plants and fruits and fragrances, gold, silver, and precious stones such as ruby for the simple version with additional ingredients for the compound drug). The formulas for *mufarrih al-nafs* are classified according to the different temperaments of patients as well as their social class. The upper class formula included jewels and other expensive ingredients, while the ingredients used to treat the lower class were simpler. Theriac or *tiryaq*,[2] a miracle drug, was recommended very frequently for the mentally ill. Ibn Abi Usaybi'a (d. 1270) described how at Nur Al-Din Hospital in Damascus, a doctor prescribed opium to be added to the barleywater for a man with *maniya*, that is, the bestial madness *(al-junun Al-sabu'i)*. The man improved and the condition disappeared (Dols, 1992).

There are many historical accounts of Islamic mental institutions such as those by the twelfth century traveler Ibn Jubayr (Broadhurst, 1952); Leo Africanus (1896) (15th and 16th century); and Eviliya Chaleby (17th century) (Leiser and Dols, 1987). The hospital is also described in popular literature such as in *The Thousand and One Nights* in the stories of "The Sleeper Awakens" and "The Three Madmen's Tales." These hospitals were neither the dungeons described by Foucault (1965) nor

---

[2] The terms *tiryaq* or *ma'jun* (paste) are used in many Islamic countries to cover a variety of hallucinogenic drugs including hashish.

the bedlams whose inhabitants were objects of curiosity. Hospitals described by Al-Maqrizi, the Egyptian historian, and by Eviliya Chelebi, the Turkish traveler, show that they were built in the center of cities rather than in isolated places (Leiser and Dols, 1987). Patients were in constant contact with the community. Visits from relatives, friends, and members of the community made the hospital a social center and reduced the isolation of patients. In these communal Islamic societies, sickness was considered as an occasion for the group to show social support and be charitable to other Muslims who were in distress. The following episode related by Al-Maqrizi show how disturbed patients could easily interact with an important visitor to the hospital such as Ibn Tulun, the governor of Egypt:

> Once he entered the hospital and stopped before one of the madmen who was shackled, and the madman shouted out to him: "Oh Amir, hear my words: I am not mad as you think, for I only acted that way as a ruse. I have a strong desire in my heart for a large pomegranate." So the governor ordered one for him immediately, and the man was delighted with it, tossing it in his hand and weighing it. Then, the madman, taking Ibn Tulun by surprise, threw the pomegranate at him. It splattered over his clothes, covering his entire chest. Thereupon, Ibn Tulun ordered them to guard the madman, and the governor did not return again after that incident to inspect the maristan [Dols, 1992, p. 117].

In the Islamic hospital, patients were frequently restrained, suggesting that only the most severely ill who posed a danger to themselves or others were hospitalized. Muslims are reluctant to send their relatives to mental institutions unless they are violent and cannot be controlled. This tendency to keep most patients at home may reflect Islamic cultural attitudes which emphasize that the basic responsibility for the insane is the family. The Qur'an states: "Do not give to the incompetent (sufaha') their property that God has assigned to you to manage; provide for them and clothe them out of it; and speak to them honourable words" (Sura 4:5). Al-Naysaburi in The Book of the Wise Fools (Kitab Uqala al-Majanin) reported cases of severe psychopathology that were cared for at home. Baja is a wise fool who lived in medieval Kufa, a town in the center of Iraq. She became raving mad but her family confined her to a room in the farthest part of their house where she received medical attention. Another case is that of Jasas, the Deluded, who seemed to present a picture of mania: he overslept, but when he woke up he spread terror and alarm by his raving and wandering about aimlessly. Yet, his Bedouin tribe in Arabia looked after him.

PSYCHOLOGICAL TREATMENT IN ISLAMIC MEDICINE

The humoral theory in Islamic medicine based on Galenism suggests that by manipulating the physiological state of the patient through drugs or diet, it is possible to change emotions and other psychological states. However, the hospital gave Muslim physicians the opportunity to observe a large number of patients for a long period and to evaluate the outcome of organic treatment. In the middle of the eleventh century, Sa'id ibn Bakhtishu was one of the first physicians who questioned the Galenic interpretation of mental illness and its treatment. In his book *Risalah fi Tibb,* he pointed out how the staff of the *bimaristan* use psychological methods with patients by pacifying their nerves, distracting them, and entertaining them with songs. He argued in favor of psychological causes of mental illness including passionate love *('Ishq).* Although organic therapies dominated Islamic medicine, psychological methods were also used (Dols, 1992).

Bürgel (1973) devoted an article to the psychological treatment in medieval Islamic medicine of both physical and psychological problems. He indicated that many titles of medical volumes included both the psyche and the soma; for example, a volume entitled *Book about the Welfare of Bodies and Souls (Kitak masalih al-abdan wal-anfus)* by Abu Zaid in the third century A.H. and another *The book of Guidance for the Welfare of Souls and Bodies (Kitab al irshad limasalih al-anfus wal ejsad)* by Ibn Jumai in the sixth century.

Music is used for the relief of physical and psychological distress by medieval Islamic physicians. An Arab legend narrated by Bürgel is that the first medical men of mankind were the inventors of the reed pipe in Physgia and Mysia. Their flute playing healed the suffering of the souls and thereby relieved physical pain (Ibn abi Usaibia, cited in Bürgel, 1973). Bürgel also cited Ibn Hindu, an author of the tenth century, in his *Miftah at-tibb, The Key to Medicine,* explaining the relationship between music and mood: "We know that there is a sort of melody and a way of beating the drum and blowing the flute and a kind of rhythm which evoke sadness, and that there is another kind evoking joy, one which appeases and relaxes, another which disquiets, and oppresses, another which makes one sleepless, and another which lulls one to sleep, and in the therapy of melancholics we prescribe [listening to music in] the gamuts that are fitting and useful to them" (Bürgel, 1973, p. 163).

Ishaq ibn 'Imran advocated both music and dancing for the treatment of melancholia. The emphasis on the spiritual effects of music, particularly as a means of revelation, was part of sufi rituals in the later medieval era (Farmer, 1929). Music therapy may be traced back to David's healing of Saul with music. In the Qur'an, birds and mountains joined David in song (21:79–80). In *Rasa'il* or Epistles, of the tenth century *Ikwan as Safa,* it was suggested that music melodies may relieve suffering from pain and illness, reduce violence, and heal sickness. In the Islamic hospital, music was used as a method of treatment.

In using music in therapy, its orthodox prohibition was disregarded by physicians. Similar attitude was taken towards the use of wine in therapy. Bürgel gives the example of Maimonides, the Jewish physician and philosopher of the twelfth century, who lived in Egypt and gave the following advice to Al-Malik Al-Afdal, Saladin's son, after recommending music and wine: "May our Lord not blame this modest servant because he recommended in this prescription the preparation of wine and listening to music, both of which are abhorred by religious law. Yet, he does not prescribe the use of these things; he only mentions and recommends everything necessary for the medical art. Religion prescribes what is helpful for the other world, while the physician, on the contrary, has to indicate what is beneficial, and to warn of what is noxious, in this world" (Bürgel, 1973, p. 164).

Bürgel (1973) described two psychotherapeutic methods, one is based on suggestion, which he concluded was an extension and elaboration of the Greek psychotherapeutic techniques, and second, based on arousing fear, shock, or shame, which was an original contribution of Islamic physicians. I will present case examples to illustrate the two techniques where suggestion was extensively used in the treatment of delusions by both the Greek and Islamic physicians. For example, Ishaq bin Imran at Qairawan used a method reported earlier during the first century A.D. by Rufus of Ephesus, to treat men who imagined that they had no heads. They were treated by having them wear a leaden helmet which by its weight reminded them constantly of the existence of their heads. Galen also used suggestion in the treatment of a man who believed that he had swallowed a snake which was causing severe stomach pain. He gave the patient an emetic and bandaged his eyes. When the patient vomited, Galen put a snake similar to the one described by the patient into the vomit and the bandage was removed. The patient thought that his pain had been cured.

In the same vein, Ibn Sina treated a deluded prince who imagined himself to be a cow. He would low and urge that he should be killed so that his flesh would be cooked into a stew. He stopped eating and his life was in danger. The patient was told that a butcher was coming to kill him. With a knife in his hand, Ibn Sina entered the patient's room with two attendants saying, "Where is this cow that I may kill?" The patient made a noise like a cow. Ibn Sina ordered that the patient's hands and feet be bound. Putting his hand on the patient's side, he said, "He is very lean and not fit to be killed; he must eat fodder until he is fat." The patient ate in the hope that he might become fat and they might kill him, but within a month he was completely recovered (Browne, 1921). Ibn Abi Usaybia cited by Bürgel (1973) reported a similar delusional case treated by Ibn Malka. The patient believed that he carried a precious vase on his head and feared its being knocked off. Ibn Malka arranged it so that one of his assistants threw a similar vase down from the roof at the same moment when another assistant pretended to knock down the imagery vase off the patient's head. This was a shock to the patient who believed that it was his vase that was broken and in this way he lost his delusion. It is important to note that both ancient and medieval physicians tended to reinforce the patient's delusions as an initial point in the process of therapy instead of denying the "reality" of these delusions as it is usually practiced in modern psychiatry.

Cases demonstrating the effects of suggestion on physiological responses reported by Bürgel (1973) would have been difficult to conceive within a narrow biomedical model, but recent development in psychoneuroimmunology and holistic medicine in the West make them more relevant. Ibn Abi Usaybia relates a story of a traveling merchant bitten by a venomous snake while he slept; he was persuaded by a companion that it was a thorn and pretended to pull it out of his foot to relieve his pain. However, when he was told later that it was a snake bite, he lost consciousness and died. Ibn Abi Usaybia explained the interaction between psychological and physiological factors in this case: "the reason was that imagination *(awham)* exerted strong influence on the body. After realizing that the injury he had received was a snake bite, the man was so impressed by this idea that the remainder of the venom still in that spot started to flow through the body. When it reached the heart, it killed him" (cited in Bürgel, 1973, p. 168).

The concept of illusion or *wahm* as a result of suggestion has also played an important role in popular medicine. In his textbook, *Firdaws al-hikma fit t-tibb,* the ninth century physician Ibn Rabban Al-Tabari attributed the effects of many magical and religious prescriptions such as talismans to the patient's illusion *(wahm).* He suggested that it was only the person who had the illusion *(mutawahhim)* and who is vulnerable to illusive persuasion could benefit from such treatment.

The other therapeutic techniques using emotions of fear, shock, and shame were illustrated in several cases by Bürgel (1973). In one case 'Issa, the advisor to Harun ar-Rashid, did not follow the diet which was expected to reduce his overweight. The court physician, Abu Quraysh told 'Issa that his illness was incurable and he would live only for a few weeks more. The patient was so frightened that he lost much weight within a short time. A second case is that of the concubine of

caliph Harun Al-Rashid, who suddenly suffered from a paralyzed arm. The physician rushed toward her in the presence of
the royal court and stretched his hand as if he intended to lift
her skirt. Afraid to be shamed in public she used her paralyzed
arm to stop him. A third case is of Mansur Ibin Ishaq, the Amir
of the city of Bukhara, treated by Al-Razi for rheumatism that
totally paralyzed him. After attempting several therapies, Al-
Razi used a combination of physical and psychological treatment: After a long hot bath and a potion, he suddenly threatened the Emir with a knife which forced him out of rage and
fear to jump to his feet. Al-Razi ran away to tell him from a
distance that "he had applied a psychotherapeutic method
('ilaj-e nafsani) to avoid a lengthy treatment. Al-Razi wrote to
the Emir: I provoked you intentionally in order to increase the
natural warmth which hereby became strong enough to dissolve the humours already softened by the bath and the drugs"
(Bürgel, 1973, p. 171).

One form of melancholia treated during the medieval Islamic period is lover's grief. The word *soda* in Persian and Urdu
means both melancholy and passion. In some cases of this love
sickness a man has to conceal his love for some reason or another. The physician's usual procedure is to exclude physical
causes, then to find out the psychological nature of the illness.
Ibn Sina described a procedure whereby he could discover the
name of the beloved. In order to make the patient think of his
beloved, the physician recites the names of families, persons,
countries, towns, streets and houses, and at the same time feels
the pulse of the patient until he identifies the loved person:
Ibn Sina suggested that if all other cures did not work (see p.
49) uniting the two according to religious rules (i.e., marriage)
is the final solution.

PROPHETIC MEDICINE AND ISLAMIC HEALING

The Qur'an gives little guidance on medical matters. However,
the medical tradition of the prophet *(Hadith)* provided Muslims
with certain values and behavior regarding their physical well-
being, and perpetuated those aspects of Arabian folk medicine
which were compatible with Islamic beliefs.

The Prophetic Medicine (Al-Tibb Al-nabawi) by Ibn Qayyim Al-Jawziya (d. A.D. 1350) is one of the best examples of Islamic and prophetic medicine (abstracted by Dols, 1992). Ibn Qayyim refers to the Qur'anic verse "those in whose heart is a sickness" clearly showing that the heart or soul is distinguished from the body—physical health is determined by the state of the soul as expressed in religious piety. Illness is conceived as a trial or a blessing for the faithful, and those who endure fatal or chronic illnesses such as plague and epilepsy are considered martyrs who are assured a place in paradise. The reward of the faithful as a result of endurance of suffering is illustrated in the following hadith:

> Ibn 'Abbas said: "Shall I not show you a woman who is one of the people of paradise?" "Yes indeed," I said. So he replied, "This black woman came to the Prophet and said: 'I am an epileptic, and when I have a seizure, I am uncovered. So will you supplicate God on my behalf?' He answered, 'If you wish, you may bear the affliction patiently and be assured of paradise, or I can beseech God to heal you.' She declared, 'I shall be patient, But will you pray to God that I will not be uncovered?' So he prayed for her" [Dols, 1992, p. 251].

Unlike Christianity, illness is not sent as punishment of Muslim believers and they are not to be blamed for their afflictions: "There is no fault in the blind, and there is no fault in the lame and there is no fault in the sick, neither in yourself . . . there is no fault in you that you eat all together, or in groups separately" (Sura 24:61; see also 48:17). The concept of original sin and illness as a result of the inherent sinfulness of human beings does not exist in Islam. The dichotomy between the "heavenly soul" and the "earthly sinful body" (Dols, 1992) in Christianity is not seen in Islam. The mind and body are united in health and sickness.

Prayer is recognized in prophetic medicine as a method of healing the sick. Bürgel (1973) cited the fifteenth-century scholar, Al-Suyuti, from the comment on a prophet tradition *(hadith)* which prescribed prayer against toothache:

> First there is the divine command to worship. Secondly there is the psychological aspect, i.e., the sufferer will forget his pain in

his prayer so that his feeling of pain will grow less and so finally his strength will overthrow the pain and cast it out. And thirdly it teaches that the best doctor is he who uses all manner of guile to strengthen the faculties. At one moment he will give strength by food, at another by setting in motion joy and grief or even hope and fear. But prayer is the best of them all.

There is no miraculous healing or exorcism described in the Qur'an except that of Jesus' healing of the blind and leperous as well as raising the dead (3:49; 5:113). However, healing is mentioned several times in the Qur'an. Since the Qur'an itself is described as a healing or *shafa* (17:82; 41:44), its verses were used in incantations, invocations, and prayers for the sick. Although exorcism is not part of Muslim religion, the *jinn* or spirits are recognized in the Qur'an. The *jinn* may possess persons, harm them, or drive them mad. Indeed, opponents of the prophet accused him of being possessed by the *jinn (majnun)* but the Qur'an defended him against such accusation and affirmed his position as the messenger of God. However, in pre-Islamic Arab society, the concept of the prophet, the *majnun*, the diviner and the poet, tended to overlap with each other because they all have contact with the supernatural world (Dols, 1992). While the prophet receives his message directly from God, the diviners *(kahana)* receive messages from the *jinn* during ecstatic experience. The poet is also believed to be inspired by the *jinn*. Like the *majnun*, he can receive secret or special knowledge (the Arabic word *sha'ir* for a poet literally means the conscious or the knower).

Both exorcism and magical practices seem to have been allowed in Islamic society as long as they are practiced in the name of God to help people (e.g., use His sacred names in amulets and talismans) rather than inflict harm on them in collaboration with the devil. White magicians, who include exorcists, work through God's power. The exorcists *(mu'azzimun)* usually start by asking for God's help, speak with the *jinni*, and demand that the *jinni* depart from the possessed body. The incantations of the exorcist are quite similar to the invocations of God during ordinary Muslim prayer. In contrast, black magicians claim that they control the demons by offerings and actions that violate Muslim law. This distinction between exorcists or white magicians and black magicians is expressed by Ibn Al-Nadim in his *fihrist,* an extensive bibliography on magic written between A.D. 987 and 1010.

After the death of the prophet, the cult of saints developed as a result of the influence of paganism and Christianity. These healing cults are in conflict with fundamental Islamic beliefs, even though they still exist today in the Muslim world. Visits to the tombs of these saints may be a remnant of the cult of Asclepius (the Greek God of medicine) modified by Christians, and still surviving in the Mediterranean region. Visits to the saints in Muslim countries are described by Gilsenan (1973) and Lane (1860) in Egypt, by Crapanzano (1973) in Morocco, and by Özturk (1964), and Özturk and Volkan (1977) in Turkey. The visits to the tombs of Sidi 'Ali ben Hamdush and Sidi Ahmed Dghughi in Morocco described by Crapanzano (1973) are typical of the healing shrines in Muslim countries. Clients of these shrines may simply seek the blessing *(baraka)* of the saint or the control of the possessing *jinn.* Temple sleep (incubation) may result in a dream that gives patients instructions about the treatment and prognosis of their illness. The visitor may undergo purification and is expected in some shrines to take part in an ecstatic dance *(hadra),* and eventually offer a sacrifice.

In his book, *Prophetic Medicine* (1978), Ibn Qayyim Al-Jawziya discussed belief in the evil eye in medieval Islamic societies. It is believed that the person with the evil eye may have a poisonous power or may emit a harmful ethereal substance to injure his or her victims. The influence of the evil eye may simply be through the will of God when the eyes meet, or the working of the spirits which are connected with the evil eye. The transfer of the evil may not be necessarily through contact or sight, but through the spirit. Among the methods recommended for prevention and treatment of the harmful effects of the evil eye are recitation of the *Fatiha* (the opening verse in the Qur'an), the Throne Verse, or the writing out of verses

from the Qur'an, to be soaked in water and drunk by the
sick person.

CONCLUSION

The history of Islamic psychiatry raises many questions about
psychopathology in Islamic society. Similar to ancient physicians, Muslim physicians extensively discussed depression and
melancholia, but the concept of psychosis was not formulated,
even though both hallucinations and delusions were reported
as symptoms of mental illness. It may be that psychotic behavior
was more accepted in these societies and was less recognized
as a mental illness by the general population. Even in present
Muslim countries such as Turkey, vignettes of a paranoid psychotic and a simple schizophrenic were recognized as mental
illness by only 10 percent of villagers and 15 percent of an
urban sample (Özturk and Volkan, 1977). In contrast, corresponding data from a small town in the Canadian prairies show
that 70 percent noted that there was something wrong with the
simple schizophrenic and 69 percent considered the paranoid
schizophrenic as mentally ill (Cumming and Cumming, 1957).
The presence of only severe cases in Islamic mental institutions
suggests that various types of disturbed behavior is tolerated
or dealt with outside the medical sphere. Of course, medical
authorities may have been selective in reporting depression,
which may have been more successfully treated by them than
psychosis. It is also possible that hallucinatory behavior such as
visions was accepted in medieval Islamic society and may not
have been considered as mental illness (Al-Issa, 1995b).
    Alcoholism was also not discussed by Muslim medical au-
thors. Alcohol is described in the Qur'an as nourishing (16:67),
and drinking was initially allowed, except that intoxication was
forbidden during prayer (see chapter 9). However, since Muslims have to pray five times per day, disturbing behavior associated with drunkenness was almost inevitable during communal
prayer. This situation eventually led to the complete prohibition of drinking: "Satan only desires to precipitate enmity and

hatred between you in regard to wine and gambling, and to bar you from the remembrance of God, and from prayer" (5:93). Thus, there was, in general, some ambivalence about drinking during the early Islamic period and in medieval Islamic society. It is possible that although alcoholism and dependence on alcohol did exist, they were not considered as mental illness and were not treated by physicians.

Suicide was also rarely mentioned as a symptom of mental illness, which is consistent with contemporary reports suggesting that this behavior is very rare in Africa and Asia (Al-Issa, 1995a). Ibn Zohr or Avenzoar (1092–1162), in his book *Kitab al-Taissir (Facilitation),* was the first Muslim physician to list the desire to die as a symptom of melancholia. He reported that he had seen many people who committed suicide by hanging or drowning (el-Otmani and Moussaoui, 1992). It may be that in Islamic society suicidal behavior was not usually used as a means of coping by patients and its low rates did not attract the attention of many other medieval physicians.

Unlike medieval Europe in which theology dominated medicine, Muslim scholars developed secular institutions in which a rational system of medicine was practiced without religious interference. For example, physicians such as Averroës or Ibn Rushd (1126–1198) contributed to the separation of religion from science. He suggested that there is a double truth, one is related to faith (i.e., religion) and the other is related to rational philosophy. He established the tradition that a doctor or a scientist can keep his religious conviction and still believe in scientific theory and practice (Browne, 1921). Thus, many medical practices were accepted even though they were incompatible with Muslim religion. In this nascent Islamic society, the prescription of alcohol is tolerated by the public even though it is forbidden by Muslim religion.

It is this tolerant attitude and the sponsoring of science by the rulers that enabled Muslim physicians to reformulate Greek theories of medicine and adapt them to different countries in the Islamic empire. Science became a successful and flourishing enterprise in which not only Arab Muslims took part, but also scientists from different ethnic and religious groups.

Although Galenism and medical theories of medieval Muslim physicians are not compatible with modern scientific thinking, psychiatrists in Muslim countries have to deal with patients whose concepts of health and illness are rooted in the past. Historical data of Islamic psychiatry are necessary, in order to understand the health beliefs of Muslim patients. Muslim psychiatrists have to work side by side with native healers who practice modified versions of Galenism or traditional therapies which are transmitted from one generation to another and have become part of native Islamic medicine.

REFERENCES

Abu-Zaid al-Balkhi (1966), *Kitab masalih al-abdan Wal-anfūs*. Damascus: Universiy of Damascus Press.

Alexander, F. G., & Selesnick, S. T. (1966), *The History of Psychiatry: An Evaluation of Psychiatric Thought and Practice from Prehistoric Times to the Present*. New York: Harper & Row.

Ammar, S. (1987), Histoire de la psychiatrie maghríbine. In: *Manuel de psychiatrie du praticien maghríbin*, ed. S. Douki, D. Moussaoui, & F. Kacha. Paris: Masson, pp. 1–15.

Broadhurst, R. J. C. (1952), *The Travels of Ibn Jubayr*. London: J. Cape.

Browne, E. G. (1921), *Arabian Medicine*. Cambridge, U.K.: Cambridge University Press.

Bürgel, J. C. (1974), Psychosomatic methods of cures in the Islamic middle ages. *Humaniora Islamica*, 1:157–172.

Campbell, D. (1926), *Arabian Medicine and Its Influence on the Middle Ages*, Vol. 1. London: Kegan Paul.

Crapanzano, V. (1973), *The Hamadasha: A Study in Moroccan Ethnopsychiatry*. Berkeley: University of California Press.

Cumming, E., & Cumming, J. (1957), *Closed Ranks: An Experiment in Mental Health Education*. Cambridge, MA: Harvard University Press.

Dols, M. W. (1992), *Majnūn: The Madman in Medieval Islamic Society*. New York: Oxford University Press.

El-Otmani, S., & Moussaoui, D. (1992), Système nerveux et neuropsychiatrie chez Ibn Rochd (Averroes) et Ibn Zohr (Avenzoar). *Histoire des sciences médicales*, 26:1–6.

Farmer, H. (1929), *A History of Arabian Music in the XIIIth Century*. London: Luzac.

Foucault, M. (1965), *Madness and Civilization: A History of Insanity in the Age of Reason.* New York: Random House.

Giffen, L. A. (1971), *Theory of Profane Love among the Arabs: The Development of the Genre.* London: University of London Press.

Gilsenan, M. (1973), *Saint and Sufi in Modern Egypt: An Essay in the Sociology of Religion.* Oxford: Oxford University Press.

Hatfield, E., Brinton, C., & Cornelius, J. (1989), Passionate love and anxiety in young adolescents. *Motivation & Emotion,* 13:271–289.

────── Rapson, R. L. (1996), *Love and Sex: Cross-Cultural Perspective.* Boston: Allyn & Bacon.

Ibn al Jawzi, Abu-Faraj Abdul Rahman (1962), *Them l-hawa.* Cairo: Darl-Kutub al-Haditha.

────── (1345 A.H.), *Akhbār al-Hamqua wal mughafalín (The News of the Stupid and the Imbeciles).* Damascus: Al-Tawfiq Press.

Ibn Jamai, Kitab al irshad limasalih al-anfus mal ejsad (n.d.), *Arabische und Persiche Handschriften.* Preface by A. Fischer.

Ibn Qayyim al-Jawzia, Shams ad-Dīn (1957), *at-Tibb an-nabawi (Prophetic Medicine).* Beirut: Darl-Kutub al-Ameh.

Ibn Al-Nadim (1964), *Al-fihrist.* Beirut: Dar al-Maarif.

Ibn Sina, A. A. (1877), *al-Qanum fi t-tibb,* 3 Vols. Cairo: Bulaq.

────── (1889–1899), *Risala fil-'ishq.* Leider: Brill.

Ibn Abi Usaybi'a (1882), *Uyun al-anba' fi tabaqat al-atibba'.* Cairo: Wahbey Press.

Ibn Zohr (1983), *Kital al-Taissir.* Damascus: al-Mūnadhama al-Arabia lil terbia wa al thakafa wal ūlūm.

Ikwan as Safa (1957), *Rasa'l.* Beirut: Dar Beirut.

Al-Isbahani, Abu l-Faraj (1868), *Kitab al-aghani,* 20 vols. Original Bulaq printing 1868–1869. Beirut: Dar-al-Tawjīh al-Lūbmani, 1980.

Ishaq ibn 'Imran (1977), *Maqalah fi l-malikhuliya.* Hamburg: H. Buske.

Al-Issa, I. (1995a), *Handbook of Culture and Mental Illness: An International Perspective.* Madison, CT: International Universities Press.

────── (1995b), The illusion of reality or the reality of illusion: Hallucinations and culture. *Brit. J. Psychiatry,* 166:368–373.

Kakar, S., & Ross, J. M. (1986), *Tales of Love, Sex and Danger.* Delhi, India: Oxford University Press.

Lane, E. W. (1860), *Manners and Customs of the Modern Egyptians,* ed. E. S. Poole. London: Aldine Press.

Leiser, G., & Dols, M. W. (1987), Eviliya Chelebi's description of medicine in seventeenth century Egypt. *Sudhoffs Archiv.,* 71:197–216.

Leo Africanus (1896), *The History and Description of Africa,* 3 vols., tr. R. Brown. London: Hakluyt Society.

Lewinson, P. M., & Graf, M. (1973), Pleasant activities and depression. *J. Consult. & Clin. Psychol.*, 41:261–268.

Mace, D., & Mace, V. (1980), *Marriage: East and West.* New York: Dolphin Books.

Al-Majūsi, Ali ibn al-Abbas (1294 A.H.), *Kitab al-Malaki (kámil as-Sina'a t-tibbiya),* 2 vols, ed. Bulaq. Cairo, 1877.

Al-Maqrizi, Taqī d-Dīn Ahmād ibn 'Ali *al-Mawa'iz wa l'-itibar fi dhiker al-khitat wa l-athar.* (Bulaq, 1854).

Masters, W., & Johnson, V. C. (1970), *Human Sexual Response.* Boston: Little, Brown.

Al-Najjar, M. R. (1978), *Juha the Arab.* Kuwait: The National Council for Culture, Arts and Literature.

Al-Naysaburi (1924), *Kitab 'Uqala' al-majanin.* Beirut: Dar Al-Kutub Al-'Ilmia.

Al-Razi Abu Baker Ibn Zakariyah (1955), *al Hawi fi t-tibb,* 21 vols. Hyderabad: Oriental Publication Bureau.

Nizami, Ilyas ibn Yusuf (1966), *Layla wa Majnun,* tr. R. Gelpke, E. Matlin, & G. Hill. Moscow: Idaiet Intisharat Dansh.

Özturk, O. M. (1964), Folk treatment of mental illness in Turkey. In: *Magic, Faith and Healing,* ed. A. Kiev. New York: Free Press, pp. 343–363.

———— Volkan, V. (1977), The theory and practive of psychiatry in Turkey. In: *Psychological Dimensions of Middle Eastern Studies,* ed. L. C. Brown & N. Itzkowitz. Princeton, NJ: Princeton University Press, pp. 330–361.

Said ibn Bakhtishu (1977), *Risalah fi tibb.* Beirut: Dar al-Mashriq.

Al-Sarraj, Abu Nasr Abdallah ibn Ali (n.d.), *Masari' al-'ushaq.* Beirut: Dar Sadir.

Shah, I. (1971), *The Pleasantries of the Incredible Mulla.* New York: E. P. Dutton.

Al-Tabari, 'Ali Ibn Rabban (1928), Firdaws al hikma fi t-tibb. Berlin: Meyerhoff.

Winterson, J. (1987), *Passion.* New York: Vintage International.

3.

Forensic Psychiatry and Islamic Law

Kutaiba Chaleby

In order to understand the meaning of insanity in Islamic law, it is important to understand the concept of mental competence and legal capacity of a free Muslim citizen. Competence *(ahlia)* in Islamic law includes entitlement to rights and duties by virtue of being a human, a state referred to as *themma* (Khisro, 1300 A.H). For example, the fetus while inside the mother's womb is entitled to receive an inheritance, carry the father's name, be the subject of a will, receive appropriate medical care, and so on. *Competence of entitlement* also obliges the individual to fulfill certain duties regardless of his or her comprehension of these duties. For example, a person of any age or mental function is obliged to pay blood money for a relative who has committed homicide or manslaughter.

In addition to competence of entitlement, there is also *competence of performance* which involves legal capacity to carry out certain activities or perform a certain task. It is stated in Islamic law that everybody who reaches the age of maturity is mentally competent unless he or she is declared otherwise. The mentally competent possess reason *('agil)*, are fully responsible *(mukallaf)* and capable of deliberate intent *('amad)* (Schacht, 1964). The *majnūn* lacks reason *('adim al'aqil)* and deliberate intent and is therefore liable to interdiction or legal incompetence.

COMPETENCE TO MAKE A CONTRACT

The sanctity of a contract is essential for dealings of daily life. Secular law states certain criteria for competence to make a contract that include an understanding of the nature, terms, and effect of the particular transaction. In the case of incompetence, the lack of understanding must be due to an illness and not to ignorance or lack of sophistication.

Islamic law does not provide specific criteria for mental competence to make a contract. It does, however, address this issue under different headings. It requires different criteria and sets limits that vary with the type of disorder, the mental state, the biological state, and the circumstances involved. For example, it explicitly describes different competence levels under which a minor, between the age of 7 and puberty, is held competent. Minors below the age of 7 cannot be involved in any kind of contract. Above the age of 7, they may do so with the consent of a guardian, unless the contract involves risk to money or property. Besides minors, Islamic law dealt with the *ma'tuh,* someone who is deficient in reason *(Naqis al-'agil),* and *majnūn,* someone who lacks reason *('adim al-'agil).*

The rule that covers mental deficiency *(atah)* regarding contractual competence is the same as those that apply to the 7-year-old child. That is to say, they may carry out certain contracts that do not involve risking their money or property and they can enter risk-taking contracts with the approval of their guardian. They are, however, forbidden from entering contracts that include losing money, such as making gifts and donations, regardless of the desire of their guardian (Al-Aini, n.d. *Sharh Al-Manar,* p. 950).

A person identified as retarded can assume the function of a deputy for others for duties he is assumed competent to perform. These include certain kinds of transactions like selling and buying merchandise or property. However, when the retarded person sells or buys for others he cannot be held responsible or liable for the price of the merchandise bought or for delivering sound merchandise. Those will be the responsibility of the person who deputized him in the first place (Amir Badshah, 1350 A.H., p. 424).

In general, the insane are considered unable to make a contract, and since insanity is known to vary in intensity and duration, the rule was made to cover the time when a person is recognized as being actively insane. However, during periods of remission or recovery, he or she is considered to be competent and his contract is considered binding. Competence is to be specified according to the level of mental functioning required in order to consider the so-called insane ineligible to make a contract. Criteria for the assessment of mental functioning are not addressed in the Islamic literature as compared with similar issues of the mentally retarded or demented *(atah)*. Since many jurists believe that the insane can follow the same ruling as the retarded or the demented, we can probably extrapolate the same criteria for both. Because contemporary treatment in psychiatry has modified the course of mental illness and what has been described as partial insanity (for example, the foolish or *safeeh* and the imbecile or *dhu l-ghafla*), transient psychosis has become the rule rather than the exception among individuals recognized as insane. It follows that more detailed studies to update the issues of mental competence in Islamic jurisprudence will be necessary.

COMPETENCE TO MAKE A WILL (TESTAMENTARY CAPACITY)

It has long been recognized under the law throughout the history of mankind that a mentally incompetent person cannot make a valid will. Recently, forensic issues in psychiatry have become more sophisticated and require that more specific criteria be applied in order to consider the testator incompetent to make a will. It is no longer that the mere presence of mental illness would render a person incompetent to make a will. Under most international popular laws, the criteria required to make a will include that the testator understand the following:

1. The nature of the will or bequest and its meaning, as a means of disposition of his property after death.

2. The extent of the assets: "bounty or property." It might not mean knowing every penny, but should be broadly accurate.
3. Who are the natural heirs or natural objects of his bounty.
4. The testator should understand and appreciate the effect of the will on others. This criterion may not be required in some countries.
5. The testator should be free from delusion.

The above provide the understanding that mental illness of any type, if it is not associated with delusion and does not interfere with any of the above criteria, would not affect the person's competence to make a will (Applebaum and Gutheil, 1991).

In Islamic law there are two main limitations to writing a will that are not related to competence: (1) The will cannot involve a donation to any party other than the natural heirs in excess of one-third of the bounty. (2) The testator cannot give any part of his bounty to any heir of his choosing. In other words, each heir will have his share regardless of the wish of the testator. The bounty will be divided among the natural heirs according to the laws of inheritance as they are written in the Holy Qur'an.

Islamic law clearly states that mental competence is required for making a legally valid will. Islamic jurists have dealt with changes in mental competence after writing the will. There are different rulings regarding this issue. Al-Kasani has stated that "if mental incompetence, i.e., insanity, took place after the writing of the will, the document would not be valid because it is not a permanent contract" (1974, p. 394). This will be the case if the person involved does not recover from the state of insanity before he or she dies. Ibin Abdeen (1966) seconds that opinion by adding that "the document will be invalid if the state of insanity lasted longer than six months." However, the Malki school does not agree with this point of view and states that the will should remain valid because the insane person cannot make a will unless he is in remission or has recovered. It was also stated that since the will is a valid document even after death, it cannot be invalidated by a mental illness (Ibn Abdul Salaam, 1388 A.H., p. 125; Ibn Abdeen, 1966; Al-Kansani, 1974, p. 394).

COMPETENCE TO DEAL WITH OWN BOUNTY

The term *safeeh* is derived from the root *safah*, which literally means "lightness of weight and movement," but in its current use, it indicates "recklessness." Interdiction or legal incapacity *(hajr)* may be imposed on a person who is not necessarily mentally ill, but foolish *(safeeh)* or reckless in dealing with his or her money (Al-Jabouri, 1988, p. 137): "but do not give fools *(sufaha)* their property that God has assigned to you to manage; provide for them and clothe them out of it, and speak to them honorable words" (Sura 4:5). Foolishness *(safah)* involves spending and dealing with wealth in an unacceptable manner. The term foolish or *safeeh* includes those who are not behaving properly according to the teaching of Islam, which could imply that the religiously nonobservant could be deprived of control of their financial affairs. Some jurists would not allow the testimony of a *safeeh* in court and would prevent him from deputizing others as well as performing certain professions or making contracts (Al-Qurtubi, 1965, p. 37).

COMPETENCE TO MARRY AND DIVORCE

Under most secular laws, to marry requires a certain level of mental competence. In Islamic law, to hold a legal marriage contract does not require a particular age or any level of competence. The marriage contract is valid at any age or any level of mental competence provided it is either approved or actually carried out by the guardian if the person involved is too young or mentally incompetent. For minors who are below 7 years of age, the marriage contract cannot be valid legally if carried out by the child. It can only be done through a guardian. Above the age of 7 and before reaching puberty, the boy can make a marriage contract but he requires the approval of his guardian in order for the contract to become binding. After puberty, however, a male can make a marriage contract on his own. Females who have never been married require the approval of their guardian at any age according to the majority of Islamic law schools (Al-Haj, 1317 A.H., p. 174).

The mentally incompetent can marry through their guardian's authority as well (Badran, n.d., p. 47). Divorce, on the other hand, cannot be carried out through another person, such as a guardian, according to the more popular schools. It requires complete mental competence and follows more complicated regulations which are covered under family laws.

The marital contract could be annulled by the wife under certain circumstances. The presence of insanity in the husband is one of them. However, the husband's choice in breaking the marital contract if his wife is mentally ill does not pose any problem since he already has the power of divorce without giving reasons for his actions. The wife's choice of annulment of marriage is viewed differently by Islamic schools of jurisprudence.

The Malki school gives the choice of annulment to the wife if insanity was present at the time of making the contract. This is valid whether the wife knew about it or not at the time of making the contract. However, if the man becomes insane after the marriage contract, the wife has no choice. The Shafii as well as the Hanbali schools rule that if the wife knew about the presence of insanity at the time of the marriage contract, she has no choice in breaking it later. The Hanafi school, on the other hand, has taken a completely different position. It rules that the wife has no choice in annulling the marriage for reasons of insanity under any circumstances. Under certain circumstances, the judge can rule to have the wife divorced according to her wishes only if she can prove that serious harm is being done to her in the marriage. This would be the grounds for separation under the Hanafi rule. Such separation, however, is considered a divorce rather than an annulment of the contract.

Although mental competence does not constitute a major issue in getting married, divorce on the other hand requires a relatively high level of mental competence. The level of mental competence which qualifies a man to divorce his wife is not limited to the presence or absence of mental illness but includes freedom from intoxicating substances and not being in a state of anger.

The special attention Islam has given mental health issues in divorce is attributed to several reasons. Some are related to the seriousness of the problem of divorce itself. Islam, protective of family unity, tries to limit divorce to the ultimate necessities. The other reason might be the fact that divorce is a prerogative of the husband only. He has the full power and authority to *legally* divorce his wife without presenting reasons or excuses. We stress the word *legally* to note that even if a man unfairly divorces his wife and the divorce is legally valid, that does not mean Islam condones it. Indeed, a man who threatens his wife unjustly with divorce or otherwise commits an improper act is expected to be punished by God.

Since divorce is left to the man to decide on, Islam has put many conditions for the divorce to be valid; one of which is well-identified mental competence. The other reason believed to have created stringent restrictions requiring mental alertness in the divorce process is the fact that the oral tradition of Islamic culture means that the mere utterance of the words, "You are divorced," if said by the husband with the intention of divorce, will validate the act of divorce on the spot. This is coupled with the fact that a husband can only return to his wife after these utterances (repeating "I divorce you" three times) if she marries another man and is in turn divorced by him. Such an irreversible verbal declaration is considered a serious matter in Islamic law.

There is a complete consensus among all schools that a mentally ill person cannot be competent to decide on divorce. The insanity rule is also applied to the mentally retarded, to those in delirious states of any cause, or under the effect of legally acquired drugs (Al-Mawsoo'a Al-Fiqhia, 1989). The jurists, however, have not identified a test or standards for judging the severity of the degree of the mental defect that would qualify a person as incompetent to divorce for reasons of insanity. This is expected to be studied and standardized by contemporary religious scholars in association with qualified psychiatrists.

Undoing of the marriage is a unique concept in Islamic law. The term used for it in Arabic, *khala'a,* literally means *removal.* Unlike divorce, *undoing* of a marriage is an agreement between the husband and the wife. Divorce, on the other hand, is the choice of the husband alone. Mental competence to undo marriage is a requirement for both male and female partners. Competence to divorce, on the other hand, is a requirement for the husband because he is the only one who can divorce his partner. Since the *undoing* process involves a form of compensation which may include money, competence in financial dealings is necessary for the wife.

A woman who is declared financially incompetent *(safeeh)* and is a mentally healthy adult cannot practice undoing because she is not competent to deal with money. If this ever happened, it would be a form of divorce and no compensation is awarded to the husband. Some scholars (Al-Jazeery, 1987, p. 298) believe that even if the woman is not officially declared financially incompetent, she cannot have the right to consent to *undoing* if she was known to be reckless with money or an excessive spender. The *safeeh* woman, however, can consent to *undoing* if her officially appointed guardian approves it, according to some schools. The Hanbali school, however, disagrees and does not give the right to the guardian to accept compensation for the financially incompetent woman.

As for the husband's competence, there are slightly different rules. If the husband is a minor or incompetent to divorce by reason of insanity or financial incompetence, the *undoing* process cannot take place (unlike a minor wife, where the *undoing* does take place but the compensation is not awarded). According to the Hanafi school, the guardian cannot divorce for the incompetent. The same is true in the case of undoing a marriage (Al-Jazeery, 1987, p. 298).

INSANITY DEFENSE AND CRIMINAL RESPONSIBILITY

The Concept of Crime and Intention in Islamic Law

The concept of *mens rea* (a Latin term meaning a bad intent) is well accepted under Islamic law and there is no crime if there is no intent. The insane, under Islamic law, are recognized to be lacking or not capable of having an intention because of disturbed reasoning; therefore, they are not liable for the crime they commit. This is well expressed in the following *Hadith* of the prophet reported by Al-Hujmiri in his book *Kashf al-Mahjub:* "The pen does not record (evil actions) against the sleeper until he awakes, or against the boy until he reaches puberty, or against the mad man until he recovers his wits."

Under Islamic law, crimes in general fall under two major categories as far as *mens rea* is concerned. Deliberate intent is called *amad,* while unintentional acts are called *khatta* which means "by mistake." Islamic law, however, recognizes a third kind of crime which is quasi-intentional *shubha al-amad.* The recognition of the third type of crime is restricted to murders. For example, in some cases of murder, a person may not intend to kill, but during an assault he or she uses a weapon that leads to death (Al-Zaila'e, 1315 A.H., p. 98; Ibn Qudama, 1965, p. 321).

Murder with deliberate intent is defined as an intentionally carried out crime leading to death. Islamic law, however, does not judge differently premeditated and unpremeditated crime. Both of these crimes are punishable by death. It is important to note, however, that if the family of the victim decides to accept blood money and not punish the murderer, the murderer may be set free unless there is a decision by the ruler of the country to give the murderer an additional punishment. The kind of punishment a murderer receives will be decided by the governor, who might free the culprit. However, if the family of the victim decides not to accept blood money, the governor would not have the authority to modify the sentence (Aoda, n.d., p. 6).

The quasi-intentional crime is only applied to murder. Among the four major schools of Islamic law, three recognize this kind of crime. The school of Malik, however, does not recognize it and classifies murder in only two categories: the intentional and those committed by mistake. According to the Malik school, an assault that unintentionally leads to death is still treated on the same level as premeditated murder. The school of Shafii recognizes quasi-intentional crime in assault and battering; while part of the school of Hanbali and also the school of Hanafi do not recognize quasi-intentional crime in assault and battering (Al-Shafii, 1321 A.H., p. 45; Al-Hattab, 1328 A.H., p. 231; Al-Ramli, 386 A.H., p. 235).

It is important to note that the civil part of crime that has to do with compensation is fully recognized in Islamic law, and whether the crime was fully intentional, partially intentional, or by mistake, civil liability holds and compensation is expected.

THE INSANITY RULE IN ISLAMIC AND SECULAR LAWS

Islamic law has given full attention to mental competence and insanity. Texts in Islamic jurisprudence have dealt with this issue (Al-Mawsoo'a, 1989). However, we will focus here on the rules of criminal responsibility. In Islamic law, there is no disagreement about the rule of insanity and criminal responsibility; that is, an insane person is not deemed culpable for any action he or she might commit. There are, however, various definitions and conceptions of what constitutes insanity. One definition of insanity is "impairment of the mind and speech in terms of reasoning." A second definition is "impairment of the capability to distinguish the *hassan* (the good) and the *khabith* (the evil) and to conceive the consequences of it. This capability is no longer in evidence or does not function properly." The third definition is "the impairment of the capability in which the conception of the whole, from its parts, is achieved." Key phrases in these definitions are: "the distinguishing capability," "the good and bad," and "the conception of the whole." We believe that the use of the word *whole* in the third statement reflects a very deep understanding of the nature of mental illness. It denotes that the mentally ill person might not be able to differentiate the whole from its different parts. It reflects an understanding that mental health might be intact in certain areas but impaired in others. The disturbance in integrating all these parts, in different aspects of life, to make the "whole" is the essence of mental illness. If one understands the two words *good* and *bad* it is the equivalent of knowing right from wrong, under the McNaughton rule.[1]

---

[1] The McNaughton Rule was established in 1843 by the Law Lords of England, following an order from Queen Victoria. She was outraged by the not guilty verdict by reason of Insanity, of Mr. McNaughton. Mr. McNaughton had publicly murdered

Islamic law has not ignored mental retardation and dementia by acknowledging the presence of diminished mental capacity with an absence of psychosis. Furthermore, these were classified into different levels and grades, such as *atah* (mentally deficient) and *al-ghafla* (imbecility).

THE COGNITIVE ARM OF INSANITY RULE

Islamic law has a similar ruling as Durham law,[2] which refers to the insanity state as the product of a diseased mind or a defect. It states that there is "no duty or punishment for the insane," as well as that "the pen is withheld from the insane until he or she recovers." These two rules can have the same interpretation as the Durham law, since they do not place any restrictions on the state of mind that is called insanity.

The Durham law was instituted in 1954 and was quite popular all over the United States until 1972 when it was replaced by the guidelines of the American Law Institute (The American Law Institute, 1962, p. 66). The American Law Institute guidelines have two distinct arms. The first arm stresses the phrase "lacks substantial capacity to appreciate the criminality of his conduct." This arm, which is embedded in the McNaughton Rule, is modified to add the term *lacks substantial* and the other word is *appreciate.* The two words *substantial* and *appreciate,* rather than *knowing,* add a new affective element to the *knowledge* of right and wrong. This was also implied by the Islamic scholars and certain schools when they defined insanity as impairment of the distinguishing capacity to conceive the consequences of an act. The phrase "distinguishing capacity" and

---

a high British official mistaking him for the Premiere. The Law Lords responded that the standard should be, "To establish defense on the insanity, it must be clearly proved that at the time of committing the act, the party accused was laboring under such defect of reason, from disease of mind, as not to know the nature and quality of the act he was doing, or if he did know it, that he did not know he was doing what was wrong."

[2] Judge Bazelone of District of Columbia Court of Appeals, authored what was known as the product test of insanity. In the famous "Durham vs. United States," the test simply stated "An accused is not criminally responsible if his unlawful act was a product of mental disease or defect."

"able to conceive" has the same connotation of meaning as the sense of *appreciation* or the *substantial capacity to appreciate,* adding an effective element to knowing. The American Law Institute guidelines also, in a sense, combined the McNaughton Rule and the irresistible impulse criterion.

THE INABILITY TO REFRAIN ARM

Some Islamic scholars have included *dahash,* "the startled or perplexed" in the insanity defense. *Dahash* could be considered as similar to the irresistible impulse in the Model Penal Code. Since a perplexed or startled person temporarily carries the same status as the insane, he is not guilty and should be ruled innocent by reason of insanity. The *dahash* state is a condition which temporarily renders the mind and reason beyond voluntary control, and is thus quite similar to "temporary insanity." Thus, Islamic law, at least in certain schools, has covered the principle of the inability to refrain, which is part of secular law. Islamic scholars have gone a step further even in addressing the issue of irresistible impulse by including severe obsession in the insanity defense (Abu Zahra, 1972).

The concept of irresistible impulse could be deduced by analogy from other rules. Irresistible impulse could be exemplified by a state of profoundly provoked anger that put the person in a state of rage. An extreme state of rage according to Islamic law would render the person not competent to make the decision to divorce. Islamic law recognizes the similarity between rage reaction and the state of insanity by declaring that a man who divorces his wife while under extreme rage and unaware of his immediate reality is subject to the same rule as the insane whose declaration of divorce is not valid (Al-Jazeery, 1987, p. 281).

THE EFFECT OF ALCOHOL AND DRUGS

Most of the secular laws around the world do not consider taking an intoxicating drug of any kind as an excuse for committing a crime (Sadoff, 1988). In other words, a person is responsible for his or her actions while voluntarily using these substances. The fact that the person was not aware of his actions during intoxication cannot be grounds for freeing the person from responsibility. That case is understandable for acts regarded as crimes. However, in Islamic law, the announcement of divorce during intoxication is, according to the majority of schools, still valid even though it is not a criminal act.

Islamic law views the use of alcohol and illicit drugs by analogy as a major sin, which makes the issue more complicated. Consuming alcohol is not only prohibited under Islamic law but carries with it two kinds of punishment. One is dictated religiously as a *Hadd*, which is considered a kind of punishment legislated by God, and is eighty lashes according to the opinion of the majority. The other punishment is designed by the governing body and can vary according to what the ruler considers proper at the time. According to the Hanafi school of Fiqh, the religiously dictated punishment is only applicable to a certain state and degree of drunkenness. The *Hadd* or religious punishment can only be applied if the severity of drunkenness reached a level at which the person was unable to distinguish the earth from the sky, or unable to tell the difference between a man and a woman. This is, indeed, a clear test that indicates whether mental functions are seriously impaired. The majority of Islamic jurists, in spite of their acknowledgment of the same test of mental incompetence, have decided that a drunk man at any level of consciousness or mental impairment, who utters a statement to the effect that his wife is divorced, will have a valid divorce which would be irreversible. They have based their reasoning on the fact that the divorce of a wife, when it is regretted, will be a kind of punishment for the man because he has consumed a forbidden substance. The argument presented by some other jurists is that this might be an unfair punishment because it affects innocent people (wife and children), but this was refuted by the idea that a man who gets drunk is not worth living with. There were two scholars in Islamic history (Al-Faraz and Abu Alhasan Al-Karkhi) who rejected the rule that the decision of incompetence is valid even when it unfairly affects others. Both have asserted that if a man announces a divorce while under the influence of alcohol, even to a mild degree, the divorce should not be valid unless he makes the same decision when he later becomes sober (Badran, p. 314). Because of the leniency of those two scholars, many Islamic countries now have accepted their rule and rejected the majority's opinion. In Egypt and in Saudi Arabia, however, a divorce decision made while intoxicated is not valid.

Ibn Qayem Al-Jawzia (n.d., p. 59) was the main authority to state that if a divorce was declared on the spur of the moment, as long as it fulfilled two criteria, it should be ruled invalid. These criteria are that anger was present to the point of temporarily taking over judgment and that the man's intention was impaired. The emphasis is put here on impaired intention and not impaired mind or mental incapacity. Al-Jawzia, a highly respected jurist of the Hanbali school, was among the minority who supported this view. His ruling is the most popular among jurists in the Muslim world today. The kind of anger or a rage state is at a mild intensity that does not cause any impairment of judgment or intention. It could be the result of any marital argument. The man declaring the divorce may be angry, but he was fully aware of his intentions. There is usually no emotional outburst. The divorce will remain valid by the consensus of all Islamic jurists.

COMPETENCE FOR EXECUTION

While there is a clear consensus about an insane person's lack of responsibility for a crime committed during the time of his insanity, opinion varies if an individual commits a crime in a clear mental state and then becomes seriously mentally ill after the conviction. According to the Shafii and Hanbali schools, the execution should still be carried out because he was fully conscious when he committed the crime. However, the Hanafi school has looked at the matter in more detail. It will not allow the execution to be carried out if the offender became insane after the crime but before or after the trial. The Hanafi school believes that if the offender was surrendered to the victim's family for execution, as might be the case on certain occasions, and becomes insane after his deliverance, the family of the victim has the right to kill him if they decide to do so. The Hanafi school has recognized the value of the official trial in this matter. It has decided that the point at which insanity has to be evaluated is during trial, so if the offender was convicted without the appearance of insanity, he is expected to be delivered to the family of the victim immediately afterward. If he was delivered in an insane condition, it would be the family's decision to execute him or not.

The Malki school is divided on this issue. The Imam Malik thinks that a convicted person who is insane should be kept in custody until he recovers and then be executed while his insanity is in remission. Ibn Al-Mawaz adds that if his recovery is not as hoped for, he should give the blood money from his own bounty but would not be executed. Another jurist, Maghera, believed that the decision should be given entirely to the family of the victim; it would be up to them to let him live or have him executed but they cannot accept blood money. Al-Lakhmi, however, believed that the family of the victim will have the choice as to whether the offender is executed, set free, or they accept blood money (Ibn Abdeen, 1966, p. 342; Al Hattab, 1328, p. 232; Al-Zarqani, 1971, p. 322).

PSYCHIATRIC MALPRACTICE AND LIABILITY

An intentional act of harm from a physician through whatever means—surgical, medical, or negligence—is considered a criminal act. Therefore, it should not be listed as a form of malpractice. However, some Islamic jurists have included the act of treating a patient without his or her consent under the same rule of intentional harm if it has caused harm to the patient. Al-Nawawi, who was a recognized Islamic jurist, was quoted to have made a statement to the effect that if a physician excised a diseased part of a patient without his consent, and if that act has caused damage or death, the physician should be penalized by *Qassas,* a punishment given only to intentional acts (Al-Nawawi, n.d., p. 179). This view, however, is not shared by the majority of jurists. Some jurists have even considered treating a patient without his or her consent even in good faith, a form of malpractice even if it has caused an undisputed harm.

The Islamic literature covers the issue of unintentional harm caused by a medical or a psychiatric practice. As the case in the secular laws, the medical error is seen at many levels: (1) an error caused by negligence; (2) an error caused by ignorance; or (3) an error that was unrelated to either negligence or ignorance. Although the classifications of these errors is almost identical in both Islamic and secular laws, the judicial rules on these consequences are by no means the same.

If an unintentional harm was caused by an error that is not likely to be made by a professional of similar qualification, the damage will be classified as a form of ignorance. In that case, the physician will not only be liable for compensatory restitution, but he might be punished by a *Qassas,* a punishment that can include a jail sentence or cutting off part of the physician's body, or even a life sentence, depending upon the severity of the damage done. Imam Al-Shafii, the founder of the Shafii school, made the following statement about damage caused by a physician's error:

> [T]he expert in medicine should be investigated about the nature of that error; if the error was of the kind that can be encountered by a professional and known to happen, and the physician involved admits his mistake, and swears that it was an unintentional error, that physician should not be prosecuted. However, his family has to make monetary restitution for the damage done and blood money if death was encountered. If the expert testimony was to the effect that no prudent physician could have made such a mistake, the physician involved would be tried as fully responsible and can receive the *Qassas* accordingly [Al-Shafii, 1321, p. 154].

The conclusion is that an error by a physician is considered to be a negligent act, if it was done by sheer ignorance; the physician should be tried as a criminal if the act was intentional. If, however, the error was not caused by proven ignorance, the physician is still liable for monetary compensation (Al-Shaikh Mubarak, 1991, p. 154). This judgment was thought to be fair because the liability for damages carries no relevance to the intention in Islamic law. Al-Jawzia (1397 A.H.) has been quoted to the effect that "both intentional and nonintentional mistakes are treated equally in regard to the compensation awarded" (p. 152). The issue of whether that act was religiously lawful or not, that is, if the physician in question has actually sinned by his damaging act, is to be decided by God. The Qur'an has made it clear that God does not punish anyone for an act that was done without malice (Sura Al ahzab, 5). However, liability for compensation or for punishment of any sort in this life still holds. The above ruling is not shared by some scholars of the Hanafi school. Al-Hassaki, a prominent Hanafi jurist, declared that the physician is not liable for any compensation as long as he has practiced within the acceptable standard of his profession (Al Hasqafi, 1966, p. 69). Other Hanafi jurists have taken a middle position. They thought to impose half of the acceptably awarded compensation on the physician who caused unintentional damage without being ignorant or negligent; that is, half the blood money in case of death (Group of Indian Scholars, 1319 A.H., p. 34).

The Malki school has confirmed the traditional position that any mistake by a physician will make him liable for compensation regardless of intent or the professional skills and standard followed (Malik, n.d., p. 614).

The Shafii school takes the same position as the Malki: the physician's mistake should be treated as any other unintentional mistake, making him liable for full compensation. Some have attributed this rule to the fact that a physician's mistake must have involved an act by the physician which was beyond the implied consent of the patient; for example, damage caused by inappropriate dosage is considered an act that was made beyond the consented contract between the physician and the patient which implied proper medication (Ibn Al Ikhwa, 1937, p. 164).

The Hanbali school takes a similar stand to the Malki and Shafii schools: the physicians are liable for monetary compensation for damages regardless of the standard they followed in that practice (Ibn Mufleh, 1391, p. 474).

In every school of Islamic jurisprudence there are a number of jurists who have taken a stand contrary to the ones stated above. Those jurists have ruled that a physician, as long as he was following an acceptable professional standard, is not liable for any damages and is not expected to pay any compensation so long as there is no evidence of negligence or ignorance.

The overwhelming majority of the classical Islamic jurists have concluded that there is a liability of the physician for an erroneous act regardless of the type of act involved and the prudence of the physician. The contemporary practice of medicine and psychiatry in the Islamic world has taken the view of the minority. It is not customary to find a physician liable for damages caused by nonnegligent acts. This view was largely supported by some classical scholars on the basis that, if the physician is held liable for ordinary, everyday practice, there will be no person on earth who will be willing to practice this inherently risky profession (Qa'ed, 1987, p. 195).

VIOLATION OF PROFESSIONAL STANDARDS

Following the professional standards of medicine is considered a prerequisite for waiving liability for damages resulting from any medical or surgical procedure. In addition, proper consent has been accepted by many Islamic jurists as the basis for the legally safe practice of medicine (Ibn Al-Shahnah, 1973, p. 292).

Islamic jurisprudence has looked at professional standards as being of two types: constant standards and variable standards. Constant standards are those parts of medical practice that are never expected to change with time in spite of the progress of medical science. They include looking out for the best interest of the patient, keeping the terms of the treatment contract with the patient, choosing the safest and simplest medical means of possible treatment, and observing the Islamic religious codes in treatment.

The variable standards, on the other hand, will include any scientifically acquired knowledge of treatment, which can be updated all the time. The constant standards are considered universally acceptable ones. There is no dispute among physicians, nor among scholarly jurists, that violation of any of them will make the physician liable. However, violation of the variable standards is subject to disagreement and debate. If a physician chose a kind of treatment that is not conventional, it is considered a violation of professional standards only if that procedure or method of therapy was not an acceptable practice, as judged by an expert. In other words, if the method of therapy was not conventional it would not be considered malpractice if there was no identified professional view stating that the method of therapy was harmful. This rule is particularly useful in treating conditions that do not have a universally acceptable method of treatment, which can include many of the psychiatric disorders.

IGNORANCE

Islamic jurists have identified three types of ignorance in medical practice: (1) the physician may be a mere impostor; (2) a partially knowledgeable physician who has not been well trained; and (3) a recognized legally practicing physician, who entertains a medical treatment that he has no proper knowledge of, or he has not kept himself up-to-date on an issue that he is expected to know about.

In the first kind of ignorance, there is no dispute about the liability of the practitioner. The second type, however, might be judged on a case-by-case basis, since consenting to treatment, even knowing when a physician is partially trained, can decrease some of the liability. In the third case, the liability of the physician is undisputed if he was found to be ignorant in a medical area he was expected to be knowledgeable about.

Imam Al-Gazali, a very prominent jurist and scholar, has declared that medical practice, especially when it involves invasive procedures, is considered a forbidden act by God, not to be carried out, except under necessary circumstances. Some jurists have called for the governor to screen physicians and test their knowledge so that no unqualified person will practice medicine (Al-Gazali, 1939, p. 216; Ibn Al-Munassif, 1988, p. 354). Observation of the Islamic Code of Ethics in medical practice is essential to maintain a religiously sound medical and psychiatric practice. This may include moral values, such as not hurting a patient by unnecessary treatment with dangerous medications or surgery. It includes also avoiding forbidden substances, like alcohol or pork products in the composition of pharmacological agents, when alternative remedies are available.

An issue that might be raised is whether the patient or the physician are held liable for noncompliance with these codes, if either one of them is not aware of the forbidden nature of his act. This is rarely a judicial matter, but rather a matter which is expected to be left to God's judgment. However, conditions may arise when somebody feels that he or she has become spiritually unclean because of the use of a forbidden substance in treatment. In such a case, a person may submit a claim against the physician for moral or other kinds of reasons. The basis of Islamic jurisprudence is that ignorance of the codes may not be used as an excuse to break the law. The Imam Al-Shafii has pointed out that, if ignorance is used as an excuse for wrongful acts, then it follows that ignorance will be more favorable than knowledge. If that was the case, then people will prefer ignorance to knowledge (Al-Zarkashi, 1982, p. 17). On the other hand, there are several incidences when great Islamic figures, like the Caliph Omar, have refrained from inflicting punishment on some individuals because of ignorance of the Islamic law. The Islamic law requires the physician to treat patients if no other person is around to perform the duty. This rule was derived from the basis of analogy with the prophet Mohammad's instruction that no man should withhold water or food that was in excess of his need from a person who is in dire need of it (Ibn Hanbal, 1313 A.H., p. 33). The Imam Al-Qurafi has gone further by declaring that if a man passed by an animal caught in a trap and he was able to get it out and deliver it to its owner, but instead left it to die, he would be liable for complete compensation of the price of the hunt (Ibn

Al Qassim, n.d., p. 436). The extension of this example to physicians is obvious.

CONSENTED TERMINATION OF LIFE

In contemporary society, with advances in life support systems, and technology that prolongs life, many complex and controversial issues have been raised. Topics like euthanasia, assisted suicide, and discontinuation of life support measures are rarely discussed in the current Islamic literature. Yet similar problems have been raised by many Islamic jurists throughout the years, with various and rather interesting points of views.

Many Islamic jurists have argued that although killing is an act of murder and it should be a forbidden sin, a killing consented to by the deceased person may be a sin that should be left to be punished by God, and not by the court of Sharia. Ibn Hazm (1350 A.H., p. 471), a renowned Islamic scholar, was one of the few who felt that killing the patient with his own consent is an act that should be punishable in court—a division of the Malki school also holds this view.

Most of the Hanafi jurists support the notion that killing a patient at his own request is not a punishable crime, although it should be considered a sin. The same position is taken by some Malki jurists (Al Tahtawi, 1238 A.H., p. 266; Al Hattab, 1328 A.H., p. 235; Al Baghdadi, 1308 A.H., p. 160). The Shafii school, with few exceptions, does not stop at withholding punishment for that kind of killing; it goes further and waives monetary compensation and blood money (*Diya*) (Ibn Mufleh, 1932, p. 633). The Malki school holds the same permissive rule of the Shafii, thus making the physician who kills a patient, upon the patient's request, immune from punishment and so not obligated to pay blood money to the patient's relatives (Al Nawawi, n.d., p. 138; Al Zarkashi, 1982, p. 176).

This issue could be tackled from another point where a logical conclusion can be made from the fact that in Islamic law the killer can be set free, if the victim's family decides to forgive him or to accept blood money. Granted, the ruler might have his own additional punishment, but this is decided outside the court system. A consenting person who requests that he or she be killed has in effect forgiven his assailant by virtue of the fact that he is asking for his own death. It would be illogical to assume that the deceased would want a person punished for killing him at his own request and fulfilling his suicidal wishes.

The present discussion raises issues related to euthanasia, assisted suicide, and the discontinuation of life supports. Euthanasia and the discontinuation of life support measures probably fall beyond the scope of psychiatry. Consented killing and assisted suicide are very much part of forensic psychiatry, since evaluation of mental competence to consent to termination of life is a major psychiatric issue. We believe that contemporary Islamic jurists have to cooperate with psychiatrists in order to identify criteria or tests for competence to consent to have one's life terminated.

INVOLUNTARY HOSPITALIZATION AND TREATMENT IN ISLAMIC LAW

There is a definite consensus among Islamic scholars that, under ordinary circumstances, patient consent is mandatory before any medical treatment or procedure can take place. However, Islamic scholars disagree on whether merely obtaining consent will free the physician from liability for compensation in case of damage. There are basically two different schools on this issue. The first school states that the physician is liable for damages if the treatment is without the consent of the patient. His liability is affirmed whether he performed the treatment by good medical standards or not. This opinion is compatible with the position taken by most secular laws. The *Fiqh* (Islamic law) schools that go along with this opinion are the Hanafi, Shafii, Malki and Hanbali. This position is exemplified by a statement in the *Dusouqi* comments which states that "if an incompetent physician, negligent or otherwise, treated a patient without an accepted informed consent, that physician is fully liable, whether he performed his professional duty properly or not" (Al Dusouki, n.d., p. 355; Group of Indian Scholars, 1320 A.H., p. 499; Ibn Al Najeem, n.d., p. 33). Such opinion was taken by the majority of Islamic legal scholars and represented the official position of the four major schools of *Fiqh*. It was, however, opposed by two famous and highly recognized legal authorities in Islamic law.

The first is Ibn Qayem Al-Jawzia, a scholar of the Hanbali school, who deviated from the official position of his school to formulate his own opinion. In his book *Aalam Al-Mawaqin*, he stated the following:

> A skilled physician who does the best he can in surgery and excises a part of a man, a young boy, or an insane person without obtaining their consent or their guardian's, or performs circumcision on a child without the consent of his father or guardian, is guilty of causing damage. Our colleagues said he is liable because he performed a procedure without consent; had he done it with the consent of the adult patient or consent of the child's or insane person's guardian, he would not have been liable for the damage. I believe that he might not be liable at all, since he did it in good faith and his actions were meant for the welfare of the patient (Al Jawzia, 1397 A.H., p. 22).

The other scholar who took a similar position on liability was Ibn Hazm. He was a well-recognized authority in his field and had separated himself from the four main schools of jurisprudence and established his own school, which continued for hundreds of years. He made the statement that "On the issue of someone who amputated a hand which is used for eating, or extracted a painful or decayed tooth without the consent of the patient, we should consider God's two statements in the Holy Qur'an, the first, 'cooperate and help each other for good deeds and pious work and do not cooperate on sins and animosities' (Sura 5:2). This verse should be understood in contrast with the second verse which states that 'whosoever assaults you do assault them as they have assaulted you' (Sura 1:193). These two verses may be applied to the case of the hand amputation or extraction of a painful or decaying tooth. If it was carried out as the only treatment possible, there is no compensation for the lost hand and the physician should be praised, because the treatment was a good deed and the Prophet has ordered us to get treated. However, if the action of the physician was interpreted as an assault, adequate punishment would be in order." Ibn Hazm continued to say that since pain and suffering prevent people from praying to God or performing their daily duties to make a living, treatment must be considered a good deed (Ibn Hazm, 135 A.H., p. 444).

In contrast to Ibn Hazm's view, contemporary practice under Islamic law holds the physician liable for damages if he administered medication or performed a procedure without the patient's consent (Al Shaikh, n.d., p. 202). It should be noted that Islamic rules do not specify emergencies. Thus, this conclusion is assumed to be valid only under ordinary circumstances.

Muslim jurists have also specified certain limits to consent. They have required a special permit for every medical procedure. Imam Ibn Farhoum pointed out that "the absolute consent only applies to ordinary and common medical procedures." Also, one jurist was asked about a man who hired a physician to treat knee pain: if the patient was not given information about the type of treatment and the equipment used, would that not be a proper consent? The jurist answered that in an absolute consent, the patient should be given enough information about the procedure and the tools used; otherwise, the patient-physician contract will not be valid (Ibn Farhoun, 1301 A.H., p. 245).

In the case of minors, they cannot consent under any circumstances. The guardian, who is usually the father, is the one to give his consent for them. The age of consent is that of sexual maturity, or around 14 or 15 years for boys and 12 to 14 years for girls (Ibn Qadhi, 1300 A.H., p. 186; Al-Shafii, 1321 A.H., p. 53).

REFERENCES

Abu Zahra, Mohamad (1972), *Al welaia Ala Al Nafs*. (Guardianship on Self.) In the 4th Conference on Research of Law, Khartoum.

Al Aini, Abdul Rahman, *Sharh Al Manar*. (Interpretations of the Enlightenment Book.) Script No. 3827. Baghdad, Iraq: General Library of Endowment.

American Law Institute: "Model Penal Code of 1962." In: *Synopsis of Psychiatry,* ed. H. Kaplan, B. Sadock, & J. Grebb. Baltimore, MD: Williams & Wilkins, 1994, pp. 1171–1175.

Amir Badshah, Muhamad Amin (1350 A.H.), *Tayseer Al Tahreer.* (To Facilitate Writing of Sharia.) Cairo, Egypt: Mustafa Al Halabi Press.

Aoda, AbdelQader (n.d.), *Al Tashree' Al Jina'e Al Islami,* vol. 2. (Criminal Law in Islam.) Bierut, Lebanon: Dar Al Ketab Al Arabi.

Applebaum, P. S., & Gutheil, T. G. (1991), *Clinical Handbook of Psychiatry and the Law.* New York: McGraw-Hill.

Badran, Badran Abu Al-ainain (n.d.), *Al Zawaj Wa Al talaq fe Al Islam.* (Marriage and Divorce In Islam.) Alexandria, Egypt: Shabab Al jamea' Institute.

Al Baghdadi, Ghiath Aldin (1308 A.H.), *Mujamaa' Al Dhamanat.* (Collection of Securities.) Cairo, Egypt: Al Matb'a Al Khayria.

Al Dusouki, Muhamad Ben Arata (n.d.), *Hashiat Al Dusouki Ala Al Sharh Al Kabeer,* vol. 4. (Dusouki Commentary on the "Great Description.") Cairo, Egypt: Al Halabi Press.

Al Ghazali, Abu Hamid (1939), *Ihiaa' Uloum Al Deen,* vol. 2. (Revival of the Islamic Religion's Science.) Cairo, Egypt: Al Halabi Press.

Group of Indian Scholars (1319 A.H.), *Al fatawi Al Hindia,* vol. 6. (The Indian Interpretation of Sharia.) Cairo, Egypt: Bolaq Press.

Al Haj, Ibn Al Amir (1317 A.H.), *Al Taqreer Wa Al Tahbeer,* vol. 2. (The Decision and Scripting of Sharia.) Cairo, Egypt: Al Amiria Press Bolaq.

Al Hattab, A.B.B.Y. (1328 A.H.), *Mawahib Al jalil Lesharh Mukhtassar khalil,* vol. 6. (The Gifts of Jalil in Explaining Khalil Brief on Sharia Law.) Cairo, Egypt: Al Saada Press.

Holy Qur'an. Sura Al ahzab Aya 5.

Al-Hujmiri, Hasan Ibn Ali (1969), *Kashf al-Mahjub.* Cairo, Egypt: Mansouni Press.

Al Husqafi, M Aladin (1966), *Al dur Al Mukhtah Sharh Tanweer Al Absar,* vol. 6. (The Chosen Jewels in Explaining the Book, Vision Enlightenment.) Cairo, Egypt: Al Halabi Press.

Ibn Abdeen, Mohamad Amin (1966), *Hashiat Ibn Abdeen, Rad al Muhatar ala al durar Al mukhtar, Sharh tanweer Al absaar.* (Commentary of Ibn Abdeen, Answering the Perplexed on the Book the "Chosen Jewels.") Cairo, Egypt: Mustafa Al Halabi Press.

Ibn Abdul Salaam, Abu Mohamad (1388 A.H.), *Quaa'ed Al Ahkam Fe Masaaleh Al Anaam,* vol. 2. (The Rules Foundations on Public Responsibility.) Cairo, Egypt: Dar Al Sharq Press.

Ibn Al Ikhwa, Muhamad Al Qurashi (1937), *Maalem Al Qurba fi Ahkam Al Hisba.* (Teaching the Law of Moral in Sharia.) Cambridge: Dar Al Furoun Press.

Ibn Al Munassif, Muhamad Bin Issa (1988), *Tanbeeh Al Hukkam Ala Maa'khith Al Ahkam.* (Alarming the Rulers About the Rules of Rules.) Tunisia, Tunis: Kar Al Turky Press.

Ibn Al Najeem, Zain Al Abedeen Ben Ibrahim (n.d.), *Al bahr AL ra'eq Sharh Kanz Al Daqaaeq,* vol. 8. (The Clear Sea, on Explaining the "Minute Treasures" Book.) Bierut, Lebanon: Dar Al Maaref Press.

Ibn Al Qassim, Abdul Rahman Ibn Mohamad Al Assimi (n.d.), *Hashiat Ibn Qassim Ala Al Rawdh Al Murabaa,* vol. 7. (Commentary of Ibn Qassim on the Square Garden Book.) Cairo, Egypt: Al Halabi Press.

Ibn Al Qayem, Shams Aldin Al jawzia (1397 A.H.), *A'alam Al Muaqein An Rab Al Alameen,* vol. 2. (The Celebrities Among Sharia's Scholars.) Bierut, Lebanon: Dar Al Fikr.

Ibn Al Shahnah, Abu Al waleed Ibrahim (1973), *Lisan Al Hukam fe Maariat Al Ahkam.* (The Rulers' View of The Rules.) Cairo, Egypt: Al Halabi Press.

Ibn Farhoun, Ibrahim Ben Ali (1301 A.H.), *Tabserat Al hukkam fe Issoul al aqdhia wa manahej al ahkam,* vol. 2. (Enlightening of the Rulers on Basics of Judging and Methods of Rules.) Cairo, Egypt: Al Amera Al Sharafia Press.

Ibn Hanbal, Al Imam Ahmad (1313 A.H.), *Al Musnad,* vol. 2. (The Supported Book on Sharia.) Cairo, Egypt: Maymaniya Press.

Ibn Hazm, Ali Ben Ahmad (1350 A.H.), *Al Muhalla Sharh Al Mujalla,* vol. 10. (The Sweetened Description of Clear Sharia.) Al Muneeria Press.

Ibn Mufleh, abu Abdulla Al Maqdisi (1391 A.H.), *Al Adab Al Shri'a wa al Menah al mariea,* vol. 2. (The Literary of Sharia.) Riyakh, Saudi Arabia: Maktaba Al Riyadh AL haditha.

Ibn Mufleh, Abu Abdula (1932), *Al Furou,* vol. 5. (The Branches.) Cairo, Egypt: The Egyptian Press.

Ibn Qadhi Al Sumawa, Badraldin (1300 A.H.), *Jame'a Al Fussulain,* vol. 2. (The Gatherer of Seasons.) Cairo, Egypt: Al Azharia Press.

Ibn Qayem Al Jawzia (n.d.), *Zad Al Miaad fe Huda khayr Al Ebad.* (The Satisfactory Food of Knowledge in the Guidance of the Worshipers of God.) Cairo, Egypt: Al Halabi Press.

Ibn Qudama, Zain Al abedeen (1965), *Al Mughni Sharh Mukhtasar Al Khirqi,* vol. 9. (The Enrichments in Explaining the Al Khirqi Brief.) Cairo, Egypt: Al-Imam Press.

Al Jazeery, Karim, Saed (1987), *Al Fiqh Ala Al Mathaheb Al Arba'a,* vol. 4. (Fiqh i.e. Sharia Law, in the Four Schools of Jurisprudence.) Cairo, Egypt: Al Rayan for Turathe Press.

Al Jabouri, Husain Khalaf (1988), *Awaridh Al Ahlia,* (Impediments of Competence.) Saudi Arabia: Om Al Quraa University Makkah.

Al Kansani, Ala Aldin (1974), *Badaea Al Sanaea' fe Tartib Al sharaea,* vol. 17. *(The Best Made in Explaining Sharia Law.)* Bierut, Lebanon: Dar Al Kitab Al Arabi.

Khisro, Mulla Muhamad bin Feramouz (1300 A.H.), *Miraat Al Isoul fe sharh mirqat Al wisoul.* (Mirror of the Foundations for Explaining the Book "The Ways to Achieve Understanding of Sharia Law.") Istanbul: Muhammad Asaad Press.

Malk, Bin Anas (n.d.), *Al muataa.* (Malik's Book of Sharia.) Bierut, Lebanon: Dar Al nafa'es.

Al Mawawi, Abu Zakaria (n.d.), *Rawdhat al talibeen,* vol. 10. (The Garden of Students of Sharia.) Demascuss, Syria: Al Maktab Al Isalmi Press.

Al Mawsoo'a, Al Fiqhia (1989), *Encyclopedia of Fiqh.* Kuwait: Ministry of Endowment publication.

Al Nirdadi, Aldin Al hanbali (1968), *Al Inssaf Fe Maarifat Al rajeh men AL Khilaf,* vol. 9. (Fairness in Recognizing the Favored Opinion Among Differences.) Bierut, Lebanon: Dar Ihia' Al Turath Al Arabi.

Qa'ed, Osama Abdula (1987), *Al Masu'lia Al Jina'ia Lel Atibaa.* (Criminal Responsibility of Physicians.) Cairo, Egypt: Dar al Nahdha Al Arabia.

Al Qurtubi, Abu Abdulah (1965), *Al Jamea' Le'ahkam Al Quraan,* vol. 5. (The Quraanic Rules.) Bierut, Lebanon: Dar Ihiaa' Al turath Al Arabi.

Al Ramli, S.M.A. (1386 A.H.), *Nehayat Al muhtaj ela sharh Al minhaj,* vol. 6. (The Needs Objectives in Explaining the Methods of Sharia.) Cairo, Egypt: Mustafa Al Halabi Press.

Sadoff, R. L. (1988), *Forensic Psychiatry: A Practical Guide for Lawyers and Psychiatrists.* Springfield, IL: Charles C. Thomas.

Schacht, J. (1964), *An Introduction to Islamic Law.* Oxford: Oxford University Press.

Al Shafii, A A M. (1321 A.H.), *Al Om.* (The Mother of Sharia Law.) Cairo, Egypt: Bolaq Press.

Al Shaikh Mubarak, Qays Bin Mohamad (1991), *Al tadawi wal Mas-'ulia Al Tubia fe Al Sharia Al Islamia.* (Medical Treatment and Medical Liability in Islam.) Demascuss, Syria: Al Farabi Books.

Al Sharbieni, M. A. (1377 A.H.), *Mughni Al muhtaj fe Ma'rifat Maani Al faz al menhaj,* vol. 4. (Fulfillment of the Need for the Meanings of the Sharia Methods Vocabulary.) Cairo, Egypt: Al Halabi Press.

Al Tahtawi, Ahmad Ibn Mohamad (1238 A.H.), *Hashiat Al Tahtawi Ala Al Durar Al Mukhtar,* vol. 4. (Al Tahtawi's Commentary on The Chosen Jewels.) Cairo, Egypt: Al Amera Press.

Al Zaila'e, Fakhr Aldin (1315 A.H.), *Tabyan Al-haqae'q Sharh Kanz Al Daqae'q,* vol. 6. (Finding Truth in Commentaries on the Treasures of Details of Sharia Law.) Cairo, Egypt: Bolafq Press.

Al Zarkashi (1982), *Almanthour Men Al Qauaa'ed,* vol. 2. (The Scattered of Rules.) Kuwait City, Kuwait: Al Felaij Press.

Al Zarqani, A Baqi (1971), *sharh Al Zarqani Ala Mukhtassar Khalil,* vol. 8. (Al Zarqani Commentary on Khalil Brief of Sharia Law.) Cairo, Egypt: Mohammed Afandi Mustafa Press.

II.

Psychopathology in an Islamic Context

4.

Culture and Mental Illness in Algeria

Ihsan Al-Issa

There have been many recent reports dealing with the influence of cultural factors on the incidence, symptoms, and treatment of mental illness in the African continent, particularly sub-Saharan Africa (German, 1972, 1987a,b; Odejide, Oyewunmi, and Ohaeri, 1989). Authors assumed that African countries are homogeneous entities, giving little attention to their social and cultural diversity. The present chapter deals with one African country, Algeria, whose cultural background reflects not only the African tradition but also the influence of the Arab–Muslim culture. Previous publications have also dealt with psychiatric problems in other non-African Muslim–Arab countries such as Iraq, Kuwait, and Saudi Arabia (Kline, 1963; Bazzoui and Al-Issa, 1966; Dubovsky, 1983) as well as with psychiatric research in the whole Arab world (Racy, 1970; El-Islam, 1982). However, the countries surveyed have been under British and American influence and tend to follow the Anglo-Saxon rather than the Francophone psychiatric model which characterizes psychiatric research and practice in Algeria. The information reported here is mainly based on a review of psychiatric

---

This chapter is a slightly modified version of the paper "Culture and Mental Illness in Algeria," *The International Journal of Social Psychiatry*, Vol. 36, No. 3, 230–240, published with the permission of the editor.

research by Algerians and other North Africans plus personal contacts with Algerian psychiatrists during a nine-month visit. Algerian cultural background is dealt with first, including traditional concepts of mental illness and its treatment, and second, the development of modern psychiatry in Algeria and some aspects of the classification of mental illness by North African psychiatrists. Finally, observations of transcultural importance on depression, schizophrenia, drug abuse and alcoholism, and other mental disorders are reported.

SOCIOCULTURAL BACKGROUND

Two historical events had a major impact on Algerian culture and personality; namely, the Arab invasion and French colonialism. The Arab invasion in the seventh century brought with it Islam which still remains one of the major forces in the life of Algerians, with Arabic as the national language. Despite the drastic effects of French colonialism on the social and cultural life of the inhabitants between 1830 and 1962, the Muslim religion remains a strong unifying factor among different ethnic groups.

The French attempt to integrate Algeria with France resulted in the destruction of the basic cultural fabric of society, the village and its communal living. Being dispossessed of cultivated land in the villages, the majority of the population became daily workers on the farms of the colonialists. Lack of employment in the countryside forced a large number of Algerians to migrate to urban centers to live in shanty towns on the outskirts of cities. Loss of the small plots of cultivated land to the colonialists and lack of paid work resulted in a degrading poverty (Camus, 1962). Although Algeria was considered as part of France, native Algerians were deprived of the advantages of French social welfare and services in the areas of education and health. For example, there were only 500 (out of 5,000) Algerian students at the University of Algiers in 1954. Double standards were applied in the segregated hospital wards. As Benaissa (1986) pointed out, there was a prevalent belief among Algerian patients that one went to a hospital to die and it was better to die at home among one's own people.

With the exodus of the French after independence in 1962, the cities were flooded with poor and uneducated peasants who lacked any experience in modern urban living. Urban living had deprived the Algerian individual of the security of village life with its social support and communal life. Although the government structure after independence is quite similar to that during the French colonial era, the administration of daily affairs tends to be run on a tribal basis: the priorities of government workers are to help relatives and friends rather than to serve the public. This is a source of frustration, conflict, and confusion to many Algerian citizens who may have no relatives in public office. Leaving the village for urban centers, they have transferred their dependency on the tribe to the government which is now responsible for their daily existence (the majority of Algerians live in urban centers and are employed by the government). In this setting, they find that their "group ego," which used to be part of communal living, is rather dysfunctional. We will see later that these social and psychological changes after independence tend to play a major part in the mental health of the Algerian individual. Cultural changes after independence seem to have influenced both the rates and the symptoms of psychopathology in Algeria.

ALGERIAN CONCEPTS OF MENTAL ILLNESS AND TREATMENT

Algerians use the Arabic word *junūn* for madness, which is derived from *jinn* (demons). The patient is considered to be possessed *(meskūn)* by supernatural beings which control his or her behavior, thoughts, and desires. Thus, the causes of madness are regarded as exterior to the person and often considered as a result of persecution and sorcery. Although the symptoms of mental illness are believed to be caused by possession, precipitating factors are intimately linked with social relationships and the position of the individual in society. Consider, for example, *tankir* (denial) which explains indifference to one's social environment, such as social withdrawal or loss of interest in the social environment. This state is induced by a witch and may be used by a woman to regain the lost love of a man or by a parent to bring back a son who has left the extended family to live separately with his wife, or by a wife to reduce the influence of the husband's family on the daily life of the couple. The evil eye, another precipitating factor, is considered as a means of sanction against anybody who exceeds the limits set by the community on positive attributes such as wealth, health, beauty, and happiness. It is often motivated by envy, jealousy, or even admiration by an enemy or a friend.

In many Arab countries such as Iraq, Kuwait, and Tunisia, the practice of traditional therapy is illegal. This is mainly the result of the association of native therapy with underdevelopment and is motivated by a desire for modernization. Following independence, similar negative attitudes might be expected to have occurred in Algeria. However, traditional healing is not only legal, but is on the increase. Bensmail, Merdji, and Touari (1984) suggested that acculturation and social change have made the new generation of educated young so insecure that they reverted to traditional therapists and remedies. However, the use of native healers may be due in part to the limited availability of psychiatric services in Algeria.

There are three traditional therapists in Algeria: the *taleb,* the *marabout,* and the clairvoyant. The *taleb* functions both as a religious teacher and a healer, and his practices are more related to Muslim religion than those of other healers. In therapy, he may recite phrases from the Qur'an or give the patient an amulet *(herz)* to carry around, or soak a paper with religious writings in water for the patient to drink. The *marabout* is more like the sorcerer in black Africa and is regarded as a saint, an exorcist, and a healer. Exorcism consists of conversing with the evil spirit through the patient, using appeal or threat by repeating a religious–magical formula, burning incense, or offering a sacrifice such as a black cock. Beating the patient with a stick may be the last resort to get rid of the evil spirit. The Algerian countryside is dotted with shrines of *marabouts* which are visited by patients, honoring them with offerings and food festivities *(zerda* or *casaa).* During the shrine visit a descendant of the *marabout* may carry out a therapeutic session *(hadra)* which includes exorcism. Finally, the practices of the clairvoyant are regarded more as related to magic than to the Muslim religion. He is particularly specialized in dealing with sexual and emotional problems such as impotence, frigidity, sterility, and contraception.

THE DEVELOPMENT OF PSYCHIATRY IN ALGERIA

Jonville, the first psychiatric hospital in Algeria, was built in the town of Blida in 1930. Its name was changed after independence into Franz Fanon Hospital, honoring the well-known author who worked there in 1956. Fanon associated himself with the Algerian liberation movement and this experience had inspired him to politicize psychiatry and to identify with *The Wretched of the Earth.* At the time of independence, there were only three mental hospitals in the whole country, but by 1987 this number had increased to ten, including two hospitals in Algiers. In addition, there are now outpatient psychiatric clinics and psychiatric wards integrated into the main general hospitals.

There are four medical schools with departments of psychiatry at the universities of Algiers, Annaba, Costantin, and Oran. In 1985, there were 250 psychiatrists in the whole country, only 120 of whom were Algerians (the number of Algerian psychiatrists had increased to 150 by 1987). Most foreign psychiatrists are from the Eastern block where they have undergone induction courses in French before leaving their country with no knowledge of the native languages (Arabic and Berber). In order to communicate directly with patients they often need a French translator during the psychiatric interview. Paradoxically, these foreign psychiatrists now work mostly in remote areas rather than in urban centers where the majority of the population speaks French.

The use of psychiatric services is mainly limited to emergencies. Moussaoui (1987) defined emergency cases in terms of being dangerous to the self and others (attempted suicide, delusions of persecution, acute psychotic episodes) or suffering from severe mental illness (panic attack, agitation, catatonia, and confused states). Hospital admission tends to reach a peak during the summer months, but is at its lowest during the Muslim fasting month of Ramadan. It is interesting to study the rates of hospitalization when the lunar month of Ramadan occurs during the summer.

CLASSIFICATION OF MENTAL ILLNESS

In 1986 three African psychiatrists from Algeria, Morocco, and Tunisia (Douki, Moussaoui, and Kacha, 1987) edited the first *Manual for North African Practitioners* which reflects the influence of the French psychiatric diagnostic system (Ey, Bernard, and Brisset, 1973). The translated version of DSM-III (Boyer, Guelfi, and Henry, 1985) has had only minor influence on the *Manual* such as in the definition and classification of anxiety disorders. However, it is quite similar to DSM-II (American Psychiatric Association, 1968) in combining descriptive categories and theoretical notions. Neurosis, for example, is differentiated from psychosis and related to unconscious intrapsychic conflicts.

A prominent feature of the *Manual* is its emphasis on organic problems that are not part of the Anglo-Saxon definition of mental disorders. For example, psychological problems associated with physical illness are discussed in a separate chapter from psychosomatic disorders. The authors have devoted as much space to a chapter on epilepsy as to disorders such as schizophrenia and depression. In general somatization seems to dominate the psychiatric picture in Algeria, a feature reflected in the *Manual*. There is not only masked depression, which is familiar to Anglo-Saxon psychiatrists, but also masked neurosis, which refers to phobias and obsessions, "masked" by organic symptoms.

The listing of chronic delusional psychoses, confusional psychoses, and bouffées délirantes as major types of mental illness reflect the influence of French nosology. The notion of chronic delusional psychoses is based on Esquiral's concept of monomania[1] in the nineteenth century but seems similar to the Anglo-Saxon concept of paranoid schizophrenia. One type of chronic delusional psychosis is the "psychosis of passion" which includes erotomania (the delusion that one is loved by someone else); delusion of jealousy; and delusions of revendication (claims of damages, claims of scientific discovery, and claims of political or mystical ideologies). Another type is chronic hallucinatory psychosis which is characterized by delusions of influence with auditory hallucinations. This is described as a psychosis of middle age and is more frequent among females, particularly widows. Patients are able to continue their adaptation in the social and occupational milieu despite the psychotic symptoms, including rich hallucinatory experiences.

The second group of disorders, confusional states, is characterized by an almost complete clouding of consciousness, temporal-spatial disorientation, anxious perplexity, and oneiric (dreamlike) experience. Although these states are regarded as a separate category, they are mentioned in the descriptions of other major psychopathologies (mania, depression, and schizophrenia) as well as in many organic conditions including infectious disease. Confusional states are often observed in patients brought to the hospital by family members, usually after exhausting traditional treatment. This is evident in the patients' bewildered appearance, their empty and expressionless looks, their uncoordinated, slow, and hesitant movement, and their fragmented or absent speech.

Finally, another chapter in the *Manual* which deals with bouffées délirantes, cites Magnan, the French physician, describing it in 1886 as a thunderbolt in a calm sky. It is characterized by sudden onset with vivid hallucinations, delusions,

---

[1] A term most frequently used in the nineteenth century to describe paranoid conditions, in which a single symptom related to one subject is prominent. Examples are *monomanie boulimique* or insatiable hunger; *monomanie érotique* or erotomania; *monomanie incendière* or pyromania; *monomanie du vol* or kleptomania. Individuals with monomania are expected to be abnormal on one subject but not necessarily normal or healthy in other respects. Monomania is also called partial insanity.

clouding of consciousness, and rapid mood swings. The themes of delusions are related to religion (prophetic inspiration, divine revelation, messianic conviction, end of the world, and resurrection), sexuality, jealousy, poisoning, forced marriage, sexual abuse, and incest. One type of bouffées délirantes is nuptial psychosis which happens after the wedding night as a result of the stresses involved in arranged marriages, and usually experienced by the bride.

Although bouffées délirantes is found often in patients in former French colonies in both North Africa and black Africa (Collomb, 1965; Sow, 1978; Pierloot and Ngoma, 1988) and in African immigrants in France (Johnson-Sabine, Mann, Jacoby, Wood, Peron-Magnon, Olie, and Deniker, 1983), it is not reported by Anglo-Saxon trained psychiatrists in Africa or the Arab countries (Odejide et al., 1989; El-Islam, 1982). This raises the question whether the presence of this label in French nosology facilitates the identification of cases that conform to it. As Kroll pointed out, the Anglo-Saxon classification of mental illness has no category which is equivalent to bouffées délirantes "that does not imply a known aetiology (brief reactive psychosis) or a relationship to another grouping (schizophreniform psychosis) or else is so vague that cases categorized within it may bear no resemblance to each other (e.g., atypical psychosis)" (Kroll, 1979, p. 1137).

DEPRESSION

The most frequent types of depression seen by psychiatrists are masked depression and delusional depression (Douki et al., 1987). In contrast to somatic symptoms (Boucebci, 1985; Bensmail, Bentorki and Touari, 1981), mood disturbance is either minor or not verbalized at all by the patients (Boucebci, 1985). It may be that in Algeria as well as in other Arab countries the reluctance of patients to express depressive mood is related to cultural teaching of children that public expression of feelings is shameful (Bensmail et al., 1981).

Delusional depression is characterized by delusions of persecution, bewitchment, possession, and poisoning, sometimes associated with aggressive behavior. It is often confused with bouffées délirantes and schizophrenia, but it tends to respond to antidepressives rather than to neuroleptics (Douki et al., 1987). The presence of delusions of persecution and aggression in depressive patients is also found in other Arab countries (Bazzoui, 1970; El-Islam, Moussa, Malasi, Suleiman, and Mirza, 1988). Delusions of persecution in Algeria are not specific to depression but are frequently encountered in other mental illnesses. For example, these delusions are so prevalent among hysterical patients that they are given the diagnosis of *hystero-paranoïaque* by Algerian psychiatrists (Bensmail et al., 1981). The tendency among psychiatric patients to develop delusions may be considered as an exaggeration of normal tendencies in the general population rather than being specific to mental illness. Sleim Ammar, the Tunisian psychiatrist, observed that the most frequent mechanisms in both health and illness used by North Africans are flight into fantasy and imagination, projection, and the experience of morbid jealousy and hostility (Ammar, 1975). These mechanisms are consistent with the development of delusions and aggressive behavior. Feraoun (1953), the Algerian novelist, described Algeria as a country in which distrust is considered as the highest manifestation of wisdom.

Social changes brought about by the destruction of traditional village life during the colonial era and migration to cities after independence may have deprived Algerians of social support and communal living, and thus increased their insecurity and isolation. These changes could partly explain the prevalence of paranoid delusions among psychiatric patients. The report by Algerian psychiatrists that patients with chronic delusional psychoses are able to function both socially and occupationally may raise the question of the acceptance of delusion in Algerian society. Future research into Algerian personality, and particularly the use of projection and fantasy in everyday life, may throw some light on the mechanisms involved in the development of delusion both in psychiatric patients and in the general population.

In contrast to delusions of persecution, guilt feelings and self-depreciation are rarely observed in depressive patients, although these symptoms have been recently increasing in frequency. The rarity of guilt and self-depreciation and their recent increase is found not only in Algeria (Bensmail et al., 1981) but also in other African and Arab countries (Bazzoui, 1970; Murphy, 1978; El-Islam et al., 1988).

Three groups tend to have the highest rates of depression in Algeria (Bensmail et al., 1981; Boucebci, 1986). Middle-aged women with many children whose depression is associated with their inability to have more children and their fear of being divorced. The second group consists of young adults who have existential problems expressed in aggressive behavior related to feelings of inferiority. Finally, elderly former fighters in the liberation army *(Moujahadeen)* often show depression with delusions of retribution.

Similar to other Muslim societies, the rate of suicide is low in the rural traditional setting in Algeria (Bazzoui and Al-Issa, 1966; Douki et al., 1987). However, there have been recent increases in suicide among the young and the unemployed in urban centers. Also, the traditionally higher rate of suicide among males in rural areas has been recently reversed among urban populations with females predominating in all age groups, particularly between the ages of 15 and 22 (Bensmail, Bencharif, and Bentorki, 1975; Bensmail et al., 1981). In the patriarchal structure of the Algerian family, the father or the oldest son still holds absolute power for decision making, causing severe conflicts in educated women. The rates of attempted suicide are ten times higher than those of suicide and seem to mainly affect adolescent females. The lowest rate of suicide or attempted suicide is during the Muslim fasting month of Ramadan, revealing that the Muslim religion which regards suicide as sinful still has some preventive influence on urban communities. In contrast, the highest rates are in June, which may be due to the advent of the hot season or to stresses on the young at approaching school examinations, or a combination of both. Similar to hospitalization which increases during the summer and decreases in Ramadan, which is referred to earlier, it is interesting to study the rates of suicide when the month of June and Ramadan coincide.

SCHIZOPHRENIA

It is observed that schizophrenia which was limited to the disorganized and catatonic subtypes used to be very rare during the colonial era in traditional Algerian society. Bouffées délirantes and other acute psychotic states were more noticeable. However, there has been an increase in the rates of hospitalized schizophrenic patients. After independence their number has increased from 18 percent of total admitted cases in 1964 to 30 percent in 1974, rising to 36 percent in 1977, and to 40 percent in 1985 (Douki et al., 1987). It is possible that during the colonial era sociocultural factors such as the stability, the cohesion and communal sociofamilial environment might have protected against the illness. This increase may also be due in part to greater availability of psychiatric services and to less tolerance of patients by families in the urban environment.

There has been a change in the subtypes of schizophrenia with a noticeable increase in the paranoid and a decrease in the disorganized and the catatonic subtypes (Kacha and Kessaci, n.d.). Kacha and Kessaci (n.d.) confirmed the presence of Sneiderian symptoms in 25 hospitalized patients (somatic passivity, thought insertion, thought broadcast, thought withdrawal, delusions of influence, and auditory hallucinations). Delusions are also becoming more systematized, with richer content related to scientific and sociopolitical themes rather than to witchcraft and possession.

Arranged marriage among relatives is popular in the traditional Algerian family, raising the question of an increase in parental consanguinity among schizophrenic patients. Bensmail and Moron (1979) found that 55 percent of hospitalized schizophrenics had a history of mental illness within the family and 50 percent had parental consanguinity. According to Boucebci (1981) parental consanguinity in the general population is 34 percent in rural and 29 percent in urban areas. Those patients who combine parental consanguinity and a family history of mental illness (33 percent of patients) had the most severe illness.

DRUG ABUSE AND ALCOHOLISM

Cannabis (kif, hashish) is the most frequently used and the most tolerated in traditional North African society. It was introduced in North Africa from the Middle East during the Arab invasion in the seventh century. Often smoked or ingested with pastry and sweets, it may represent some sort of substitute for alcohol, which is forbidden by Islam. It is used by the general population in a controlled manner, most often in the evenings and during special occasions such as feasts and mystical dancing. Thus, the drug user is hardly distinguishable from the average adult citizen. However, the traditional picture has recently changed, with a more compulsive intake of cannabis alone or in combination with prescribed drugs (Douki et al., 1987). Legislation against the use of cannabis has made its use more secretive and outside social control.

Since alcohol use is forbidden in the Muslim religion, it has never become popular in Algeria. Its use has, however, increased since the nineteenth century after the arrival of Europeans who started the production of wine and beer in urban centers. Drinking in Algeria still remains a male activity limited to Westernized persons and carried out outside the home. There is a strong taboo against bringing alcohol into the home in the traditional Muslim family, limiting its availability for drinkers. Similarly, there is an almost complete abstention from drinking during the fasting month of Ramadan. These social and religious factors restricting drinking may explain the observation that chronic alcoholism and cirrhosis of the liver are rare in Algeria and that alcoholics and heavy drinkers can abstain from drinking without major problems. Long periods of abstention from alcohol in the Muslim culture may provide the therapist with ideal conditions to initiate detoxification of long-term alcoholics, facilitating complete recovery.

There is a higher association between alcoholism and other psychiatric disturbances in Algeria than in Western countries. In one mental hospital, 68 percent of cases suffered from psychiatric illness (Kacha and Akrour, 1986). In contrast, a Spanish researcher (Fernandez, 1980) found only 3 percent of alcoholics suffered from psychiatric disturbance. With recent social changes, such as urbanization and breakdown of the traditional Muslim family, psychiatrists observe that drinking is also becoming associated with social and family problems such as traffic accidents and divorce. Admission of cases of alcoholism and psychosis associated with addiction has increased from 1 percent to 6 percent of total admissions to a mental hospital in the city of Costantin between 1964 and 1975 (Bensmail et al., 1975). In a more recent study, Kacha and Akrour (1986) found that among 706 patients admitted to a mental hospital in Algiers, 7 percent were suffering from alcoholism and addiction, showing that substance abuse disorders are becoming more prevalent in urban areas.

OTHER CULTURE-SPECIFIC FINDINGS

In addition to schizophrenia, depression, drug abuse, and alcoholism discussed previously, we deal here with culture-specific findings related to "neurotic disorders," psychosexual disorders, and the effects of culture-specific family stresses on mental health. One interesting clinical observation is that while "hysterical" reactions are frequent, phobias and obsessive–compulsive disorders are relatively rare in the traditional setting. The rarity of obsessive–compulsive disorders *(waswās)* could be the result of simple norms of behavior and group cohesiveness which produce individual security (Douki et al., 1987). However, psychiatrists may not see these "patients" because *waswās* is not considered a mental illness but a religious experience resulting from temptations by the devil, distracting the faithful from carrying out the Muslim rituals of ablution and prayer.

Male inhibited sexual excitement seems to be the major psychosexual disorder seen by psychiatrists (Douki et al., 1987;

Bazzoui and Al-Issa, 1966). In contrast, female psychosexual dysfunctions, particularly inhibited sexual excitement or orgasmic dysfunctions rarely come to the attention of the professional. In Algeria, some cases of vaginismus are brought for treatment to the clinic by the husbands or the family. Male inhibited sexual excitement and vaginismus are often noticed on the wedding night when the whole extended family awaits the consummation of the marriage and the verification of the virginity of the bride. Premature ejaculation is not considered as a sexual dysfunction but as a sign of "hyper" virility. Homosexuality is hardly seen by psychiatrists as the primary reason for consultation (Kacha, Brahimi, Fertikh, and Taibi, 1981). In general, the treatment of psychosexual disorders is still in the domain of traditional medicine rather than modern psychiatry. Infanticide and abandoned children, a major problem in urban areas, reflects negative attitudes toward premarital sex and pregnancy outside marriage. This problem is not related to mental illness but to the fear of loss of social status (Boucebci, 1977).

CULTURE-SPECIFIC FAMILY STRESSES

In Algeria as well as in North Africa, there are many stresses associated with the family, such as the large number of children, polygamy, and the absent migrant father who works in France (Ammar, 1975). The number of children in an Algerian family could be as high as 17, with an average between 8 and 10 (Boucebci, 1979). Families with a large number of unemployed children are a source of stress. Boucebci (1990a) described the psychological suffering and the profound self-depreciation with loss of self-esteem of children and adolescents who spend all their days with no occupation or amusement in the streets of the cities because of small and crowded family accommodation. A neologism used in the capital, Algiers, is the term *hittiste* to describe this sociocultural phenomenon; a term derived from the Arabic word *hit* meaning wall, to describe the young who spend many hours sitting in the street with their backs against walls (Boucebci, 1990a).

Before independence, all members of the extended family looked after children. But parents who now live alone in large cities tend to reject their last-born children (the most frequent names given to these children are *ameziane* ["the little one"] and *barkahun* [enough of them]). The rejection of these younger children and the deterioration in the quality of care with the disappearance of social support and multiple mothering, are found to be related to an increase in the risk of mental illness (Boucebci, 1979). Boucebci (1985) observed that although childhood psychosis tended to be rare in the traditional setting, it has been increasing among the last-born children. Similarly, the rate of adult schizophrenia is found to be highest among the last-born children (Kacha, n.d.). Young mothers with large families, particularly those from the lower class, are also at risk with high rates of confusional psychotic states (Boucebci, 1979) and postpartum depression (Boucebci, 1977). Finally, families of migrant fathers who have gone to work in France tend to have a high risk of mental illness, particularly the oldest son who replaces the father in taking responsibility for the family; he represents the highest risk for psychosis and other psychiatric disorders (Boucebci, 1981).

One serious problem in Algerian cities is that of abandoned infants and infanticide, which is a result of negative attitudes toward premarital sexuality and pregnancy outside marriage. The behavior of the majority of these women who commit infanticide or abandon their children and who are single, divorced, or widowed, is not motivated by mental illness (depression, schizophrenia) but by their fear of loss of social status. A single mother cannot pursue the father in the courts or give the child for adoption (fostering a child is possible, but adoption is illegal). Giving the child the mother's family name implies promiscuous sexual behavior which brings disgrace, shame, and social rejection. Therefore, infanticide or simply abandoning the child may be the only alternative for the mother (Boucebci, 1977). Abandoned children tend to suffer identity problems since the Algerian family law makes adoption illegal and patrilineal descent is basic to the development of individual and group identity in this culture. Statistics reported by Boucebci (1990b) and Yaker (1979) reveal a high rate of mortality and psychiatric morbidity among institutionalized abandoned children. These negative effects are the result of a deficiency in psychological and physical care (maternal deprivation and malnutrition) in nurseries and hospitals. A study (Boucebci, 1990b) of a group of 24 abandoned infants hospitalized in Algiers reveals that with the exception of one normal case, all remaining infants were mentally ill, suffering from psychosis and mental retardation. That some statistics show 75 percent of abandoned infants available for adoption in France are Algerians (Boucebci, 1990b) demonstrates that factors associated with Algerian culture are mainly responsible for this problem, and remain influential even among Algerian immigrants in France.

A pathogenic stress related to arranged marriages and affecting the newly wed young girls in Algeria is reported by Pfeiffer (1982). He noted that:

> For the bride, often still a child herself, such a marriage means the first separation from the parental home, and, at the same time, a meeting with an indifferent, often internally opposed partner who becomes the cause of an unprepared for sexual experience, which is often traumatic. Added to this is the foreignness of the situation and the feeling of being delivered up to the husband, and particularly to his family. Reports from North Africa describe nuptial psychoses, in which the patient shows a hypochondriacal, confused, and hysterical character. In India, suicidal acts and possession states are stressed in similar circumstances [Pfeiffer, 1982, p. 263].

Algeria still remains a patriarchal, male-dominated society. Despite the educational and professional achievement of urban women, they still retain their traditional subservient role. Future research on the relationship between sex role conflicts and psychopathology may explain the higher rate of suicide in women in Algeria.

SUMMARY

This chapter reviews research and observations on the association between cultural factors and the rates and symptoms of mental illness in Algeria. In addition to traditional concepts and practices, modern psychiatric services and the classification of mental illness are discussed. Research on depression, schizophrenia, drug-abuse, and alcoholism are reported. Two major sociocultural factors related to mental illness are emphasized: the Muslim religion and social changes during both the colonial and postcolonial eras. Many culture-specific family stresses are also related to mental illness.

REFERENCES

American Psychiatric Association (1968), *Diagnostic and Statistical Manual of Mental Disorders,* 2nd ed. (DSM-II). Washington, DC: American Psychiatric Press.

——— (1994), *Diagnostic and Statistical Manual of Mental Disorders,* 4th ed. (DSM-IV). Washington, DC: American Psychiatric Press.

Ammar, S. (1975), Ethnopsychiatrie et psychiatrie transculturelle: Introduction aux problèmes posés par l'impact de l'acculturation sur la santé mentale au Maghreb. *La Tunisie Médicale,* 6:315–330.

Bazzoui, W. (1970), Affective disorders in Iraq. *Brit. J. Psychiatry,* 117:195–203.

——— Al-Issa, I. (1966), Psychiatry in Iraq. *Brit. J. Psychiatry,* 112:827–832.

Benaissa, A. M. (1986), *Contribution à l'étude de l'histoire de la santé en Algérie.* Algiers: Offices des Publications Universitaires.

Bensmail, B. M., Bencharif, A. K., & Bentorki, H. (1975), Considerations sur l'assistance et la morbidité psychiatriques dans l'est Algérien. *La Tunisie Médicale,* 6:393–406.

——— Bentorki, H., & Touari, M. (1981), La Depression en Algérie: Aspects culturels et evolution épidémiologique. *Psychiatrie Francophone, 0–4e trimestre,* 10–19.

——— Merdji, Y., & Touari, M. (1984), Pensée magique et thérapies traditionelles. *Psychiatrie Francophone,* 3–4:28–33.

——— Moron, P. (1979), Culture traditionelle, consanguinité et facteurs génétiques psychiatriques. In: *Comptes Rendus du Congrès de Psychiatrie et de Neurologie de Langue Française.* Charleroi, Belgium, June 26–July 1, 1978. Paris: Masson.

Boucebci, M. (1977), La psychiatrie infanto-juvenile en Algérie. *Acta Psychiat. Belgica,* 77:587–622.

—— (1979), Grande multiparité et incidences psychiatriques. Paper presented at the Congrés de Psychiatrie et de Neurologie de Langue Française, Angers, June 25–30.

—— (1981), Santé mentale du fils de migrant. Paper presented at the Congrès de Psychiatrie et de Neurologie de Langue Française, LXXXIX Session. Colmar, France, June 28–July 4.

—— (1985), Le handicap mental: Aspects épidémiologiques de prise en charge et preventifs en Algérie. Paper presented at the Congrès Medical Meghrébin. Monastie, Tunisie, May.

—— (1986), Les depressions au Maghreb. *Population et Santé au Maghreb,* 12:2–4.

—— (1990a), Aspects actuels de la psychiatre en Algérie. *L'information psychiatrique,* 101:952–962.

—— (1990b), L'enfance abandonné au l'adoption foreclose. *L'information psychiatrique,* 10:981–988.

Boyer, P., Guelfi, J. D., & Henry, J. F. (1985), *DSM III manuel diagnostique et statistique des troubles mentaux,* tr. & coordinated by P. Pichot & J. D. Guelfi. Paris: Masson.

Camus, A. (1962), *Actuelles III chroniques Algériennes 1939–1958.* Paris: Gallimard.

Collomb, H. (1965), Les bouffées délirantes en psychiatrie Africaine. *Psychopath. Africaine,* 1:167–239.

Douki, A., Moussaoui, D., & Kacha, F. (1987), *Manuel de psychiatrie du praticien Maghrébin.* Paris: Masson.

Dubovsky, S. L. (1983), Psychiatry in Saudi Arabia. *Amer. J. Psychiatry,* 140:1455–1459.

Ey, H., Bernard, P., & Brisset, C. L. (1973), *Manuel de psychiatrie,* 5th ed. Paris: Masson.

Fanon, F. (1968), *The Wretched of the Earth.* New York: Grove Weiderfeld.

Feraoun, M. (1953), *La terre et le sang.* Paris: Editions du Seuil.

Fernandez, F. A. (1980), Aspects actuels de l'alcoolisme en Espagne. *Annales Medico-Psychologiques,* 138:74–80.

German, G. A. (1972), Aspects of clinical psychiatry in sub-Saharan Africa. *Brit. J. Psychiatry,* 121:461–479.

—— (1987a), Mental health in Africa I: The extent of mental health problems in Africa today. *Brit. J. Psychiatry,* 151:435–439.

—— (1987b), Mental health in Africa II: The nature of mental disorder in Africa today—Some clinical observations. *Brit. J. Psychiatry,* 151:440–446.

El-Islam, M. F. (1982), Arabic cultural psychiatry. *Transcul. Psychiatry Res., Rev.,* 19:5–24.

———— Moussa, M. A. A., Malasi, T. H., Suleiman, M. A., & Mirza, I. A. (1988), Assessment of depression in Kuwait by principal component analysis. *J. Affect. Disorders*, 14:109–114.

Johnson-Sabine, E. C., Mann, A. H., Jacoby, R. J., Wood, K. H., Peron-Magnan, P., Olie, J. P., & Deniker, P. (1983), Bouffée délirante: An examination of its current status. *Psycholog. Med.*, 13:771–778.

Kacha, F., & Akrour, A. (1986), Approche du toxicomane hospitalisé en milieu psychiatrique. 2ième *Journée de Psychiatrie Algérien*. Algiers, Algeria.

———— Brahimi, A., Fertikh, A., & Taibi, D. (1981), Le psychiatre face aux troubles sexuels. *Psychiatrie Francophone, 0-4e trimestre:* 49–53.

———— Kessaci, M. (n.d.), 25 schizophrènes deux ans après: Résultats préliminaries. XIe *Journées medico-chirurgicales de l'Armée Nationale Populaire*. Algiers, Algeria.

Kline, N. S. (1963), Psychiatry in Kuwait. *Brit. J. Psychiatry*, 109:766–774.

Kroll, J. (1979), Philosophical foundations of French and U.S. nosology. *Amer. J. Psychiatry*, 136:1135–1138.

Moussaoui, D. (1987), Urgence en psychiatrie. In: *Manuel de psychiatrie du practicien Mahgrébin*, ed. S. Douki, D. Massour, & F. Kacha. Paris: Masson.

Murphy, H. B. M. (1978), The advent of guilt feelings as a common depressive symptom: A historical comparison on two continents. *Psychiatry*, 41:229–242.

Odejide, O. A., Oyewunmi, L. K., & Ohaeri, J. U. (1989), Psychiatry in Africa. *Amer. J. Psychiatry*, 146:708–716.

Pfeiffer, W. M. (1982), Culture-bound syndromes. In: *Culture and Psychopathology*, ed. I. Al-Issa. Baltimore: University Park Press.

Pierloot, R. A., & Ngoma, M. (1988), Hysterical manifestations in Africa and Europe: A comparative study. *Brit. J. Psychiatry*, 152:112–115.

Racy, J. (1970), Psychiatry in the Arab East. *Acta Psychiat. Scand.*, (Suppl.) 211.

Sow, I. (1978), *Les structures anthropologiques de la folie en Afrique Noire*. Paris: Payot.

Yaker, A. (1979), *Carence maternelle sévère, développement et problème de santé mentale*. Doctoral dissertation, 3e cycle, Paris V, René Descartes.

5.

Mental Illness in Kuwait and Qatar

M. Fakhr El-Islam

The Arab communities living along the Western coast of the Gulf that separates Persia from Arabia are mostly descendants of migrants from the Arabian peninsula. They share their pre-Islamic as well as Islamic cultural heritage with other Arabs living in the peninsula. The present account is based on 25 years of clinical psychiatric experience in Qatar and Kuwait, the former being closer to the mode of socioeconomic and cultural developments in the Gulf region.

SOCIOECONOMIC CHANGE AND INTERGENERATIONAL CONFLICT

Because of the increase in wealth associated with the discovery of oil, communities have gone from an eighteenth century lifestyle to a twentieth century one over just a few decades (El-Sendiony, 1981). Among the more welcome changes has been the introduction of adequate health services. However, the dramatic changes in people's value systems, beliefs, attitudes, and traditions have created a lot of social upheaval. These changes have been attributed to educational and occupational factors that have widened the gap between older people following a

121

traditional way of life and younger more modern people who are more open to new ideas. Secular education has provided the young not only with facts but also methods of thinking which are alien to their parents. It has demanded achievement in school and exposed the shortcomings of those less well endowed intellectually who if able to live the nomadic life of earlier generations would have been able to live quite easily. New occupations in skilled, technical, and professional fields sometimes lead to the break-up of the extended family, and are often the object not only of envy but also disapproval on the part of the older generation. It has become possible for many young members of the extended family to move away and live in nuclear family households. However, in spite of this geographic separation, most nuclear families consider themselves a part of their original extended families and maintain close ties (e.g., to arrange marriages, mediate disputes, or negotiate to secure certain benefits or even to solve everyday problems [El-Islam, 1985a, 1995]). Of the informational factors that have widened the generation gap, mass media, tourism, and employment of expatriates have been blamed most. The mass media, including availability of international television channels and communication networks, have given access to an overload of information that contains different value systems and life experiences from those in orthodox Arab–Islamic traditions. Affluence has made tourism possible for many members of the indigenous population of Arabian Gulf communities. They tour Western and more developed Arab countries with exposure to "modernity" in all its forms and degrees. Because of the need for new technical and professional skills to run a modern society the relatively young states of the region have to employ a large number of expatriates. These expatriates bring with them not only their expertise, but also their traditions and ways of life which are often at variance with the local culture, but which offer an alternative for the young generation.

Investigation of intergenerational conflict was carried out in both clinical (El-Islam, 1974, 1976, 1979) and community (El-Islam, Abu-Dagga, Malasi, and Moussa, 1986; El-Islam, Malasi, and Abu-Dagga, 1988) studies. The conflict mainly involves three areas: family relationships, marriage, and emancipation of women (El-Islam, 1983). Authoritarianism was characteristic of the family in the Arab peninsula even before the advent of Islam (Kurani, 1953). Tradition maintains a hierarchical order in the family in which dominance of male over female and older over younger is observed. The family offers security to its members in return for behavior that is in harmony with the cultural code. Respect for and obedience to elders top the list of family traditions, and paying respect to parents is held to bring about prosperity, success, health, and happiness. Tradition favors living with parents after marriage in an extended family. Filial relationships are more important than marital relationships. A son is given more freedom, authority, and responsibility than a daughter.

The preference of Arabs for male children is surpassed by only a few cultures, for example, the Chinese, who have a saying: it is better to raise geese than daughters (Tseng and McDermot, 1981), and who also share the belief that a woman determines the sex of her babies. The traditionally disadvantaged status of Arab women (El-Islam, 1975, 1982a) emphasizes submission and dependency as important feminine attributes in the upbringing of girls. Females are expected not to show any interest in sex. Arab culture puts a premium on premarital virginity and a sexual role is allowed only through marriage. The culturally accepted and only role for women is to marry and produce children. Traditionally parents have the "right" to arrange marriages for their children of both sexes, sometimes disregarding the views and preferences of the children themselves. Cousin marriage is preferred to marriage to nonrelatives; and husband and wife should come from families of equal status.

What is traditional and what is Islamic have been closely identified with each other in everyday life and in Arab interpersonal relationships. Most transgressions of tradition are also transgressions of the Islamic religious code. The young who had a secular education adopt objective explanations for phenomena (e.g., ill health) which their parents attribute to religiously endorsed supernatural forces (e.g., the evil eye). Young people prefer individuation and equality of rights and duties in the family. Many opt for love marriages and call for emancipation of women. Material possessions play a greater part than in the past for the young in defining their identity (Melikian, 1981).

However, many young people lack motivation to achieve. Freedom from economic insecurity has apparently deprived the youth of learning how to cope with frustration. The lack of a constructive attitude to work is attributed to the fact that the national income is not the consequence of productivity of the native population but rather is dependent on the discovery of oil, which is found inland and offshore (Sayyigh, 1971). Members of the old parental generation had to work hard in such dangerous occupations as diving for pearls for the sake of a relatively small income. They are disappointed at and critical of their children's lack of drive. In a study of the factors that precipitated depression (El-Islam, Mohsen, Dermerdash, and Malasi, 1983) work-related factors were much less involved in indigenous Qatari and Kuwaiti depressives when compared to expatriate depressives in Qatar and Kuwait. This seems to reflect the small value of work for indigenous Arab Gulf citizens.

Clinical studies of intergenerational conflict show it plays a significant role in parasuicide (57%), schizophrenic disorders (17%), and emotional (neurotic) disorders (20%) of young patients (El-Islam, 1985b). Community studies, however, revealed no covariance of intensity of intergenerational conflict with scores of symptoms of mental ill health on the general health questionnaire (Goldberg and Hillier, 1979). It was therefore suggested that the role of intergenerational conflict in clinical material is more likely to be a precipitant of help-seeking rather than of the symptoms themselves. Families with prominent intergenerational conflict are more likely to seek the external help of professionals for a member's symptoms or problems which families with less conflict solve through support within the family.

ILLNESS BEHAVIOR IN ARABIAN GULF COMMUNITIES

Defined by Mechanic (1962) as ways in which individual symptoms are differentially perceived, evaluated, and acted (or not acted) upon by different persons, illness behavior seems to pass through four stages of appraisal in order to decide (1) that the change is adverse; (2) that action is required to reverse the change; (3) what action is required; and (4) how to secure such an action (El-Islam and Abu Dagga, 1990b, 1992). Individuals acquire cognitive schemas in which various appraisals are coded as a result of cultural, family, and individual experiences. Arab culture in the Gulf region takes somatic symptoms as being very serious and definitely worthy of medical attention. On the other hand, emotional and behavioral symptoms are regarded as being supernatural in origin and thus call for the involvement of a traditional–religious healer (El-Islam and Ahmed, 1971; El-Islam, 1978). The effects of cultural factors on assessment are so deeply imprinted that the best secular education does not reduce the likelihood of supernatural interpretation of psychotic experiences (El-Islam and Malasi, 1985).

Common somatic and emotional symptoms from patients' records were investigated in order to find out how nonpatients explain, and what they would do, should they have any of these symptoms. Among lay explanations of symptoms, supernatural forces are well recognized by most Gulf Arabs. The belief in God's will as a fatalistic determinant of events is quite common. Symptoms, like any other event, may be attributed to God's will, and this leads some people who have symptoms not to attempt to appraise them at all because this fatalistic belief implies that whatever appears through God's will also disappear by God's will. Humans can only pray for the disappearance of symptoms. Envy is another supernatural force which is believed to arise from the evil eye representing the evil wishes of others. They may envy the greater status, health, or prosperity of the victim. Unpleasant personal change in a person's mental health (e.g., depression) is attributed to the evil eye (envy by others). In Western postindustrial societies increased effort is expected of lower achievers so they may reach the level of higher achievers. In the noncompetitive Arab Gulf communities, envy removes the inequality or restores equality by the almost magical, envious, wish-fulfilling powers of low achievers that make higher achievers come down to *their* level so that they lose their higher position. Sorcery is believed to be another means of inducing harmful mental effects on others by employment of evil spirits *(jinn)* for revenge or even out of spite.

Older individuals are more likely to attribute symptoms of mental ill health to supernatural forces. A psychosocial etiology of mental symptoms is more likely to be entertained by females who are culturally conditioned to feel that they are the weaker sex and that they are therefore more vulnerable to psychosocial stresses. There is no one-to-one correspondence between culturally shared attributions on the one hand and methods of traditional treatments on the other. Patients and their relatives often go from one method of traditional healing to another in search of a cure; from religious amulets to Qur'anic recitation, and from rituals undoing sorcery to exorcism, and finally cautery.

SOCIAL AND CULTURAL BOUNDARIES OF MENTAL HEALTH

In Arab Gulf communities, the components of mental health are implicitly defined on sociocultural grounds. The positive component of mental health, successful adaptation to work and family, is normally defined by the balance between individual input abilities and environmental requirements. In these communities the indigenous population has very little motivation to achieve in the work situation because jobs are created for indigenous citizens (Kline, 1963), departments are often overstaffed in order to provide them with income, while in many instances no real work is done. Work adjustment as a criterion for defining mental health is almost irrelevant here. Again the indulgent upbringing of indigenous children teaches them very little about setting limits on their behavior. According to international adjustment criteria, many of these children would probably be diagnosed with a conduct disorder in their interpersonal relationships and attitudes to authority figures. "Premarital sexual adjustment" as a criterion for good mental health cannot be applied in this society where sexual relationships are considered normal only in marriage.

Only an "emic" approach can decide which thought contents are abnormal according to socially set norms and whether the deviance falls in the domain of the medical profession or that of traditional healers. The family may bring for medical–psychiatric attention a member who consumes alcohol but has none of the medically defined alcohol-related problems. This is because, for the Muslim family, consumption of alcohol is never considered "normal." On the other hand, an individual may be tormented by obsessive thoughts and the family not seek psychiatric help because obsessions are believed to be intimations by the devil. Thus, only strong faith can counter them in the continuing battle between man and devil. In fact, the Arabic word *waswās* means both devil and obsession. More serious errors in diagnosis of states of mental ill health take place if an "etic" approach is taken to sociocultural beliefs through failure to recognize the boundaries between what is socioculturally shared and what is not. This can lead to both under- and overdiagnosis of psychotic illness (Al-Ansari, Emara, Mirza, and El-Islam, 1989). Aggressive behavior in a female calls for family disciplinary counteraggression in order to contain her physically in the family household. Similar behavior in a male leads to the family seeking professional help for the same problem.

SOCIAL AND CULTURAL FACTORS IN SYMPTOMATOLOGY PATTERNS

Somatization is in the foreground of most psychiatric disorders which present to medical (primary care or psychiatric) professionals in Arab Gulf communities (El-Islam, 1982a, 1984). An extensive somatization syndrome was described (El-Islam, 1975) in Qatari women who fail, or experience the threat of failure, to satisfy the culturally approved role of marriage and mothering. They develop a mixture of somatoform and conversion dissociative symptoms that cover the entire body. The symptoms not only elicit sympathetic attention from family members and medical professionals (e.g., through overinvestigation of somatic symptoms), but also lead to the reverse interpretation of the sequence of events as others come to believe that these women fail to marry, maintain a marriage, or have children *as a result* of their somatic ill health! Instead of being regarded as social failures these women are regarded as somatic victims.

The rarity of agoraphobia in women in these communities is in contrast to its prominence amongst Western women (El-Islam, 1994a). This has been attributed to the rarity of situations which would unmask this symptom complex in women in Arab Gulf communities. It is the exception there for women to be unaccompanied by men outdoors, and the use of public transport is rare. Moreover, homebound females are regarded as more virtuous women than those who go outdoors. Social phobias do not handicap individuals in securing their own spouses in this society where most marriages are arranged by family elders for members of both sexes even if they have mental illness (including mental retardation and schizophrenia). Coitophobia is mostly encountered in newly wed women in this society where child rearing emphasizes chastity and it is customary to tell young girls horrific tales that emphasize the physically assaultive and painful nature of sexual intercourse and its disgraceful eternally punishable consequences according to the Islamic code if it takes place outside marriage. Females learn that they have to accept sex because it is a male's prerogative. Death phobias usually include after-death fears of judgment by angels in the grave (grave torture) and of hellfire in their later postmortal life. Fear of death is usually greatest at bedtime when sleep is culturally regarded as a "micro" form of death lest it extend into the complete "formal" death in the course of the night. It is extremely rare to encounter weight-gain phobia (anorexia nervosa) in these communities where some degree of obesity is equated with strength; the obese are called *Mateen* (strong), and thin people are called *Dhaeef* (weak). Women on the plump side are considered attractive and are more likely to be sought as prospective spouses when marriages are arranged.

Obsessional disorder often relates to Islamic religious material. Obsessional doubts include the existence or oneness of God, and the number of performed prayer segments in the five daily prayers. Compulsive rituals usually involve the concept of *taharah* which is close to, but not identical with, cleanliness. *Taharah* is the state of being fit to pray or to read the holy book (Qur'an) which is achievable by ablution (washing ritual). This ritual must be performed following sleep, the passing of flatus, urine, or stools, sexual intercourse or, according to a minority of religious sects, after touching members of the opposite sex (e.g., in shaking hands). Compulsive checking rituals usually deal with the performance of *taharah* rituals or prayers.

Dissociative conversion symptoms betray the patient's own concept of what the symptom mimics. Thus a patient with a dissociative aphonia does not move the tongue, which is regarded as the organ of speech, and a patient with dissociative limb paralysis feels no sensation in the limb concerned because of the idea that a paralyzed limb is "dead" and therefore has no feeling. There is also a widespread lay belief among patients with dissociative disorder that subjective lack of awareness of their acts exempts them from responsibility for the consequences of these acts.

Depressed patients (El-Islam, Malasi, and Abu-Dagga, 1988) prove to have the same depressive core of symptomatology as in other cultures. Guilt feelings have religious contents (e.g., guilt over neglect of religious duties and fear of God's retribution for past wrongdoing). Metaphoric descriptions of depressive distress commonly involve reference to the heart. Suicidal feelings and intentions to end life by self-inflicted death are uncommon. The Islamic religion prohibits all forms of self-harm and condemns those who kill themselves to eternal hell in the afterlife. Hopelessness also contradicts the Islamic code because it is only the blasphemous who lose hope in relief of their distress by God. A somatization front usually covers background guilt which is elicited by specific probing and is rarely volunteered by the patient (El-Islam, 1969). Depressive and anxiety symptoms have been studied in Muslim women on oral contraceptives in Kuwait (El-Islam et al., 1988). Those who believed that contraception was against the Islamic code and yet took oral contraceptives out of economic necessity to limit their offspring, suffered cognitive dissonance and were very likely to develop psychiatric symptoms.

In schizophrenic patients, first rank symptoms, which are the main diagnostic criteria in recent psychiatric classifications, should be thoroughly appraised and distinguished from socio-culturally shared beliefs and experiences that simulate delusions or hallucinations (El-Islam, 1980). Delusions of passivity should have contents beyond projections on the devil who is culturally held to tempt or entice man into wrongdoing. Cultural beliefs about the devil do not include a visual or auditory perception, and reports of such perceptions have to be regarded as hallucinations. Culture-centered delusions (pathological extensions of culturally shared beliefs beyond approved norms) are more likely to disappear than delusions with secular–material contents. Once they lose their pathological components, culture-centered beliefs are readily "normalized" by containment in the repertoire of culturally shared beliefs. The better outcome for schizophrenics living in traditional extended families is attributed to the families' lower expectations; greater tolerance of abnormal behavior and brief withdrawals; individually tailored programs for securing social contacts for patients; and better supervision of medication and aftercare when compared to patients living in nuclear families (El-Islam, 1979, 1982b). A study of marriages of schizophrenic patients (El-Islam and Abu-Dagga, 1990a) revealed better marriage rates than similar studies in the West. This is attributed to the system of arranged marriages in these communities which take a large part of the burden off schizophrenics whose seclusiveness and shallow emotions grossly impair their ability to secure spouses in a love marriage.

In these communities with a lot of intermarriage within the extended family or tribe, transgenerational transmission of mental retardation and psychotic disorders is familiar to all practicing professionals. Although lay individuals are also aware of the increased inheritance risk in consanguinous marriages, cultural pressures continue to promote marriage of relatives, and especially of cousins, to the point of seeking the approval of all male cousins in the extended family before arranging the marriage of a female to a "stranger," a man from another extended family or tribe.

Dementia is widely recognized as part of aging. Unless they have overt behavioral disturbances (e.g., disinhibition or wandering) elderly demented patients are rarely seen by psychiatrists. Recently, however, there has been an increase in demands for permanent inpatient care of parents or grandparents within the health system, which is available free of charge to indigenous citizens.

Drug and alcohol dependence are not unexpected in these affluent communities. Some adolescents start substance abuse as an act of rebellion against the values of society which traditionally emphasize abstinence as the norm (Bilal and El-Islam, 1985). Early paternal loss in excess of what is seen in other psychiatric patients has been noted with drug and alcohol dependent patients. In this polygamous community it is not unusual for the elderly to marry much younger wives. They often do not survive long enough to bring up the children of such marriages, who suffer paternal deprivation during their childhood and adolescence and grow up without adequate paternal identification figures. Iatrogenic benzodiazepine dependence was recently overcome in the Qatari community through heightened awareness on the part of psychiatrists who together voluntarily limited benzodiazepine prescriptions to a maximum of three weeks for any psychiatric disorder. However, free availability of these drugs in neighboring Gulf countries prevented the full eradication of iatrogenic benzodiazepine abuse.

Ischemic heart disease was studied as a psychosomatic disorder in relation to type A personality characteristics (Emara, Abdella, Saadah, Al-Asfoor, and El-Islam, 1986). As expected from the attitude of the endogenous population to work, Kuwaiti patients with myocardial infarction were found to be much less likely to have the drive and job involvement components of type A behavior than expatriate Arabs with myocardial infarction in Kuwait, although both groups had similar physical risk factors.

The psychosocial profile of parasuicidal patients in Kuwait showed demographic characteristics in common with parasuicidal individuals in the West (e.g., a preponderance of young females), but a much higher proportion was precipitated by intergenerational conflict (Suleiman, Nashef, Moussa, and El-Islam, 1986; Suleiman, Moussa, and El-Islam, 1989; Emara et al., 1988). Three types of family reaction to the parasuicidal family member were detectable. The family may adopt an aggressive attitude by ostracizing the parasuicidal member because of disgrace to the family through the suicidal attempt. Other families adopt a permissive attitude and provide whatever they would have felt guilty about failing to provide had the parasuicidal family member died. The third type of family reaction has never been reported outside this community; it is a combined reaction where a family member (usually a senior female) adopts the permissive attitude and another family member (usually a senior male) simultaneously adopts an aggressive attitude toward a parasuicidal family member.

TREATMENT OF MENTAL ILLNESS

The large mental hospitals in the region (e.g., in Kuwait and Bahrain) were the first to develop a form of psychiatric service that replaced the old purely custodial care which was provided for the rich within the extended family, while the state provided for the poor by imprisoning them. Qatar has never had a hospital exclusively for mental patients (El-Islam, 1995). Specialist psychiatric services in Qatar have always been provided by psychiatric wards in a general hospital setting. Specialist psychiatric outpatient clinics have been available in general hospitals and some primary care centers in Kuwait. The majority of hospital admissions are informal and there is no mental health legislation. Families usually accept doctors' advice to have psychiatric patients compulsorily admitted to the hospital against their will when they are considered dangerous to themselves or to others. Collaboration with families has provided a readily available alternative to mental health legislation (El-Islam, 1994b). This does not seem strange in communities where the family is expected to run the affairs of all its members whether they are healthy or unhealthy. Moreover, families collaborate with psychiatrists in the care of patients before they need hospitalization and in their care after discharge from the hospital, functions which are rarely covered by mental health legislation. Recently, daycare and community psychiatric nursing services have been provided in Qatar to boost patients' regular treatment and rehabilitation in the community. Home visits are paid to all psychotic patients who fail to attend for follow-up. Families often provide transport for nurses to visit their homes to supervise patients' maintenance on medication, encourage self-care, and participate in problem solving.

There is a preponderance of males among psychiatric inpatients and outpatients in Arab Gulf communities. The general population in these communities has a male majority because men come to work there, leaving their spouses and children in their home countries. When dangerous to self and/or to others, males are more difficult to control, and hence are more likely to need professional psychiatric intervention at outpatient or inpatient levels. Marriage prospects are put much more in jeopardy for females than males by the stigma of psychiatric disorder, and hence families are very reluctant to bring their unmarried female members to see a psychiatrist. Males have to be outdoors (e.g., at work) to earn a living and cannot be kept at home for long periods like females when mentally ill; this makes professional help for males all the more necessary.

Some form of family therapy, to secure the support of family members, is the rule for all patients living in families. This is of prime importance for crisis intervention (e.g., in cases of parasuicide or bereavement). Inclusion of family members is essential in therapy of patients with excessive intergenerational conflict, and in the case of psychotics who are not likely to comply on their own with treatment outside the hospital. Intergenerational conflict is amenable to psychotherapeutic amelioration in most cases as families accept the need of each member to achieve some degree of individuation and accept diversity as normal. Family sessions demonstrate that intergenerational conflict is associated with intrapersonal conflict in members of both the older and younger generations. Parents have conflict about the education they provided for their children which is held responsible for their rebellion against traditional parental values. Youth experience guilt over the conflict between internalized parental values and peer values, feeling caught between two worlds: one dying and another not yet born!

Family participation in rehabilitation of schizophrenics is facilitated by prior psychoeducation by psychiatric staff (El-Islam, 1989). Families help to organize new social networks from young people in the extended family to replace the drug abusing companions of drug dependent family members. The family is the best social agent, recently rediscovered in the West after public social services have dwindled as a result of budget cuts.

The relationship between psychiatric professionals and traditional–religious healers, if present at all, is neither supportive nor complementary in most Arab Gulf communities. Claims of cooperation or even integration in other countries are not sympathetically viewed by most psychiatrists. A famous traditional healer from Saudi Arabia admitted, after more than 20 years of practice, that all his clients were psychiatric patients who should be exclusively handled by psychiatrists; he gave up his practice and advised other healers to follow suit.

The state of Qatar provides the handicapped (including the mentally retarded and unemployable psychotics) with a monthly income for life. The economic status of indigenous patients' families was difficult to assess. It is customary to hide the reality of one's income from strangers for fear of envy. No effort to convince patients' relatives of the confidentiality of information could persuade them to yield information on family income. The psychiatric department in Qatar provides, free of charge, all standard pharmacological, electroconvulsive therapy, behavior, supportive, and cognitive therapies through community, day, outpatient, and inpatient services.

For a total population of about 400,000 (Central Statistics Organization, 1992) in Qatar there is one comprehensive psychiatric service in Doha which is within a two-hour drive from the furthest part of this country (total area 11,000 square kilometers). During 1994 and 1995, 2,502 patients made their first contact with the clinic. Table 5.1 shows their age distribution in comparison to the age distribution in the general population. There is an overrepresentation of adolescents (13–19 years old), young adults (20–29 years old), and old people (aged 60 or more years). Forty percent were females while the proportion of females in the general population is 31 percent. The

TABLE 5.1. First Contacts with Psychiatric Service (1994 and 1995)

Age	Psychiatric Patients % (N = 2,502)	Total Population % (N = 384,090)[a]
3–12	13.4	19.3
13–19	15.7	9.7
20–29	26.7	22.3
30–39	24.8	24.5
40–49	9.3	10.8
50–59	4.9	4.0
60+	5.2	1.9

[a] 11,989 infants under age 3 were deducted from the total population as no individuals in this age group were seen at the clinic.

majority of outpatients (67%) have nonpsychotic disorders. The inpatient unit can accommodate a maximum of 36 patients and the proportion of new admissions to readmissions is about 1:1. During 1994 and 1995 the community nursing service dealt with 146 cases and the consultation liaison service dealt with 600 cases.

REFERENCES

Al-Ansari, E. A., Emara, M. M., Mirza, I. A., & El-Islam, M. F. (1989), Schizophrenia in ICD-10: A field trial of suggested diagnostic guidelines. *Comprehen. Psychiatry*, 30:416–419.

Bilal, A. M., & El-Islam, M. F. (1985), Some clinical and behavioural aspects of patients with alcohol dependence problems in Kuwait psychiatric hospital. *Alcohol & Alcoholism*, 20:57–62.

Central Statistical Organization (1992), *Annual Statistical Abstract*, 12th Issue. Doha: Al-Ahleia Press.

Emara, M. K., Abdella, N., Saadah, A., Al-Asfoor, A., & El-Islam, M. F. (1988), Attempted suicide by drug overdose. *Saudi Med. J.*, 9:182–187.

——— El-Islam, M. F., Abu-Dagga, S. I., & Moussa, M. A. A. (1986), Type A behaviour in Arab patients with myocardial infarction. *J. Psychosom. Res.*, 30:553–558.

El-Islam, M. F. (1969), Depression and guilt. *Soc. Psychiatry*, 4:56–58.

——— (1974), Hospital referred parasuicide in Qatar. *Egypt. J. Ment. Health*, 15:101–112.

——— (1975), Culture bound neurosis in Qatari women. *Soc. Psychiatry,* 10:25–29.

——— (1976), Intergenerational conflict and the young Qatari neurotic. *Ethos,* 4:45–56.

——— (1978), Transcultural aspects of psychiatric patients in Qatar. *Compar. Med. East & West,* 6:33–36.

——— (1979), A better outlook for schizophrenics living in extended familes. *Brit. J. Psychiatry,* 135:343–347.

——— (1980), Symptom onset and involution of delusions. *Soc. Psychiatry,* 15:157–160.

——— (1982a), Arabic cultural psychiatry. *Transcult. Psychiat. Res. Rev.,* 19:5–24.

——— (1982b), Rehabilitation of schizophrenics by the extended family. *Acta Psychiatr. Scand.,* 65:112–119.

——— (1983), Cultural change and intergenerational relationships in Arabian families. *Internat. J. Fam. Psychiatry,* 4:321–329.

——— (1984), Some transcultural aspects of depression in Arab patients. *Islamic World Med. J.,* 2:48–49.

——— (1985a), Psychiatric rehabilitation: The role of the extended family. *Postgrad. Doctor,* December:820–824.

——— (1985b), Intergenerational complex in Arabian families. In: *Psychiatry, The State of the Art,* Vol. 8, ed. P. Pichot, P. Berner, R. Wolf, & K. Thau. New York: Plenum.

——— (1989), Collaboration with families for the rehabilitation of schizophrenic patients and the concept of expressed emotion. *Acta Psychiatr. Scand.,* 79:303–307.

——— (1994a), Cultural aspects of morbid fears in Qatari women. *Soc. Psychiatry Psychiatr. Epidemiol.,* 29:137–140.

——— (1994b), Collaboration with families: An alternative to mental health legislation. *Care in Place,* 1:256–260.

——— (1995), Psychiatry in Qatar. *Psychiatr. Bull.,* 19:779–781.

——— Abu-Dagga, S. I. (1990a), Marriage and fertility of schizophrenic patients in Kuwait. *Med. Princip. & Pract.,* 2:18–26.

——— ——— (1990b), Illness behaviour in mental ill-health in Kuwait. *Scand. J. Soc. Med.,* 18:195–201.

——— ——— (1992), Lay explanations of symptoms of mental ill health in Kuwait. *Internat. J. Soc. Psychiatry,* 38:150–156.

——— ——— Malasi, T. H., & Moussa, M. A. A. (1986), Intergenerational conflict and psychiatric symptoms. *Brit. J. Psychiatry,* 149:300–306.

——— Ahmed, S. A. (1971), Traditional interpretation and treatment of mental illness. *J. Cross-Cult. Psychol.,* 2:150–154.

———— Malasi, T.H. (1985), Delusions and education. *J. Operat. Psychiatry,* 16:29–31.

———— ———— Abu-Dagga, S. I. (1988), Interparental differences in attitudes to cultural changes in Kuwait. *Soc. Psychiatry Psychiatr. Epidemiol.,* 23:109–113.

———— Mohsen, M. Y. A., Demerdash, A. M., & Malasi, T. H. (1983), Life events and depression in transit populations. *Internat. J. Soc. Psychiatry,* 29:13–20.

Goldberg, D., & Hillier, V. F. (1979), A scaled version of the general health questionnaire. *Psychol. Med.,* 9:139–145.

Kline, N. S. (1963), Psychiatry in Kuwait. *Brit. J. Psychiatry,* 109:766–776.

Kurani, H. (1953), Evolution in education. In: *Evolution in the Middle East: Reform, Revolt and Change,* ed. S. K. Fisher. Washington, DC: The Middle East Institute.

Mechanic, D. (1962), The concept of illness behaviour. *J. Chron. Dis.,* 15:189–194.

Melikian, L. H. (1981), *Jassem. A Study in the Psychosocial Development of a Young Man in Qatar.* London: Longman.

Sayyigh, Y. (1971), Problems and prospects of development in the Arabian peninsula. *Internat. J. Mid. East. Studies,* 2:40–58.

El-Sendiony, M. F. M. (1981), *The Effect of Islamic Sharia on Behavioural Disturbances in the Kingdom of Saudi Arabia.* Mecca: Ummal Qura University.

Suleiman, M. A., Moussa, M. A. A., & El-Islam, M. F. (1989), The profile of parasuicide repeaters in Kuwait. *Internat. J. Soc. Psychiatry,* 35:146–155.

———— Nashef, A. A., Moussa, M. A. A., & El-Islam, M. F. (1986), Psychosocial profile of the parasuicidal patient in Kuwait. *Internat. J. Soc. Psychiatry,* 32:16–22.

Tseng, W. S., & McDermot, J. F. (1981), *Culture, Mind and Therapy.* New York: Bruner/Mazel.

6.

Mental Health in Iran

Fereydoon Mehrabi, Seyed-Akbar Bayanzadeh, Mohammad-K. Atef-Vahid, Jafar Bolhari, Davoud Shahmohammadi, Seyed-Ahmad Vaezi

GENERAL FEATURES OF THE ISLAMIC REPUBLIC OF IRAN

The Islamic Republic of Iran is situated in the South West of Asia. The total area of Iran is 1,648,195 km^2 and is divided into 26 provinces. There are 227 districts, 497 cites, 596 towns, and 66,000 villages. Tehran is the capital of Iran. The official language is Farsi, although other languages such as Turkish, Luri, Kurdish, Gili, Balochi, and Arabic are spoken in some parts of the country. Muslims make up 99.6 percent of the population, 91 percent Shiite and 8.5 percent Sunni; 0.07 percent Zoroastrian; 0.05 percent Jewish and 0.2 percent Christians.

A 1991 census placed Iran's population at 58.5 million of whom 56.6 percent live in the cities and 43.4 percent live and work in the villages. The sex ratio of males to females is 105 and, on average the family size is five people. From the total

Acknowledgments. We would like to express our gratitude to the following staff of the research department of Tehran Psychiatric Institute for their contributions in preparing this chapter: Miss Robabeh Noori, M.A., Mr. Mojtaba Ehsanmanesh, M.A., Mrs. Safieh, A. Amin, B.A., Ms. Razieh Shomali, B.A., Mr. Issa Karimi, B.A., and Miss Sudabeh Taheri.

population, 53.4 percent work in the service industry; 24.9 percent in agriculture; and 21.7 percent in manufacturing.

The average life expectancy for both men and women is estimated to be 63 years. The divorce rate in Iran is estimated at 9.1 percent. The rate is higher in the cities (11.2%) than in the villages (5.1%). The average marital age for men is 23.6 years as compared to 19.8 years for women. In Iran, the birth rate is reported at 31 percent and death rate at 4 percent. The population growth rate is 2.7 percent (Shad-pur, 1993).

In the health field, the 29th Act of the Parliament of the Islamic Republic of Iran mandates that the use of the national health service should be the basic right of every individual. Iran, which is the signatory of the UN Almata declaration, is working toward achieving the goal of making primary health care available to all by the year 2000. In addition to working toward achieving primary health care, in the past few years there has been an extensive effort in the field of mental health.

THE HISTORY OF PSYCHIATRY IN IRAN

In ancient Iran, the attitude toward the mentally ill was influenced by superstition. The control of evil spirits in the body, possession of the soul by a *jinni* (spirit), reported by Egyptians, Greeks, and Romans, were the dominant beliefs of people in Iran and perhaps in most places in the world. Treatment of all patients involved expelling evil spirits, which was performed by priests.

When the Aryans emigrated to Iran, the oldest method of medicine began to take shape, around 3000 B.C. According to Zoroastrians, the first well-known Iranian physician was called Thrita. There was no relation between the widely used medicine in Iran in 500 A.H. with the medicine of other countries at the time. According to the Zoroastrian school, treatment of mental illness was approached through religion and was carried out by priests (Khoda-Bakhshi, 1953).

In accordance with Zoroastrian belief, Ormuzd is the creator of goodness whereas the devil is the creator of pain and illness. Therefore, fighting illnesses was the responsibility of priests, who were representatives of Ormuzd.

The Avesta are the Zoroastrian scriptures, and according to the Avesta there were three groups of physicians: (1) *Mang Pezeshk* who used the *inspiration method* whereby divine influence is brought to bear on the soul; (2) *Gla Pezeshk* who used herbs to treat patients; and (3) *Kareto Pezeshk* who used surgical techniques. These treatment methods were carried out by the Zoroastrian priests and continued until the emergence of Islam, in 641 A.D., which brought the Sassanian period to an end.

Iran was also influenced by Hippocrates, Socrates, Plato, and Aristotle in Greece and the evolution of science and medicine. The school and hospital of Jondi Shapoor was established at the end of the Sassanian period, and the medical school there became very famous. The importance of this school so far as psychiatry is concerned lies in the significance it gave to the influence of the brain over the body. In addition, they believed that the brain plays an important role in developing physical symptoms. A good example was demonstrated by Jebraeel (a physician). He treated Harron Al-Rashid's servant who suffered from hysterical paralysis by undressing her in front of others. This is an example of his awareness of the psychogenic root of this illness. Furthermore, there were sections in the hospital where mental patients were cared for (Najmabadi, 1987).

After Islam was established, such notable physicians as Muhammad Zakariay Razi (865–925 A.D.) and Sayed Esmail Jorjani (433–531 A.H.) are recorded.

Muhammad Zakariay Razi not only contributed at a considerable level to a medical encyclopaedia, but was also an expert in mental disorders. In one of his works, the *Mansur Book*, he has given detailed information on mental illnesses. Avicenna (980–1037 A.D.) was the leading neurologist and psychiatrist not only of his own day, but between 1100 and 1500. He emphasized the reciprocal effects of the body and the soul. In *Ghanūn* or canon, a chapter is devoted to the head and brain which discusses 12 signs that are representative of brain states (third book). This chapter also discusses the five senses and explains illnesses such as paralysis, tremors, memory difficulties, thought processes, and hallucinations. Incidentally, the literature at the end of the twentieth century confirms Avicenna's description of delirium.

Razi and Avicenna utilized the principles of logical science in the analysis of their observations and findings. These two scientists refined methods of observation and clinical experimentation, and removed medicine from philosophical discussions. However, they applied philosophical methods for the affirmation or rejection of their findings.

Razi (1964) believed that whatever all physicians agreed upon should be born in mind. Avicenna, who was also a famous philosopher, did not consider items such as the four elements, temperament, and so forth, necessary in medicine. He believed that in medicine there were methods that doctors should use to observe, analyze, and accept by reasoning and hence use them in practice (Avicenna, 1991). In this way theoretical medicine found a rational justification and the practice of medicine was accepted as a discipline.

Jorjani (433–531 A.H.), in discussing diagnostic methods, considered the following as the primary duty of any physician: knowing the body's state (i.e., distinguishing between illness and health) and diagnosis and prognosis of illnesses. In addition, he believed that it is not possible to diagnose an illness unless the doctor is aware of the patient's background and his or her premorbid functioning (Jorjani, 1966).

The great Iranian physicians in the past appreciated the reciprocal effects of the body and soul and based their analysis of the condition of the patient both on his or her internal state and on environmental factors. In other words they chose a psychosomatic approach, which is recognized by modern medicine.

It is apparent that other famous physicians, who lived before Avicenna, also turned their attention to psychological problems. Movafagh Heravi, who was probably a doctor, compiled a book based on Razi's opinions and ideas, the author has mentioned medicines such as *Afrimun*, *Bladur* (Akajo), *Gharzegh*, and *Gol-E-Gav-Zaban*. These were prescribed for illnesses such as compulsion, amnesia, insanity, and melancholia.

Drug therapy was the main treatment procedure for the mentally ill, but physicians also used "soul management" which was intended to stabilize the patient's condition (Nezami Aruzi-Samarghandi, 1948).

The above mentioned methods were considered to constitute the skill and art of the medical profession and applying them depends on the physician's expertise, skills, and medical knowledge. Other methods used were inducing long sleep and entertaining patients, as strongly recommended by Avicenna. In addition, Avicenna recommended that patients not be left unsupervised, believing that loneliness and seclusion were very bad for sick people. Occupational therapy was also considered important.

Psychiatry in ancient Iran is well documented but it is unfortunately not widely studied. According to writers and biographers, in addition to Jondi Shapoor hospital which existed until the end of the third century A.H., the Azodi hospital, which was built in the tenth century A.H., admitted mental patients as well as other patients (Algood, 1992). In addition to the Dar-al-Shafa hospital, in the city of Yazd, there were other hospitals in the main cities of Iran. In addition there were centers for mental patients. *Harghel* and *Aghel* were two of the most famous hospitals, and were situated near Basreh and Madaen (Davidian, 1995).

It is important to note the public's attitude toward insanity and the insane. According to the early literature only a few mental patients were sufficiently agitated to need restraints; and these were chained up via a collar round the neck. Most of the insane were free from the standard responsibilities and were free from life attachments, and lived in their own different world. These patients suffered from children making fun of them and throwing stones at them. In Persian literature Attar Nayshaboori writes that an insane person, fed up with children teasing him, took refuge in the governor's palace. He saw a number of servants keeping flies away from the governor's face. When asked by the governor what he was doing in the palace, he said: "I came to complain about children throwing stones at me, but I see that you are unable to disperse flies from your own face. Therefore, how could you possibly help me?"

Attar Nayshaboori described some mental patients as confidant, wise men, faultless and holy, etc. These attributes were in agreement with beliefs of the public about such patients. The insane were respected, helped, sheltered, and given treatment in hospitals. It is thought that the public religious beliefs played an important role in the positive way they behaved toward the insane.

In the middle ages, at the time that insane people were burned to death in Europe, in Iran there were institutions where the insane were cared for. The most famous center was the Dar al-Shafa hospital in Yazd, built in 666 A.H. Unfortunately there is no precise date as to when this hospital was closed (Jafari, 1959).

DEVELOPMENT OF MODERN PSYCHIATRY IN IRAN

The establishment of Tehran University in 1934 paved the way for the development of psychiatry as a formal discipline in Iran. In 1940, the Department of Psychiatry was created at the Medical Faculty of Tehran University, and Dr. Rezaaei, a French-educated psychiatrist, became the first chairman of this department. Later on, Dr. Mirsepaasi, another French-educated psychiatrist, became the codirector of Tehran Psychiatric Hospital along with Dr. Rezaaei; and in 1944, they founded the Society for the Protection of the Insane. In 1945, Rūzbeh Hospital was built as the first university affiliated psychiatric hospital. This was followed by the opening of the first psychiatric unit within a large general hospital. In Shiraz, the first psychiatric unit in a general hospital was opened in 1968 (Langsley, Barter, and Amirmoshiri, 1983). Five years after the creation of the World Psychiatric Association, the Iranian Psychiatric Association was founded in 1966 under the leadership of Dr. Mirsepaasi. In 1971, Iran became a member of the World Psychiatric Association, and in the same year, Dr. Davidian was selected as a WPA committee member.

In the 1970s, in line with modern approaches in psychiatry, many new changes were initiated in Iran. This was started by the introduction of a number of disciplines, including psychology, social work, psychiatric nursing and occupational therapy, into the psychiatric setting. Moreover, opening of a series of day facilities and introduction of the strategy of a "catchment area" enabled service users to receive psychiatric treatment without having to travel far from home. By 1978, three psychiatric residency programs had been developed and instituted in Shiraz, Tehran, and Isfahan (Langsley et al., 1983).

EPIDEMIOLOGY OF MENTAL ILLNESS

The first epidemiological study of psychiatric disorders was carried out by Bash in villages near the city of Marvdasht in Fars province in 1962 (Saheb-al-Zamani, 1963). This study showed that 11.9 percent of the population suffered from some kind of mental illness. In another study, Bash and Bash (1969) found that 14.9 percent of his sample population evidenced some form of psychiatric problem, with the psychotic disorders accounting for 2.2 percent of the cases. In 1971, Davidian and his colleagues conducted a preliminary study of the prevalence of psychiatric illness in a sample consisting of 488 persons, age 15 and older, in the city of Roodsar (Davidian, Izadi, Nehapetian, and Moghber, 1974). The results indicated that 17 percent of the sample population suffered from psychiatric illnesses.

In a study carried out as part of a project aimed at integrating mental health into primary health care (PHC), Shahmohammadi (1990) explored the incidence of psychiatric illnesses in rural PHC centers around the city of Shahr-e Kord. His sample included 28,903 rural inhabitants. The prevalence rate of mental illness was found to be 13.45 per thousand. The prevalence rates for specific illnesses were as follows: severe psychiatric disorders, 5 per thousand; mental retardation, 5.1 per thousand; and epilepsy, 3.25 per thousand.

In one study of the epidemiology of mental disorders among the rural population of Bagheri-Yazdi, Bolhari, Shahmohammadi (1994) found that 12.5 percent of the population suffered from mental disorders. Within this group, the prevalence rates for specific disorders were as follows: mood disorders (5.75%), anxiety disorders (5.50%), generalized anxiety

(4.75%), obsessive–compulsive disorders (0.25%), agoraphobia (0.25%), posttraumatic stress disorder (0.25%), organic mental disorders (0.50%), and schizophrenia (0.25%). Also Javidi (1993) in a similar study reported a prevalence rate of 8.7% for mood disorders, with dysthymia accounting for 5%, and bipolar disorder, major depression, and unspecified depressive disorders each accounting for 1% of the cases.

Yaqubi, Nasr, Shahmohammadi (1996) studied the prevalence of psychiatric disorders among the urban and rural population of the city of Some'eh Sara in the province of Gilan. The researcher employed the DSM-III-R clinical interview Check List in this study. The results indicated that in the category of mood disorders, major depression ranked the highest with an incidence of 6.24 percent. In the anxiety disorders, generalized anxiety was found to be the most prevalent disorder (5.12%) followed by panic disorder (0.96%), posttraumatic disorder (0.64%), obsessive–compulsive disorder (0.48%), and social phobia (0.16%). The prevalence rates for other types of psychiatric disorders were as follows: somatization (1.76%), schizophrenia (0.8%), adjustment disorder and mental retardation (0.8%), organic anxiety (0.8%), psychosomatic disorder (0.8%), organic mood disorder (0.32%), conversion disorder (0.16%), sexual disorders (0.16%), impulse control (0.16%), and dementia (0.16%).

Based on his review of the epidemiological studies of psychiatric illnesses, Davidian (1992) estimated a prevalence rate of 7.77 percent for all types of depressive disorders. Bash (1984) reported the following prevalence rates (per 1000) for psychiatric disorders in Iran: rural 149, urban 166, tribal 21. The prevalence rates for psychosomatic disorder were rural 17, urban 23, and tribal 9. He also found that the prevalence rates for all types of psychiatric disorders among the tribal populations were significantly lower than those for urban and rural population.

Hashemvarzi (1992) studied the rate of schizophrenia among 8000 psychiatric patients in the province of Isfahan and reported the prevalence rate of 3.95 percent among men and 16.7 percent among women. Comparing the prevalence rates for different age groups, he found that the age group 15 to 24 had the highest rate (44%). Moreover, among schizophrenics, rates for the unemployed and unmarried patients were 33.58 and 52 percent, respectively. This study also revealed that schizophrenia is five times more prevalent among poor people in urban areas than in the rural population.

Dezhkam and Sohanian (1992) studied the incidence of posttraumatic stress disorder (PTSD) in 163 survivors of the 1991 earthquake in the cities of Manjeel and Roodsar in northern Iran. They found that 68.1 percent of the survivors (72 women and 39 men) met the criteria for PTSD and 38 individuals exhibited symptoms of mild PTSD. Furthermore, 59.46 percent suffered from major depression and 29.73 percent displayed symptoms of moderate depression. The results also indicated that PTSD was more prevalent among the young and unmarried individuals. However, the highest incidence of PTSD was observed in the 15- to 17-year-old group. Those in the 18 to 25 age range showed the second highest incidence rate.

CHARACTERISTICS OF PSYCHIATRIC ILLNESSES IN IRAN

Epidemiological studies in Iran show a significant sex difference in the rates of psychiatric disorders. Bageri-Yazdi (1994), as an example, reported a higher prevalence of psychiatric illnesses among women over the age of 15 than for men (18.1 compared to 6.6%). Similarly, Javidi (1994) reported prevalence rates of 22.1 percent and 6.1 percent for women and men, respectively. In another study, Bahadorkhan (1994) found a prevalence rate of 19 percent for women and 12.4 percent for men. Kokabeh (1994) also reported a significant sex difference in the incidence of psychiatric disorders. In Palahang's study, higher rates of psychiatric disorders were noted among women (16.7%) when compared with men (6.41%) (Palahang, 1995). The rate for anxiety disorders showed similar trend (15.47% for women and 6.42% for men). Yaqubi (1996) found that women twice as much than men (30.84% compared to 15.8%) suffered from psychiatric disorders. In his epidemiological studies of psychiatric illnesses in the villages of Khuzestan and Fars provinces, the cities of Shiraz and Roodsar, and the village of Darreh-e Zereshk in Yazd province, Davidian (1992) found a higher incidence of depression in women than in men in all sites (ranging from 3.53 times in urban women in Shiraz to 2.48 times in Yazd). It appears that women are more susceptible to depression than men. The slightly higher rates in urban areas may reflect the specific effects of urban life (Davidian, 1992). Some investigators (e.g., Yaqubi, 1996) have attributed the higher incidence of psychiatric illnesses in women to their limited social roles, having to take care of a home, being expected to work in the fields, and general dissatisfaction with life. Several studies have found that psychiatric problems are more prevalent among widowed and married women and least prevalent among single women (Javidi, 1994; Palahang, 1996; Yaqubi, 1996).

Seghatol-Eslam (1989) investigated factors leading to suicide in men and women. He found that the causes of suicide in women were family problems (59%), personal problems (14%), mental illnesses (9%), and divorce (8%). However, in men, the leading causes of suicide were mental disorders, especially depression (42%), followed by divorce (20%), addiction (16%), and family problems (12%). He also found that suicide attempts in men were more often planned and premediated and that they had prior histories of attempts, while in women suicide attempts were usually a response to an immediate stress, unplanned, and less serious. Furthermore, in men, stress ranked second after mental illness in causing suicide, but in women, stress was a leading cause of a suicide attempt. Muslemi and Kamalzadeh (1994) reported a higher rate of suicide attempts among adolescent and young females followed by married individuals, unemployed persons, those with no college education, and individuals in the 21 to 30 age range. First-born children had the lowest rate of suicide attempts. Men are more apt to hang themselves, while women attempt suicide by setting fire to themselves. Adolescents and young adults are more likely to attempt suicide by setting fire to themselves.

In their investigation of the epidemiology of suicide in the city of Kerman, Yasemi and Sanei (1994) found that the rate of attempted suicide was 1.5 times more in women than in men, while the rate of completed suicide was 15 times more in

men than in women. Self-immolation was the leading cause of
death among suicide attempters. The effects of married life in
preventing successful suicide were more pronounced in the
case of men than women. The most prevalent method of suicide was drug overdose followed by self-immolation. Of the
four seasons, suicide attempts were least frequent in autumn,
and the lowest rate of suicide occurred in the mouth of Azar
(December). It is interesting to note that this finding is similar
to those reported in Western countries.

Regarding the relationship between birth order and psychiatric illness, research has shown that contrary to findings in
other countries, in Iran first-born children are more susceptible
to develop psychiatric problems, such as schizophrenia (Vatankhah, 1993). Vatankhah found that 44.8 percent of all mentally
ill individuals were first-born.

The detrimental effects of the Iran–Iraq war on the mental
health of Iranians have also been the focus of much research.
In a study carried out by Vafaai (1995) on 400 patients in Razi
Psychiatric Hospital, it was found that 85.13 percent were suffering from PTSD. Symptoms of depression (insomnia, loss of
appetite, weight loss, helplessness, and desperation) were most
prevalent. Jalili and Davidian (1982) found that 88.62 percent
of those afflicted by PTSD suffered from depressed mood.
Other symptoms observed were sleeplessness, irritability, sensitivity to noise, and reduced productivity. These were followed,
in the order of prevalence, by headaches, forgetfulness, anxiety, loss of appetite, fatigue, nightmares, anger, dizziness, and
withdrawal. In their study of 500 patients receiving medical
treatment at the war zone, Dashti and Javidi (1992) reported
that physical complaints were the most prevalent—headaches,
back pains, muscle fatigue—followed by anger, depression, sadness, and nightmares. The length of hospitalization for these
patients was from one to eight days. In his study of soldiers who
had evidenced psychological breakdowns on the battlefield,
Fathi-Ashtiani (1991) found that most of them suffered from
neurotic or reactive disorders, the most prevalent being PTSD.
Moreover, the highest incident of neurotic or reactive disorders
was noted in those individuals with no prior history of mental

illness. Those with prior histories of psychiatric problems manifested psychotic disorders. The most prevalent physical complaints were nightmares, fatigue, weaknesses, headaches, dry
mouth, tremors, and dizziness. Reported psychological symptoms included sensitivity to noise, anger, aggression, depression, irritability, anxiety, preoccupations, forgetfulness, and
restlessness.

Studies carried out by Mohammadi (1992) on individuals
wounded by chemical weapons during the war indicate that
the most prevalent symptoms noted were depression, anxiety,
dissociation, somatization, PTSD, dysthymia, and adjustment
problems. Rah-gu, Motavallian, and Alavi (1993) found higher
rates of depression, anxiety, and interpersonal problems in
those wounded by chemical weapons than in other wounded
soldiers. Moreover, the effects of chemical agents on physical
organs, particularly the immune system, and repeated or continuous and lengthy hospitalization, all had led to the disruption of family relations, separation from family, and loss of
social and psychological support. These factors, coupled with
the side effects of drugs used in the treatment of their illness
and feelings of hopelessness and incurability, had led to depression in their patients. Being afflicted by chronic diseases, rapid
postwar social, economic, and cultural changes, some of which
may be at odds with the conceptions and expectations held by
these veterans, are among the difficulties commonly faced by
them. Modabbernia and Vaez-Salehi (1994) studied 1,850 hospitalized patients at Mirza Kuchak Khan Psychiatric Center in
Rasht, in the province of Gilan. Of this group, 223 had developed mental illness following their return from the front. It
was found that 65.5 percent suffered from anxiety disorders,
and among these individuals 87.7 percent showed symptoms of
PTSD. Twenty-nine percent of the total sample suffered from
various forms of psychosis, and 5 percent were malingerers.
Sixty-seven percent of the patients were single and 12.5 percent
had a history of mental illness in their families, while 3.5 percent had themselves a past history of psychiatric disorder.

Sepehri (1994) randomly selected 110 soldiers who had
fought at the war front and had developed psychiatric problems. In his study of this group, he found that 22.7 percent

had mild complaints, and the symptoms they exhibited were too limited and insignificant to meet the criteria for a diagnosis of mental disorder. Psychiatric disorders diagnosed in the remaining patients were as follows: dysthymia (29%), PTSD (17%), major depression (secondary to stress) (5%), hypochondriasis with symptoms of depression and anxiety (3%), major depression (2%), conversion disorder (1%).

Mohammadi and Noorbala (1995) investigated the causes of chronicity of psychiatric disorders due to the effects of war in 107 patients during the period from 1991 to 1992. They found that the causes for the chronicity were the nature of the illness, various life events, social and economic factors, such as loss of job, divorce, and death of loved ones. Maddahi (1993) and Ahmadi-Abhari (1995) have found that patients suffering from PTSD face numerous difficulties in adjustment to family, job, and society in general.

Much research has also been done on ex-prisoners of war. Nurbala and Narimani (1994) investigated factors leading to stress during the postconfinement period and methods of coping in Iranian former POWs. It was found that inflation, high living expenses, debts, lack of money for the purchase of basic necessities, bureaucratic tangles, a difficult family financial situation, anxiety concerning future employment and education, were among the major factors leading to stress during the postcaptivity period. Some of the coping strategies adopted by this group were reliance on past experience, resort to prayer as a means of gaining the strength required to solve problems, maintaining a positive attitude toward events, consultation with wife and relatives, and avoidance of potentially damaging situations. Negative reactions, such as internalization of problems, aggression, anger, and reactive behavior, were also widespread. Yaryari and Nurbala (1992) investigated other aspects of the problems faced by ex-POWS. Of his sample, 82.7 percent had been subjected to torture during captivity, 61.6 percent had enlisted because of religious motives, and 88.4 percent stated that their experience of captivity had strengthened their religious beliefs.

In their study of disabled war veterans, who had suffered spinal cord injuries, Nurbala and Narimani (1994) compared these veterans with a group of 40 veterans without physical disabilities. They reported that 53 percent of the wounded veterans mentioned religious belief as their motives for participating in the war. Other motives mentioned were love of the country, and following the example of friends. Sixty percent of these patients had a negative attitude toward their disability. A significant relationship was also found between low self-esteem, lack of family support, inability to accept disability or having a negative attitude toward it, marital problems and divorce, and exhibition of symptoms of psychological disorder. Mohammadi and Rostami (1993) compared 120 paralyzed veterans suffering from psychiatric disorders with 60 paralyzed but psychologically healthy veterans. According to their report, depression was the most prevalent illness (63%), caused by war related stresses, restricted movement, sense restriction (numbness), lack of mobility to carry out normal activities, divorce and estrangement, unsatisfactory and cold relationship with spouse, sexual performance disorders, and unemployment.

In her study of 1,644 war refugees, Dolatabadi (1994) found that as a result of different kinds of war related stresses, such as loss of property and loved ones, they suffered from numerous psychological problems. These included physical complaints, depression, anxiety, irritability and aggression. More than half of them had witnessed horrific scenes of artillery and aerial bombardments of their towns and villages. Many (380) had seen the dead bodies of their relatives or of others. In the face of such circumstances, some had fled from the danger zone, had experienced shock and helplessness, had been forced by others to leave the area, or had resisted the enemy advance. The results indicated that on the whole the prevalence of psychological disorders in women was higher than in men.

In a study involving 104 patients, Razmgiri (1994) investigated the possible impact of cultural factors on the pattern of clinical symptoms of depression. He found that the number of depressed women in the 25 to 34 and 45 to 54 age groups were noticeably higher than the number of men. In this study, diagnostic criteria were depressive moods, sleep disorders, lack

of interest and lack of enjoyment of all aspects of life, preoccupation with death, weight and appetite change, psychomotor
retardation or agitation, fatigue and loss of energy, unjustified
feelings of worthlessness and guilt, and decreased concentration and thinking ability. Sleep disorder was observed in 91.3
percent of the patients, while 79.8 percent experienced weight
and appetite change. Prevalence of the feeling of worthlessness
and guilt, reduction of the ability to think and concentrate,
loss of energy and fatigue, were lower in Iranian patients than
the rates reported in the literature. The rates for depressed,
sad moods and preoccupation with death were about the same
as those reported in the literature. The Iranian religious belief
and value system, which does not view the world as meaningless
but considers human life to have meaning and purpose, has
had a major role in lowering the prevalence of unjustified feelings of worthlessness and guilt. At 31.7 percent, the rate for
these disorders is much lower than that indicated by international statistics. The results of a cross-cultural study of depression conducted by WHO (Sartorius and Davidian, 1983) in
Iran, Japan, Switzerland, and Canada, showed that Iranian patients suffering from depression were comparatively younger,
were more likely to belong to the lower economic class
(55.1%), and be illiterate (43%). Lower rates of suicidal
thought were reported in Tehran (41%) and Tokyo (46%)
than in the other capitals included in the study. The study
revealed the lowest rate of hypochondria (17%) and feelings
of guilt (32%), the highest rate of somatic symptoms (57%) in
Tehran, but no depressive delusion was reported. However,
psychomotor agitation was found only in Tehran.

Studies carried out on Iranian addicts also show significant
differences between this group and their counterparts investigated in the Western countries. Daneshmand (1980) investigated the personality traits of Iranian addicts. The results
indicated that Iranian addicts were characterized by more psychoneurotic traits and less psychopathic features compared
with addicted people in Western countries. Qarahgosloo and
Beheen (1979) reported that Iranian addicts exhibit a number
of psychological symptoms, of which the most prevalent is depression. This finding is at odds with the results of Western

investigations, the majority of which depict the addicted individual with a higher level of anxiety and antisocial behavior. Tarighati (1980) reported that depression is the most important symptom of addiction in Iran.

Rasoulzadeh-Tabatabaei (1991) in his survey ranked the life event stressors for the people of Tehran and identified their coping strategies. The results indicated that the factors causing the greatest stress were, in order of priority: housing problems, death of mother and spouse, death of father, divorce, and addiction of a family member. Among 29 coping behaviors, the most widespread, in order of priority, were: drawing on past experience, praying for a solution to the problem, increasing the level of information about the problem, and consultation.

THE USE OF ALTERNATIVE MEDICINE

Until a few decades ago, various traditional healing methods, in the form of rituals, prayers, and taking herbs, were widely used for the treatment of physical, neurological, and emotional disorders. Such practices were deeply rooted in the attitudes and beliefs of Iranians in the past on the one hand, and poor provision of medical care on the other (Langsley et al., 1983). A recent countrywide "pathway" study, however, has revealed that today 14 percent of people with mental health problems may use alternative methods as the first choice (Shahmohammadi, Bayanzadeh, and Ehssanmanesh, 1997).

THE INFLUENCE OF RELIGIOUS BELIEFS

Religious beliefs and convictions have played a long-standing role in Iranian society, alleviating various psychological ailments, such as fear, worry, and various other psychological reactions, and therefore made a significant contribution to health and well-being. In a study conducted by Tahmasbipur and Kamangiri (1996), it was found that individuals with lower levels of religious faith showed higher levels of depression. Also, a significant negative relationship was also found between anxiety and religious belief. These researchers found a significantly positive relationship between religious faith and well-being.

Differences in clinical features of compulsive disorder have been found between Iranian and Western patients. For example, certain Iranian patients wash their hands to such a degree that the skin is completely destroyed. This practice leads to skin infection in some cases. From the etiological point of view the compulsive washing in Western patients is due to a preoccupation with dirt and fear of contamination by various diseases, while in Eastern cultures, such as Iran, ritual and religiously mandated purity constitute a strong motive force for this practice.

Regarding the treatment of patients suffering from such compulsive disorders, Aal-e Yassin (1995) discovered that religious therapy had a meaningful impact on patients who adhered to religious guidelines, while it failed to have any significant impact on those who did not share those religious beliefs.

In an investigation into the effect of recitation of the Qur'an on reduction of postsurgical pain, Nikbakht-Nasrabadi (1994) in his study of 39 patients who had undergone stomach surgery showed that there was a significant difference in reduction of the intensity of pain between the group that had listened to recitations of the Qur'an when compared with the control group.

Notably, the rate of psychological or psychosomatic illnesses as a reaction to loss in general, and the loss of loved ones in particular, is lower in Iran compared to what is reported in Western countries (Tariqhati, 1994). Moreover, this researcher in his study of Iranian mental patients concludes that the mourning ceremonies and the social support system provided for the bereaved person minimize the pathological grief reaction.

THE PRESENT STATE OF PSYCHIATRY IN IRAN

In the last 15 years, major changes have taken place in psychiatry in Iran; in particular various preventive measures have been adopted. At the present time, the emphasis is on outpatient treatment and provision of psychiatric care in different communities. Effort is made to minimize hospitalization, and return patients to their families and work setting. Moreover, consideration of mental health and prevention have received more attention. Also steps are taken to integrate mental health services into health care. Hence, the fundamental policy of the government of the Islamic Republic of Iran regarding mental health is currently based on this integration plan. The plan has now expanded to 143 cities and covers 40 percent of the villages. In this plan, mental health is considered as one of the fields of the public health services and is not limited to the care of the mentally ill.

At present, over 500 psychiatrists are working in the country who together with other mental health workers, such as psychologists, psychiatric nurses, and occupational therapists, provide psychiatric services in Iran. Public and private sectors jointly provide inpatient service at 20 psychiatric hospitals and 28 psychiatric wards in general hospitals—a total number of 6,250 psychiatric beds. Furthermore, outpatient services are also available at 65 public clinics and 328 private clinics.

The training of psychiatrists is being carried out at eleven universities in the cities of Tehran, Tabriz, Mashhad, Isfahan, Shiraz, Ahwaz, Rasht, and Kerman. This academic activity leads to the graduation of 50 psychiatrists per year. Additionally, every year about 40 clinical psychologists and 10 psychiatric nurses are graduated at the master's degree level.

REFERENCES

Aal-e Yassin, S. A. (1995), *The Role of Pastoral Counseling in the Treatment of Compulsive Washing in Women Who Adhere and Those Who Do Not Adhere to Religious Commandments.* Tehran: University of Tehran.

Ahmadi-Abhari, S. A. (1995), Long-term effects of war stress on PTSD patients' mental status. Proceeding Articles for the 3rd Iranian Symposium on Stress (26–29 Feb. 1996). Iran University of Medical Sciences.

Algood, C. (1992), *Medical History in Iran*, tr. E. B. Foghani. Tehran: Amirkabir Publications.

Avicenna, H. (1984), *Ghanoon, Ketaab-Avval*, tr. A. Sharafkandi. Tehran: Soroush Publications.

——— (1991), *Ghanoon dar teb (Principles in medicine)*, tr. A. Sharafkandi. Tehran: Soroush Publishers.

Bagheri-Yazdi, S. A., Bolhari, J., & Shahmohammadi, D. (1994), Epidemiological study of psychiatric disorders in rural areas of Meibod, Yazd. *Andisheh va Raftar*, 1:32–41.

Bahadorkhan, M. J. (1994), *Epidemiological study of psychiatric disorders in rural areas of Gonabad* (in Khorasan province). (Thesis submitted to T.P.I Dept of clinical psychology.)

Bash, K. W. (1984), Epidemiology of psychosomatic disorders in Iran. *Psychotherapy and Psychosomatics*, 42:182–186.

——— Bash, L. J. (1969), Studies on the epidemiology of neuropsychiatric disorders among the rural population of the province of Khuzistan, Iran. *Soc. Psychiatry*, 4:137–143.

Daneshmand, L. (1980), A study on the personality characterstics of Iranian addicts. *Internat. J. Sociological Psychiatry*, 26:142–144.

Dashti, A., & Javidi, H. (1991), Clinical profile of patients war related psychiatric disorders. Proceedings of the Symposium on Neurological and Psychological Problems Caused by the War. Tehran.

Davidian, H. (1965), Psychological analysis of Aal and Ommalsabian. *Majjaleh Sokhan*, 16:19–34.

——— (1971), The number and reason of consulting non-psychiatric physicians by psychiatric patients. *Tazehayeh Ravanpezeshki*, 1:122–133.

——— (1992), The epidemiology of depression in Iran: A literature review. *Majjaleh Nezam Pezeshki*, 11:15–23.

——— (1995), Psychiatry in Iran in the early Islamic civilization (An analytic review). *Andeesheh va Raftar, Quart. J. Psychiatry & Clinical Psychology*, 1:7–15.

——— Izadi, S., Nehapetian, V., & Moghber, M. (1974), A preliminary study of the epidemiology of mental illness in the district of Bahr-e Khazar (City of Roodsar). *Majaleh-e Behdast-e Iran*, 3:145–156.

Dezhkam, M., & Sohanian, M. (1992), A Study of the Epidemiology of PTSD among the Victims of Earthquake in Northern Iran During the Summer of 1990. Typescript.

Dolatabadi, S. (1994), *A Comprehensive Study of Psychiatric Problems of the Refugees of the Imposed War*. Tehran: Iran University of Medical Sciences and Health Services.

Elahi, A. (1994), Native play therapies. Proceedings of the Social-Cultural Psychiatry Convention. Tehran: Iran University of Medical Sciences and Health Services.

Farrokh, J. (1971), *Psychiatry*, Vol. 1. Mashhad: Mashhad University Press. (Farsi)

Fathi-Ashtiani, A. (1991), A study of presenting neuropsychiatric symptoms in a group of fighters of the imposed war. Proceedings of the Symposium on Examining the Neuropsychiatric Problems Resulting from the Effects of War.

Halimi, A., & Davidian, H. (1982), A study on war related psychiatric disorders. *Majalleh Nezam Pezeshki*, 8:293.

Hashemvarzi, M. (1992), Epidemiological study of schizophrenia in the province of Esfahan. In: *Bulletin of the 3rd Convention on Research in Psychiatry and Clinical Psychology*. Shahid Beheshti University-Tehran.

Al-Heravi, M. A. (1967), *Al-abnieh Ann Haghayegh Al-advieh*, ed. A. Bahmanyar Hossein Mahboobi Ardekani. Tehran: Tehran University Publications.

Jafari, J. (1959), *The History of Yazd*. Tehran: Bongah-e Tarjomeh va Nashr-e Ketab.

Jalili, A., & Davidian, H. (1982), A study on war related psychiatric disorders. *Majalleh Nezam Pezeshki*, 8:293–402.

Javidi, H. (1994), *Epidemiological Study of Psychiatric Disorders in the Marvdasht Region of Fars province*. M.A. dissertation, Tehran Psychiatric Institute Dept. of clinical psychology.

Jorjani, S. E. (1966), *Al-Eghraz Al-tabih-e va Al-mabaheth Al-alaieh*. Tehran: Bonyad-e Farhang-e Iran.

Khoda-Bakhshi, S. (1953), *Medicine in Ancient Persia*. Tehran: Tehran University Press.

Kokabeh, F. (1994), *A Study on Epidemiology of Psychiatric Disorders in Rural Areas of Azarshahr, Tabriz*. M.A. dissertation, Tehran Psychiatric Institute Dept. of Clinical Psychology.

Langsley, D. G., Barter, J. T., & Amirmoshiri, A. (1983), Psychiatry in Iran and China. *Internat. J. Social Psychiatry*, 29:39–47.

Maddahi, M. E. (1993), *Post War PTSD*. Iran University of Medical Sciences. Unpublished Report.

Massudieh, M. T. (1985), *Baluchestanian Music*. Tehran: Soroush Publications.

Modabbernia, M. J., & Vaez-Salehi, M. E. (1994), A study on the incidence of psychiatric disorders and related problems caused by the war in patients hospitalized during the period 1981–1986 at Mirza Koochak Khan in Rasht, Gilan. *Majalleh Daneshkadeh Pezeshki-e Gilan*, 3:17–22.

Mohammadi, M. R. (1992), Psychoneurological disorders in a group of ex POWs. Proceedings of the 1st Symposium on War Psychological Outcomes, Tehran.

—— (1993), Examination of war related stresses and other factors precipitating psychiatric disorders in paraplegic veterans. Proceedings of the 1st Seminar of the Center for Veteran's Spinal Cord Injuries, Tehran.

—— & Noorbala, A. A. (1995), A preliminary investigation of the reasons for chronicity of psychiatric disorders in injured veterans of the imposed war. *Majalleh Nabs*, 5:14–17.

—— Rostami, M. R. (1993), Examination of war related stresses and other factors precipitating psychiatric disorders in paraplegic veterans. Proceeding of the 1st Seminar of the Center for Veteran's Spinal Cord Injuries, Tehran.

Muslemi, F., & Kamalzadeh, B. (1994), An investigation of the factors contributing to suicide and suicide attempts in adolescents and young adults. Proceedings Seminar on Youth Issues with Emphasis on Iranian Youth.

Najmabadi, M. (1987), *The History of Medicine in pre-Islamic Iran*, Vol. 1. Tehran: Tehran University Press.

Nezami Aroozi-Samarghandi, A. (1948), *Kolliat-e Chahar Maghaleh*, ed. Mohammad-Ebn Abdolvahhab Ghazvini. Tehran: Eshraghi Publications.

Nezami Aruzi-Samarghandi, A. (1992), *Kolliat-e Chahar Maghaleh*, ed. Mohammad-Ebn Abdolvahhab Ghazvini. Tehran: Eshraghi Publications.

Nikbakht-Nasrabadi, A. R. (1994), *The Effects of Listening to Recitation of the Holy Qur'an on Reducing Pain Following Abdominal Surgery*. Tehran: University of Tarbiat Moallem.

Nurbala, A. A., & Narimani, M. (1994), Self-esteem and its relation to psychological characteristics in a group of veterans with spinal cord injuries. Typescript.

Palahang, H. (1995), *Epidemiological Study of Psychiatric Disorders in the City of Kashan*. Doctoral dissertation, Tehran Psychiatric Institute Dept. of Clinical Psychology.

Qarahgosloo, H., & Beheen, M. (1979), Frequency of psychiatric symptoms among 150 opium addicts in Shiraz, Iran. *Internat. J. Addicts*, 14:1145–1149.

Rah-Gu, A., Motavallian, A., & Alavi, M. (1993), The study of psychiatric problems of the victims of chemical warfare. *Tarbiat Modarress University Newsletter*, 14:16–19.

Rasoulzadeh-Tabatabaei, K. (1991), Comparative study of ranking of stress-causing life events and coping behaviors among people in north and south areas of the city of Tehran in 1990. Proceedings, 3rd Convention on Psychiatric and Psychological Research in Iran. Tehran University.

Razi, A. M. Z. (1964), *Ghessass va Hekaayat Marazi*, tr. Mahmud Najmabadi. Tehran: Tehran University Publications.

Razmgiri, V. (1994), An exploration of the social impact of cultural factors on patterns of clinical symptoms of major depression. *Bultan-e Gongereh-e Farhanki va Ejtemaei*, 1:44–45.

Riahi, A. (1977), *Baluch Zar and Baad*. Tehran: Tahuri Library.

Riahi-Nezhad, M. R. (1994), Obsessive-compulsive disorder: A new perspective on etiology and treatment, and differing symptoms of compulsion. Proceedings, Iran University of Medical Sciences Convention on Social and Cultural Psychiatry.

Saheb-al-Zamani, N. (1963), *Unsettled Soul*. Tehran: Ataei Publications.

Sanati, M., Zargahami, M., Kashufi, M., & Khazaei, A. (1989), Limitations of DSM-III-R in diagnosing PTSD: Examination and statistical comparison of symptoms of 73 PTSD and non-PTSD wounded soldiers. Proceedings for the 1st National Symposium on Stress.

Sartorius, N,. & Davidian, H. (1983), *Depressive Disorders in Different Cultures*. Geneva: W.H.O.

Seghatol-Eslam, T. (1989), A research on stress causing factors and suicide. Proceedings, 1st National Symposium on Stress.

Sepehri, H. (1994), A review of the problems in diagnosing psychiatric disorders in veterans (soldiers). *Majalleh Pezeshki Oromieb*, 5:7–15.

Shaad-pur, K. (1993), *Primary Health Care Network in Iran*. Tehran: Daftar Nashr Farhang Eslami.

Shahmohammadi, D. (1990), *Integration of Mental Health into Primary Health Care*. Tehran: Office of Disease Control.

——— Bayanzadeh, S. A., & Ehssanmanesh, M. (1997), Pathway study of psychiatric patients in Iran. *Andisheh Va Raftar-a (Quarterly Journal of Psychiatry and Psychology)*.

Tahmasbipur, N., & Kamangiri, M. (1996). *Relationship between Religious Attitude and Intensity of Anxiety, Depression, and Mental Health among a Group of Patients at Shohada-e Haft-e Teer and Mojtam-e Hazrat Rasoul-e Akram Hospitals during the First Half of 1996*. Tehran: Iran University of Medical Sciences.

Tarighati, S. (1980), Mourning and culture. *Boltan-e Ravanpezeshki-e Farhangi va Ejtemaei*.

——— (1994), Mourning and culture. *Boltan-e Ravanpezeshki-e Farhangi va Ejtemaei*.

Tarkhan, M. (1992), The incidence of mental and behavioral disorders in first-born. Proceedings, Seminar on the Etiology and Prevention of Mental and Behavioral Problems in Children and Adolescents.

Vafaai, B. (1995), A study of 400 war-related psychiatric cases at Razi Psychiatric Hospital in Tabriz. Paper presented at Social-Cultural Psychiatry Convention.

Vatankhah, H. (1993), The relationship between birth order and non-organic psychiatric disorders. First Annual Convention of Psychiatry and Clinical Psychology in Iran-Tehran.

Varzi, H. (1992), Epidemiological study of schizophrenia in the province of Esfahan. In: *Bulletin of the 3rd Convention on Research in Psychiatry and Clinical Psychiatry.* Shahid Beheshti University, Tehran.

Yaqubi, N. (1996), Epidemiological study of psychiatric disorders in urban and rural areas of Some-e Saara Township of Gilan. *Andishe va Raftar,* 1:55–65.

Yaryari, F., & Nurbala, A. A. (1992), Examination of the neuropsychiatric symptoms exhibited by Ex-POW's one year after returning to their homeland. *Bultan-e Pezeshki-e Markaz Zaye'at-e Nokhaei Janbazan.*

Yasemi, M. T., & Sanei, N. (1994), Epidemiological study on suicide cases in the Province of Kashan. Proceedings, Tehran University Convention on Research in Psychiatry and Psychology in Iran.

7.

Mental Illness and Its Treatment in Malaysia

M. Z. Azhar, S. L. Varma

The prevailing influence of culture on health is evident in every society. Cultural beliefs determine perceptions of causality, illness behavior, and treatment. In each South East Asian country several ethnic groups, religions, and languages coexist. Among the Asians the traditional belief that spiritual forces exert immense control over both physical and mental health is still dominant; this is the case in Malaysia.

Malaysia is made up of three main racial communities: the Malays form 55 percent of the population, Chinese 35 percent, and Indians 10 percent. Because of these racial differences psychiatric symptoms tend to be slightly different with each of these groups, although the rate of psychiatric disturbance is no different from the rest of the world. However, Malaysia is associated with such culture-bound syndromes as *Amok, Latah,* and *Koro,* although they have been reported in many other countries.

The Malays are the indigenous people of Malaysia. They are generally soft spoken and shy, though that has changed recently. Although many Malaysians have traveled widely and some have been educated overseas, most still hold to cultural traditions and beliefs. The belief that illnesses, and especially mental illness, can be caused by demons, evil spirits, or by being hexed by others is still widespread, even among educated people. At times the services of *bomohs* (traditional healers) are called upon before people meet with psychiatrists. It is still not uncommon for psychiatrists to give way to families who want a mentally ill relative discharged or given leave so that they can be taken to a *bomoh*. Over the last 15 years, the Malays, who are mainly Muslims, have become more aware of religion, and a religious revival has resulted in many Malays becoming more religious. This has not resulted in new psychological symptomatology but it has resulted in new health seeking behavior. Some people look for holy water that has been given *doa* (invocation) by a holy person or religious teacher. Most now also resort to *sunat hajat* (elective prayers) more frequently as an adjunct to psychiatric treatment of the mentally ill.

The Chinese are mainly involved in the business sector. They were originally migrants who came to work in the tin mines. They worked hard and their numbers gradually grew, and eventually they became established as an important population group in the country. In fact it was one of them, Yap Ah Loy, who founded Kuala Lumpur, the present capital city of Malaysia. Like the Malays, some middle class Chinese are now Western educated, but Chinese culture remains strong. Their belief in the powers of *yin* and *yang* and the ways in which balance of these powers determines mental and physical health, is still evident. Some also believe ghosts and evil spirits are the cause of mental illness. It was not uncommon a few years ago to find Chinese patients presenting to the psychiatrists with lacerations on their backs. This is part of a Chinese ritual during which evil spirits are driven away by Buddhist monks who make these lacerations on the patient's back.

HISTORY OF MALAYSIAN PSYCHIATRY

The earliest psychiatric facility in Malaysia was a lunatic asylum in Penang, in 1829, with 25 inmates. The building of the Central Mental Hospital in Tanjong Rambutan was followed by the opening of mental hospitals in Tampoi and Sarawak in 1933. In 1961, Malaysia's first native-born psychiatrist began work. The first general hospital psychiatric unit was set up in 1959 in the Penang General Hospital with outpatient and inpatient facilities. Later on, a number of decentralized psychiatric general hospitals were set up. In 1973, Malaysia began a postgraduate program in psychiatry. At present there is one psychiatrist for every 350,000 people, far below the recommended levels for developing countries. Currently the mental health facilities in Malaysia are basically hospital based. Moreover, even in places where district outpatient services have already been set up, the psychiatric facilities are based in hospitals. Perhaps the most gratifying and important development in the last 15 years has been the increase in the number of psychiatrists in the country, from 19 in 1988 to around 100 in 1996. The Malaysian government's target is to have around 300 psychiatrists by the year 2000. Another important change has been the substantial reduction in the number of beds in the psychiatric hospitals and the increased emphasis on community based mental health services. The motive behind this is the policy of deinstitutionalization. Slowly, community psychiatry, child psychiatry, rehabilitation, and other specialties have been established, placing psychiatry firmly on the road to new horizons.

MENTAL ILLNESS IN MALAYSIA

Types of mental illnesses are changing in this country, probably due to increased awareness among the general population. In the 1960s Western literature described depression as being rare in developing countries. Perhaps depression was not taken seriously as an illness in these countries and most of the patients presented to the physicians with vague somatic complaints. Although this is still generally true—most patients find it hard to accept depression and visit a doctor for treatment—studies have shown that depression is as prevalent in developing as in developed countries, although the presentation may have a more somatic coloring (Varma and Azhar, 1992) because of the inability of the patient to accept depression per se as a symptom and instead projecting the depression as physical aches and pains. A recent study (Varma and Azhar, 1995) looked at the psychiatric symptomatology in patients and their families attending a primary health care facility in Malaysia and found that the most common symptoms found were of depression (13.2%), followed by hypochondriasis (8.2%), anxiety (6.1%), and psychosis. Typically depression was missed by doctors because, as noted, most patients complain not of depression but of vegetative symptoms such as fatigue, sleep disturbance, back pain, chest pain, nausea, abdominal discomfort, or shortness of breath. This is because the culture does not consider depression to be an illness, but rather a personal weakness. For example, the attitude is that only weak people become depressed; it is unmanly to cry and show depression—but to have a backache or headache is perfectly acceptable. So the main problem of depression in this culture is its late recognition and thus its late treatment. However, the outcome, even with delayed recognition and treatment, is relatively good. The rate of suicide in Malaysia is low and is comparable with that of other Asian countries. This is probably because Malaysia is predominantly Muslim, and there is a very strong religious prohibition against suicide and this acts as a safety valve. The rate of suicide is higher amongst the Chinese than the Malays primarily because of the religious factor. Even among psychotics, the suicide rate is higher in Chinese compared to Malays (Azhar, 1991).

Most people in Malaysia believe that they have symptoms because of being bewitched or because they have lost their souls (semangat). The loss of the soul makes the body weak and patients suffer from shortness of breath, numbness, tremors, palpitations, abdominal discomfort, etc. Another group of patients have these symptoms because they believe their ancestors were possessed by the Jinn (spirits) and that now after their ancestors have passed away, the Jinn have decided to stay in their bodies, and the symptoms arise because they are weak or because they refuse to accept the Jinn. These Jinn are supposed to have special powers to help the person they possess or to help others. A patient of mine with anxiety symptoms believed the symptoms were caused by a *Jinn* that belonged to her mother who had recently passed away and that the *Jinn* had chosen to inhabit her. By her body being inhabited by the *Jinn* she would be an expert *bidan* (maternity nurse) just like her late mother. However, she was unable to accept this responsibility because she had her own future plans. The problem with this belief system is that the doctor is not the first person the patient goes to for help when symptoms develop; first they tend to see the *bomohs*. They only seek psychiatric treatment after their illness becomes chronic. These beliefs are also found among both rural and urban populations. For example, the patient described above is a schoolteacher in an urban area. Hypochondriacal symptoms too are often missed because these symptoms are not necessarily physical or clear. Worries about cancer, say, are rare. Most complaints are of vague intestinal problems that do not fit any known physical illness. Patients complain mainly of nausea and *angin* (wind) in the stomach or other parts of the body such as nerves or blood vessels. Their complaints can be easily mistaken for somatic hallucinations or delusions by the unsuspecting doctor. *"Angin"* or "wind" is commonly blamed as the source of most illnesses by the *bomohs* and this belief is shared by most people. Most patients believe doctors cannot help them since there is no such thing as wind in Western medicine and therefore doctors will not be able to detect their illness. Here, instead of going from doctor to doctor they will go from one *bomoh* to the another to look for the right *bomoh* who will be able to remove all the wind from their system.

Hysteria is another neurotic illness that occasionally occurs in Malaysia. What is more interesting is the hysteria epidemic that occurs, especially in residential schools or hostels, generally involving young female students. They are also fairly common in factories with female workers. It is assumed that these females are being "disturbed" by spirits who are supposed to inhabit the area where the schools or factories are. The reason why they only affect females is not clear, but one explanation is that females are weaker than males in their soul substance or *semangat* and thus it is much easier for the ghosts and spirits to disturb them. Usually it starts with one person "seeing" a spirit or a ghost, usually in a deserted place such as the wash-room, and becoming hysterical—generally screaming or crying and at times becoming aggressive and violent. Other female colleagues will then join her by screaming and shouting, with some becoming violent as well. The screaming and crying goes on until a *bomoh* or a religious person is called to say prayers that will appease the spirits, and only then will all the women settle down. A doctor is very rarely consulted in these instances. News of a hysteria epidemic usually gets extensive coverage in the media and this results in other schools or factories being "infected." In most cases, only the index person experiences the vision of the spirits. The "infected" friends mostly do not see the ghosts but experience the sensation of being touched or pushed. The factories and schools involved are usually those that have rather strict rules and regulations. The schools commonly affected are religious schools where the students are not allowed to openly play games or mix with males. Some schools that send their students to doctors after a hysterical attack have relaxed some of their strict rules, with positive results. However, there are no studies to accurately establish the relationship between mass hysteria and strict rules. Mass hysteria can be considered as a general coping device that is accepted by the culture.

The frequency of obsessive–compulsive disorder is the same as in the West even though the presentation is different. Although no systematic study has been done to detect the content of obsessive thoughts in Malaysia, experience of many psychiatrists indicates that very few patients present with the classical obsessive thought of dirt and the washing compulsion. We have only treated two of these patients in our practice. Most of the patients we see present with ruminations of religious content. In our clinic about 10 patients a year are referred and nine of them will have religious ruminations. Examples of these ruminations are "there is more than one god," "I have said the *talak* (divorce) to my wife, therefore our continued relationship is sinful"; "the Prophet made a mistake." Treatment would require not just psychological knowledge but religious knowledge. Most patients are given religious psychotherapy, which is described later in this chapter. At times religious teachers are called in to aid in treatment, but this at times hinders progress as we allow the patient to be reassured. In cognitive therapy, reassurance is regarded as an avoidance behavior. Avoidance is a hindrance in psychotherapy because it prevents disconfirmation of negative thoughts. At times the ruminators use these reassurances as neutralizing thoughts which, just like avoidance, maintains the symptoms. (Our religious therapy is based on the cognitive therapy model and principles.)

Regarding psychotic illness, just like elsewhere, schizophrenia affects 1 percent of the population. As expected the symptoms of schizophrenia reflect the patient's culture. Recently the phenomenology of hallucinatory experiences of Chinese patients from a predominantly Chinese area of Malaysia was compared to those of Malay patients from a predominantly Malay area (Azhar, Varma, and Hakim, 1993). Most Malay patients heard voices that they attributed to God, demons, or spirits while Chinese patients attributed them to friends, relatives, or neighbors. However, those Chinese who had been raised in Malay communities had auditory hallucinations similar to their Malay counterparts, and heard the voices of God, demons, or spirits. This clearly indicates how cultural influence can transcend race and religion. Regarding the content of voices, religious issues were significantly more common in the Malays. Visual hallucinations were also significantly more common among Malays, 51 percent of whom experienced true visual hallucinations compared with 20 percent found in most other studies. Although these symptoms do not have any bearing on drug treatment, they influence the psychosocial management of these patients. Psychological treatment directed at voices will have to be very delicately handled, for example, if they are voices of God; then the doctors cannot challenge the patients to ignore them or to go against them. Some patients who are willing to have therapy are told not to challenge the voices but to look for evidence that they are misinterpreting them as God, because while God is infallible humans are not.

Delusions among Malaysian patients have also been studied. Azhar and Varma (1996c) found that there is a higher prevalence of religious and other subculturally related delusions in Malay patients. Persecutory delusions were more common in Malay patients while grandiose delusions were more common in the Chinese. Nihilism and delusions of guilt were also more common amongst Malays. Analysis of grandiose delusions indicate that more Malay patients were deluded about being in authority or having power given by God. On the other hand, Chinese patients were deluded about their wealth and social status. Most delusions in Malay patients centered on interpretation of the Qur'an, being sinful, being specially chosen by God, being given powers by God, being a descendant of God or the Prophet. Analysis of persecutory delusions indicates that Chinese believed members of their families or close friends wanted to harm them while the Malays believed strangers wanted to harm them. Reasons for harm given by the Chinese include their wealth, knowledge, and skills. The Malays on the other hand cited jealousy of their God-given power as the main reason.

Another aspect of psychosis that has received widespread attention in the West is the role of expressed emotions in relatives in the maintenance of psychosis. Very little information exists about relatives' expressed emotion in non-Western countries and its relationship to maintenance of schizophrenia. Only one study exists so far in Malaysia and it indicates a trend in the opposite direction (Azhar and Varma, 1996b). The families of 83 schizophrenic patients who had more than two episodes of schizophrenia were studied. The most salient feature discovered was the virtual absence of high levels of expressed emotion as the cause of relapse. The majority of the families had low expressed emotion (72.3%) while only 25.3 percent had high expressed emotion (the remaining 2.4% were of families with equivocal answers). The most likely explanation for this disagreement is the cultural differences between Malaysian and Western families. Obviously this has significant bearing on how family therapy is conducted. As most families already have positive emotions, there is no sense in further developing this aspect of interaction with the patient. In the first place expressed emotion may not have any role in our patients' health, or perhaps the utilization of expressed emotion as proposed in the West in order to prevent relapse may not apply to our patients.

CULTURE-BOUND SYNDROMES IN MALAYSIA

Some disorders are found only in certain cultures, often with sudden onset, brief duration, and good prognosis. Culture is a mixture in which all biological and psychological functioning operates in the manifestation of psychopathology, and it may not be wrong to state that all psychiatric syndromes may be bound culturally in some way or other. The term *culture-bound* has generally been used by Western professionals to identify a few syndromes reported in other cultures. However, it should be understood that if a traditional healer from Asia or Africa, for example, is exposed to a Western patient, he might find certain behaviors of those patients odd and surprising. The term *culture-bound syndrome* denotes recurrent, locality-specific patterns of aberrant behavior and troubling experience that may or may not be linked to a particular diagnostic category. These syndromes are generally limited to specific societies or culture areas and have a troubling set of experiences and observations. The importance of culture-bound syndromes lies in the fact that these have been identified as important diagnostic categories, deserving mention in the DSM-IV (APA, 1994).

Trance States

Possession-trance states are not peculiar to Southeast Asia but occur in other parts of the world as well. There are, however, certain characteristic features of possession-trances that are common to the different ethnic groups in Malaysia. These are the alteration in the level of consciousness, amnesia for the period of the trance, duration of less than an hour, fatigue at the termination of the trance, normal behavior in the interval between trances, onset before 25 years, occurrence amongst those in a low social class with little education, and in those who have previously witnessed a trance. Possession-trance is akin to a hysterical episode (Kua, Sim, and Chee, 1986). It begins in a person who is under stress and unable to cope with it and thus resolves the conflict by possession-trance. During the trance the stereotyped behavior allows the release of repressed feelings. This socially sanctioned behavior is recognized as a sign of distress which evokes an appropriate response from the community. Moreover, the individual is treated with respect because he is perceived to be favored by a deity. This condition is likened to a defense mechanism for the preservation of self-dignity and self-worth, and these people are almost never referred to any psychiatric facility. Treatment is mostly sought from the traditional healers where less stigma is attached to the patient.

Koro

Koro is an acute anxiety reaction characterized by an intense fear that the person's sexual organs (commonly penis or female breast or genitalia) are shrinking and may disappear into the abdomen, leading to death. It is an acute anxiety state with panic attack (Gwee, 1968). The person may attempt to secure a hold on his penis by tying a ribbon around it or grasping it. This generally occurs in cultures where belief about *koro* is prevalent, and thus family members are disturbed by the attack. The panic over impending disappearance of the penis leads family members to help the patient in tying his genitalia with string. Although *koro* affects individuals, occasionally there is an epidemic. Some time back, an epidemic of a Korolike syndrome occurred in Thailand, where it is called *rok-ioo,* which was later on blamed on poisoned food. Most cases are reported in Southeast Asia and southern China, where it is described as *suk-yeong.* Occasional reports of *koro* from Western cultures are also seen. A few cases of *koro* have also been reported in cases of organic brain syndrome. *Koro* individuals are described as those with a low educational background and who are dependent or have immature personalities. *Koro* has usually been thought of as a psychogenic disorder resulting from the interaction of cultural, social, and psychodynamic factors in especially predisposed persons. Cultural fears about nocturnal emission, masturbation, and sexual overindulgence leading to fears about virility seem to give rise to the condition. The precipitating factors may include coitus, a sudden exposure of the penis to cold water, or hearing stories of people dying of *koro*. However, the disorder is short-lived and the person usually recovers after explanation and reassurance. The patients may be treated with psychotherapy or antipsychotic drugs. Sometimes sedation may be necessary. In a few cases modified insulin and electroconvulsive therapy may be needed. Most of the patients in long-term follow-up show improvement and do not have further attacks, although they may be prone to develop anxiety. However, the prognosis is related to the premorbid personality and any adjustment problems. A case of sporadic *koro* has been described recently where there is a complication of marital disharmony and sexual rejection (Adityanjee, Azhar, and Subramaniam, 1991). There is suggestion that there is a distinction between sporadic *koro* and epidemic *koro*. The sporadic form can present with *koro* as a symptom or with *koro* syndrome which in turn consists of classical *koro* and *koro* grafted upon underlying psychiatric illness. Classical *koro* as described by Devan and Ong (1987) is more likely to be seen epidemically whereas the *koro* symptom (Sachdev, 1985) is unlikely to occur in epidemic proportions.

Amok

First described in Southeast Asia, this word is derived from the Malay word *mengamok* meaning to engage furiously in battle. *Amok* describes the sudden onset of wild rage. It is a rare illness which has been described in Malaysia, Singapore, Philippines, Papua New Guinea, Puerto Rico *(mal de pelea)*, and Java. Examples of persons with a syndrome similar to *amok* in the United States have also been reported. Those people turned out to be suffering from schizophrenia, bipolar disorder, or depressive disorder. It was fairly common in Malaysia many decades back but of late has become rare. It is a form of dissociative disorder characterized by a period of brooding followed by an outburst of violent, aggressive, or homicidal behavior directed at people and objects. The person runs about armed with a weapon, such as a knife, and attacks everybody in his path indiscriminately, before he is eventually overpowered, or sometimes, commits suicide. Prior to the outbreak he appears to be withdrawn and depressed and he has complete amnesia of the attack. The episode tends to be precipitated by a perceived slight or insult and is common among males. The Malaysians also refer to the attack as *mata gelap* (dark eye). The attack is often accompanied by persecutory ideas, exhaustion, and return to a premorbid level later on. Some of the cases have been reported to have schizophrenia, paranoid psychosis, epilepsy, or a brain lesion. The reasons for occurrence of this syndrome in Malaysian people are not very clear but it may be a cultural expression of aggression in society where restrictions are imposed on adolescents and adults. The belief in magical possession by demons and evil spirits may be another factor. The easy availability of knives as lethal weapons has also been referred to as a contributory factor. Social stresses, role crisis, and separation from family may also be contributory factors. The attack lasts for a few hours. The treatment consists of restraint and sedation or treatment with antipsychotic medication, if psychosis is diagnosed.

Latah

This is an uncommon disorder seen among Malays and Indonesian women. It is known in the Philippines as *mali-mali* and in Thailand as *bah-tschi*. This disorder is found predominantly in Malaysian and Javanese women but also in males. However, in recent times this disease has become rare and nowadays hardly any cases of *latah* are seen. The cause of *latah* has been considered to be an intense fear reaction to a stimulus leading to disorganization of ego boundaries. The personality is stable when the person is out of the attack, which may occur to intelligent people. The Malaysian people's belief in possession states may be a factor contributing to the *latah* reactions. It has also been suggested that *latah* is a hereditary disease running in

families, having startle reactions to stimuli which would otherwise not cause that reaction in normal individuals.

   Latah occurs in two forms. The first one is the startle reaction, in which the person suspends all normal activities and
starts a behavior characterized by compulsive imitation of
words, gestures, or acts; automatic obedience may be present.
The person may also utter obscenities. The other form consists
of a chain of unusual and inappropriate motor and verbal manifestations, which are generally out of the person's voluntary
control. Any frightening incident can precipitate the behavior.
However, those afflicted with *latah* are fully aware of the situation in spite of not having control over their actions and any
attempt to control them leads to resistance. They may feel em-
barrassed after the episode as they are usually the target of
jokes. *Latah* can become a chronic disease if uncontrolled for
several years, leading to permanent automatic obedience and
echo reactions. This may also lead to personality deterioration
and the person may become reclusive. Those with this condition do not seek medical help and are viewed by family members or friends as just "odd personalities." However, once
treatment is sought, it should consist basically of psychotherapy.
If the *latah* reaction is found to be associated with some psychiatric disorder, benzodiazepines and major tranquilizers may
also be used.

PSYCHOTHERAPY IN MALAYSIA

Background

Psychiatry in its infancy in Malaysia was mainly for the treatment of psychotics who were put in asylums. Psychotherapy
was never meant for them and it developed much later in the
seventies. It was, as in Western countries, mainly used for neurotic patients and first came to be practiced by local psychiatrists in the major cities. Since these psychiatrists received their
training overseas, the most common form of psychotherapy in
the seventies and eighties was of the psychoanalytic type. The

patients were mainly those who were themselves Western educated and spoke English. This, of course, meant that the majority of patients did not receive this treatment.

The culture of most Muslim Malaysians could not readily
accept the Freudian model (1927). As such most neurotic patients visited indigenous religious faith healers with very little
prospect for improvement. Most of the symptoms were attributed to loss of *semangat* (soul substance), being bewitched by
enemies, or being disturbed or haunted by evil spirits. Various
verses and incantations are recited to free the patient of all
these spirits. At times verses of the Qur'an or *Sunnah* (prophet
tradition) are recited. Many other forms of pseudoreligious
practices are used by these healers to convince their patients
that the healers are religious and their trade is being acknowledged by God. An example of such a practice is when a so-
called religious person recites verses of the Qur'an to catch
spirits. One of these healers literally puts these unseen spirits
in bottles and throws them in the river. Others will start by
reciting the Qur'an but end by summoning some spirit that is
allied to them to fight the bad spirits inhabiting the sick person.
Yet others recite the Qur'an and see messages and future events
in a basin of water. Any Muslim knows that predicting the future or fortune telling is against the teaching of the Qur'an
and the Prophet. These practices have been going on for years
and are still being practiced in most parts of the country today.
But as more Muslims become educated and can differentiate
proper religious substance from pseudoreligious techniques,
they tend to look for more scientific forms of treatment.
Freud's psychoanalysis does not fit into either the religious or
scientific categories. As such the younger Muslim psychiatrists
practice supportive psychotherapy rather than psychoanalysis.

Supportive psychotherapy places more emphasis on supporting or maintaining a patient's existing personality structure and defense mechanisms (Tian, 1995). The key feature is
the provision of an ongoing, consistent relationship in which
the therapist aims to maximize the patient's strengths, minimize his dependence on the therapist, and help him to live as
independently as possible. Family therapy and group therapy

have also begun to be popular as patients become more sophisticated and understand that their illnesses are at times caused by or have effects on other family members.

However, a scientific approach to religious psychotherapy only started in the early nineties, in the state of Kelantan, Malaysia (Sharma, Azhar, and Varma, 1995). Controlled studies involving patients with anxiety disorder (Azhar, Varma, and Dharap, 1994), depressive disorder (Azhar and Varma, 1995a), and bereavement (Azhar and Varma, 1995b) indicate that religious psychotherapy brings about more rapid improvement compared to supportive psychotherapy.

Religious Psychotherapy in Malaysia

Psychotherapy is important and effective if carried out properly, after careful patient selection. In Kelantan, the field of psychotherapy is limited if we follow the Western concept since most patients are culturally tuned to culture-based medication. Simple psychotherapy or counseling by faith healers seems to be fairly effective anecdotally though improvement does not last.

Psychotherapy is a sociocultural institution and its issues will play a major role in the mode and outcome of psychotherapy. Ideally psychotherapy should be able to take into account the impact on therapy of religious beliefs and practices, especially those that play powerful roles in patients' lives (Koltko, 1990).

Koltko (1990) illustrates how religious beliefs are relevant to many issues in psychotherapy, such as receptivity to psychotherapy in general and relative accessibility to different specific approaches. He emphasizes that a therapist should keep in mind that religious beliefs and values held by a community have existed for much longer than the therapist's particular therapeutic orientation, and this is because they have had adaptive functions. Hence the therapist should not lightly challenge or attempt to change them. He or she should be sensitive to differences in issues affecting various subgroups of believers.

Thus, when religious beliefs are taken into account in psychotherapy, they will inevitably affect patient receptivity and the therapy's ultimate outcome.

This brings us directly to our conceptualization of religious psychotherapy (Azhar and Varma, 1996a). We hypothesize that the main problem in human emotional disorders is not in the conflicts, especially of a sexual nature, but in the person's value system and ideals, acquired over the years through learning, experience, and modeling. These ideals and values will determine our actions and emotions, and if one has negative emotions then they can be traced back to wrong ideals or values, and a modification of these ideals or values could help to eliminate or control negative emotions. This is an oversimplification of the problem. There are, of course, many factors that contribute to negative emotions, but values and ideals are the central etiological factor. We base this on Qur'anic psychology. Different values of morality produce two different individuals with different emotional makeup. We will present clinical evidence in support of this hypothesis.

Religious Psychotherapy with Muslim Patients

In our experience since 1990 with anxiety patients, we have found that there was a significant improvement in the study group given religious psychotherapy as compared with the control group (Azhar et al., 1994). Similar results were seen in depressed patients (Azhar and Varma, 1995a) and bereaved patients (Azhar and Varma, 1995b). Overall, religious psychotherapy was found more acceptable to patients and produced faster recovery than supportive psychotherapy (Azhar and Varma, 1994). However, more work needs to be done to look at its actual long-term outcome and whether it is useful in relapse prevention in comparison to drugs. At this stage, we have ample evidence to suggest that there is a significant change in the values of the patients treated with religious psychotherapy compared with those treated with supportive psychotherapy. Based on these findings, the religious psychotherapy model seems to be supported, and what is needed is a "value search" and "value change" rather than "conflict search" and "conflict resolution."

The basic technique of religious psychotherapy is borrowed heavily from the techniques used by Beck (1967; Beck, Rush, Shaw, and Emery, 1979) to treat depression. We first identify negative thoughts in the patient and attempt to modify them using cognitive techniques. Once the patient learns this we go deeper, and using the downward arrow techniques (Beck et al., 1979) or the prejudice model of Christine Padesky (Padesky and Mooney, 1993), we try to identify dysfunctional assumptions in the patient and later on the patient's "ideals" and "values." Once we attain this level, we use religious techniques in a scientific way to modify the values.

The mainstay of our technique is collaboration between patient and therapist and Socratic questioning at all levels. By collaboration, we mean we work *with* the patient to find a solution, we do not preach or teach him what he should or should not do. Socratic questioning means we ask the patient questions so that he will find the answers himself rather than the answers being given to him. For example, if he believes people are laughing at him, we ask him how he knows that for a fact, why people would want to do that, would he do the same to others, what evidence has he got to show. It must be data driven and scientific and at no time is the therapist allowed to start preaching, or force his values on the patient. He has to work together with the patient to find the patient's values using the Qur'an and *Sunnah* (prophet tradition) as guidance. A therapist who has a tendency to preach or impose his values is not suitable to carry out this form of psychotherapy no matter how religious he may be.

We can take the example of an anxious patient. He was asked to find ways of reducing anxiety the Islamic way. With his consent, we went through the *Hadith* and Qur'an together and discovered that prayer is one of the ways. When asked to relate his experience with prayers he said he could not really believe prayer was very effective. We then discussed what aspects of prayer could make him calm and he said "the ability to concentrate on God and to forget our troubles for that short duration.'' He then realized that the reason he could not relax was because he had poor concentration during prayers. It was agreed to practice increasing and focusing attention, and doing breathing exercises for the remainder of the session so that he could concentrate better, especially during prayer. Then over the next week, he was asked to rate his anxiety levels before and after prayers. He found that over time, the relaxation level increased after prayers. When we put the result on a graph, it became obvious to him that the better his concentration during prayer (which he was taught to rate on a scale of 1–100), the calmer he became. As he became more at peace with God, he grew less worried. He could see the direct relationship of calmness and prayer. Gradually his prayers increased in time and frequency to include *sunat* prayers.

At that stage, his values were examined and subsequently modified using guidance from the Qur'an and *Hadith*. We started with Socratic questioning such as, what would that mean to you, what would that say about you, to help establish what he himself thought. (At no time does the therapist help the patient to answer these questions.) Also, all his answers must be based on factual statements and evidence that we have worked on collaboratively in the sessions. Most patients worry about many worldly things, and although they are Muslims they mostly spend too much time working and have very little time to read the Qur'an. So the use of the Qur'an during the session is welcome. This particular patient, who was a worrier, was asked to choose any verse that he felt could describe his values that we had been working on in sessions. A computer program to pick verses in the Malay language translation was used. He could pick *worry* as the main topic and then press for topics related to worry in the Qur'an, which will then come up with a series of suras of either Meccan or Medinan origin. He could then choose between the two. A series of suras will emerge and he can choose which he likes. He can then choose which sura he wants and the computer will pick the verses within that sura that have the topic of worry. He chose Sura 87 *(Al A'la)* verses 15–17. *"And glorify the name of their Guardian-Lord, and (lift their hearts) in Prayer. Nay (behold) ye prefer the life of this world. But the Hereafter is better and more enduring."* His values were ''if I do not worry, I'll be doomed.'' This produced the need to constantly worry and be chronically anxious. It was modified to "if I do not worry about the right thing only, then I'll be doomed.'' The right thing was being defined collaboratively with him as the right path in Islam. Together we looked at the need to worry and discovered that it was necessary to worry but it was illogical to worry about everything. He was unnecessarily worrying about too many worldly things which were beyond his control and it was affecting his life. He would not be doomed if he did not worry about them because he was already doing well financially, his children, though not perfect, were also doing well. His wife was not demanding and his job was secure. The energy spent in worrying, if directed to those verses, would be more appropriate. It is worrying if the money he gets is not *halal* (permitted in religion) for example. He realized that it was not important to worry whether he could make enough money, but it was important to worry if it was *halal.* In truth he would be doomed if the money is not *halal* but not doomed if the money was little but *halal.* This change of perspective made him less anxious. He was anxious initially when he realized that he was neglecting his religious obligations, but many verses in the Qur'an tell us how Merciful Allah is and how Forgiving Allah is. That in itself is helpful for this patient.

After the success with the prayer session and the session dealing with the patients' values, they become very receptive to other forms of Islamic intervention. Thus in order to uphold and strengthen a patient's newly modified values we looked at the Qur'anic psychology of morality and how it can achieve calming in a human being. In a philosophical sense, to be *moral* is to be able to find a means of satisfying your desires without infringing on the rights of others. In this sense, therefore, morality is primarily a sociomaterialistic concept, insofar as its object is the equal distribution of pleasure. The Islamic religious concept of morality is, however, diametrically opposed to this. To be *religiously moral* is to exercise self-control by curbing your desires and restraining your passion in order to attain your exalted status as a human being worthy of Heaven in the afterlife, and indeed, the whole world that has been put in your service. You could never be worthy of being a master of this world until you had succeeded in mastering your own "self," that is, being fully in charge of your inner kingdom. Religious morality in this sense requires progress from the lower level of self-slavishness (slave to the self) to the higher level of closeness to God. Rather than a call for a better distribution of pleasure, morality is, in this sense, a call for breaking the shackles of pleasure.

The two approaches, the sociomaterialistic concept of morality and the religious concept of morality, are therefore different, and they produce totally different human beings. The latter would produce people who could really follow the footsteps of the Prophet, the reason being that the basic psychology is different for both. The former will produce a materialistic man who seeks immediate pleasure, an immediate materialistic reward for all human activities, hence his temporal orientation; that is to say, his approach to reality in terms of the "pleasure of the moment" and what time has to offer. But moments are by definition transitory and time perpetually flies, so that this kind of man inevitably feels he is being left behind, and paradoxically, with a lump in his throat. The greater the fulfillment of his desires, the greedier and hungrier he gets. He bets on time, with no assets for the future, for as a mortal human being, he expects death to come unexpectedly, and, as the fleeting moments give him satisfaction only to take it away from him, he lives in a state of anxiety and constant worry until death comes in the end.

The religious concept has a totally different psychological makeup and a different sense of morality based on a different human vision or set of values. One sees worldly pleasures as transitory and in a very real sense, mortal. They constitute a test which, if passed, should admit the person to higher ranks beyond this world. Indeed the whole world is nothing but a path of transition from this world to the other, with God as the only security for such a trip. God is the only Ruler who reigns supreme, and who determines his weal and woe. If all people decide to profit or do harm to the patient, they could not achieve anything that was not preordained, he believes, and that is why the patient is neither overjoyed by material gain, nor overdismayed by material loss. This discussion further helped the patient to strengthen and solidify his new, modified values. The most important thing in this part of the therapy is that the discussion must be done in a collaborative fashion and must not be a sermon or lecture.

Once patients can learn the procedure we use in psychotherapy, they can be discharged. They should be able to treat themselves the next time a problem arises. So basically this technique helps a patient to know the Islamic coping skills, and logically the outcome should be excellent and relapses are not expected. Work is now being directed toward these aspects.

Religious psychotherapy has become very popular in our practice as most of the patients are religious and almost 70 percent of them end up with this form of therapy. The relatives of the patients also support the patient in following this type of therapy (Azhar and Varma, 1994). At the moment it is only being used for neurotic patients, who must have a basic education because the therapy involves cognitive behavior techniques that require a lot of input from the patients themselves. All of them will need to carry out a lot of behavioral experiments during sessions and at home as shown above. It is also very important that they are motivated to improve themselves. However, the most important criterion is that they have to be religious, for all discussions will be based on religion as the source of guidance and evidence. In our work, for the purpose of being objective and scientific, all patients must fill out a religious scale before undergoing therapy. This is a scale that we developed initially for our study but have now been used on a regular basis. It consists of 20 questions on prayers, fasting, *zakat* (alms giving), performing the *haj, sunat* prayers, other social obligations of good Muslims, and belief in Qur'an and *Hadith*. This will help to establish if the patients are really religiously motivated to undergo the therapy. All patients who score 70 percent and above on the scale have been known to show improvement after therapy (Azhar et al., 1994).

As with other therapies, this therapy is also being tried on other disorders besides neurosis. Work has started on patients with chronic pain and other somatoform disorders. A small sample of patients with psychosis (i.e., patients with bipolar disorders) are also being tried with this therapy. At the moment there is confidence among the therapists that this therapy will be able to at least maintain improvement in these groups of patients, although it may not offer a permanent cure. The quality of life of patients who have undergone this treatment will be better. Research is also being directed in this area of the relationship between quality of life and religious psychotherapy.

SUMMARY

The influence of culture on mental health is evident in Malaysia. The types of mental illness seen in this country are changing. Depressive, hypochondriacal, and anxiety symptoms are more commonly seen and the presentation seems to favor a somatic picture. Most patients prefer to talk in terms of physical rather than mental problems and explain their problems in terms of loss of soul substance. Epidemic hysteria is another common phenomenon. Obsessive–compulsive patients present mainly as ruminators with commonly religious content. The cultural influence is also seen in psychotic patients. The content of delusions and hallucinations are mainly of a religious or sociocultural nature. An interesting aspect of relapse in schizophrenia in Malaysians is that it is not related to high expressed emotions in patients' relatives.

Culture-bound syndromes in Malaysia include trance states, *koro, amok,* and *latah.* Many of the culture specific syndromes are attributed to the traditional belief that spiritual forces exert immense control over both physical and mental health.

Freudian psychotherapy is not popular in Malaysia. Supportive psychotherapy and the behavioral therapies are well accepted by patients, however. A new form of psychotherapy using the Qur'an and *Hadith* has been developed in Kelantan, Malaysia. It uses cognitive therapy as the basic principle. It does not look for conflicts in patients but collaborates with patients to find their ideals or values. These are then analyzed to understand why they cause symptoms and subsequently modified with the Qur'an and *Hadith* as guidelines so as to extinguish symptoms. Research has indicated that those on this therapy improve faster than those on supportive therapy.

REFERENCES

Adityanjee, A., Azhar, M. Z., & Subramaniam, M. (1991), Sporadic Koro and marital disharmony. *Psychopathology,* 24:49–52.

American Psychiatric Association (1994), *Diagnostic and Statistical Manual of Mental Disorders,* 4th ed. (DSM-IV). Washington, DC: American Psychiatric Press.

Azhar, M. Z. (1991), Profile of in-patient suicides in two hospitals in Malaysia. *Med. J. Malaysia,* 46:171–176.

—— Varma, S. L., & Dharap, A. S. (1994), Religious psychotherapy in anxiety disorder patients. *Acta Psychiatr. Scand.,* 90:1–3.

—— —— (1994), Psychotherapy experience in Kelantan. *Malaysian J. Med. Sci.,* 1:12–15.

—— —— (1995a), Religious psychotherapy in depressive disorder patients. *Psychother. & Psychosom.,* 63:165–168.

—— —— (1995b), Religious psychotherapy as management of bereavement *Acta Psychiatr. Scand.,* 91:233–235.

—— —— (1996a), Religious psychotherapy: A proposed model based on the Malaysian experience. *J. Fed. Islam. Med. Assn.,* 1:64–70.

—— —— (1996b), Relationship of expressed emotion with relapse of schizophrenia patients in Kelantan. *Singapore Med. J.,* 37:82–85.

—— —— (1996c), Phenomenological differences of delusions between schizophrenia patients of two cultures of Malaysia. *Singapore Med. J.,* 36:273–275.

—— —— Hakim, H. R. (1993), Phenomenological differences of hallucinations between schizophrenic patients in Penang and Kelantan. *Med. J. Malaysia,* 48:146–152.

Beck, A. T. (1967), *Depression, Clinical, Experimental and Theoretical Aspects.* New York: Harper & Row.

—— Rush, A. J., Shaw, B. F., & Emery, G. (1979), *Cognitive Therapy of Depression.* New York: Guilford Press.

Devan, G. S., & Ong, S. H. (1987), Koro and schizophrenia in Singapore. *Brit. J. Psychiat.,* 150:106–107.

Freud, S. (1927), The Future of an Illusion. *Standard Edition,* 21:1–56. London: Hogarth Press, 1961.

Gwee, A. L. (1968), Koro, its origin and nature as a disease entity. *Singapore Med. J.*, 9:3–7.

Koltko, M. E. (1990), Religious beliefs affect psychotherapy. The example of Mormonism. *Psychotherapy*, 27:79–90.

Kua, E. H., Sim, L. P., & Chee, K. T. (1986), A cross cultural study of the possession-trance in Singapore. *Austral. & NZ J. Psychiatry*, 20:361–364.

Padesky, C. A., & Mooney, K. A. (1993), Cognitive therapy of personality disorders. Schema change processes. Workshop presented at the European Congress of Behaviour and Cognitive Therapy, London.

Sachdev, P. S. (1985), Koro epidemic in Northeast India. *Aust. N. Z. J. Psychiat.*, 19:433–438.

———— Shukla, A. (1982), Epidemic Koro syndrome in India. *Lancet*, ii. 1161.

Sharma, I., Azhar, M. Z., & Varma, S. L. (1995), Religious psychotherapy: A cross-cultural perspective. *J. Soc. Psychiatry*, 11:53–55.

Tian, C. S. (1995), Psychotherapy. In: *Psychiatry for Doctors*, ed. E. H. Kua, S. M. Ko, & L. C. C. Lionel. Singapore: Armour Publishing, pp. 319–325.

Varma, S. L., & Azhar, M. Z. (1992), Psychiatry coming of age in Malaysia. *J. Ment. Health*, 1:369–370.

———— ———— (1995), Psychiatric symptomatology in a primary health setting in Malaysia. *Med. J. Malaysia*, 50(1):11–16.

8.

Mental Illness in Pakistan

M. H. Mubbashar

HISTORICAL BACKGROUND

Pakistan is a relatively young country with an ancient and diverse cultural heritage. Its geographical location lends itself to incursions from the north as well as the south, and it serves as the gateway to the Indian subcontinent. Thus Pakistan has been the abode of numerous civilizations—Aryan, Buddhist, Greek-Roman, Islamic, and European—each of which has contributed to the evolution of the distinct culture of this land of Indus, which today retains its indigenous base. The interplay of these civilizations has resulted in an amalgam of beliefs and practices which are fascinating, not only in their range but in the diversity of their origins. Since a health belief system is an integral part of the culture, its study provides insights for identifying the innumerable influences.

Pre-Islamic, Islamic, and European influences shape the presentation of a problem, health seeking behavior, beliefs about etiology, and treatment modalities employed regarding mental illness.

In the pre-Islamic era, the earliest recorded influence on the mental health beliefs and practices was of the Aryans from the Armenian Knot. The Vedic medical text *Arthra Veda* (700

B.C.) divided mental diseases into endogenous and exogenous, and further categorized them into theories of natural causation and theories of supernatural causation (theories of mystical causation, theories of animistic causation, and theories of magical causation).

Remedies suggested included dispensing drugs (e.g., Rauwolfia serpentine), performance of sacrifices, expiatory ceremonies, purification rites, and chanting of songs. Essentially the same model was adopted by Buddhism and Jainism, with greater stress on meditation. The Greeks had their own well-developed system of medicine which came in contact with the Ayurvedic system following the invasion of Alexander the Great.

The humoral disease theory of the Greeks may have developed from the Ayurvedic concepts. The Greek model of treatment was institution-based using dialectical, rhetorical, and cathartic models, prescribed by Aristotle (384–322 B.C.) (Mubbashar, 1992).

ISLAMIC INFLUENCES

Islamic doctrine deals with a number of psychological issues, including marital relationships, child rearing, adoption, and human development, and incorporates a number of preventive and promotive strategies for psychological well-being. Muslim scholars' and sufis' approach to mental illnesses was molded by Roman influences. The development of the self was considered essential for Islamic personality. The human body was only a vessel for the soul, and its infusion into the body was ordained by God. According to Imam Ghazali, heart, soul, and intellect are all controlled by the self (*nafs*). Mental illnesses are caused by upheavals of *nafs* which is categorized into *nafs-e-mutmainna* (satisfied self), *nafs-e-lawwamah* (critical self), and *nafs-e-ammarah* (base self). It is the latter two which have the tendency to fall prey to Satanic designs leading to abnormality of thought and behaviors (Sharif, 1990).

The thought process passes through five stages: (a) *hajjis*—when it is a passing thought; (b) *hkatir*—when it persists for some time; (c) *Hadit-al-nafas*—when it causes conflict; (d) *Ham*—when it is a preoccupation; (e) *Azam*—when it becomes a decision. The etiology of mental illness is attributed to Satanic designs which take the form of *waswās* (obsessional thoughts). Mental illnesses caused by *waswās* are categorized as alienation, desacralization, dispersion into multiplicity, and crises of identity. The remedies suggested encompassed biological, psychological, and social methods with a blend of institutional and community care with the state taking responsibility of the mentally ill (Mubbashar, 1992).

EUROPEAN INFLUENCES

British colonization of the Indian subcontinent starting in the eighteenth and nineteenth centuries resulted in the decline of the traditional health delivery institutions as they lost their state patronage. A parallel system of health care was set up by the colonial masters creating a dichotomy. Mental health care models in vogue in Britain at the time were essentially curative in their thrust and institutional in their approach. It was therefore natural that these were imported into the subcontinent, with the result that mental hospitals were set up at Lahore and Hyderabad and a psychiatry unit was established at a military hospital in Rawalpindi in 1942.

The British influence continued to be the dominant one even after Pakistan's independence in 1947. At the official level, however, this system was treated by the people of Pakistan as alien and incompatible with local customs and beliefs. Thus, Western theories made few inroads on traditional theories. Certain conditions were classified as belonging to the Western system, while traditional healers and their clients retained their theories.

THE EPIDEMIOLOGY OF PSYCHIATRIC DISORDERS

Epidemiological studies carried out in developing countries are beset by a number of problems. The first relates to the concept of "caseness" which is being tackled by developing standard-ized interviewing and rating procedures on the one hand and operationally defined diagnostic categories on the other. This raises the question of "Category fallacy" (Kleinman, 1987), however, which is being tackled by development of indigenous instruments such as the Bradford Somatic Inventory (BSI) (Mumford, Bavington, and Bhatnagar, 1991).

COMMUNITY SURVEYS

Using the BSI in Chitral (northwest of Pakistan) with 515 adults (over 18 years of age), 27 percent of women and 4 percent of men had scores in the very high range; 31 percent of women and 15 percent of men had scores in the high range; 24 percent of women and 30 percent of men had scores in the middle range; and 51 percent of men were in the low range.

In a survey of mental illness in 1992, a psychiatric assess-ment schedule was used, a modified form of PSE (Wing, Coo-per, and Sartorius, 1974) to generate a psychiatric diagnosis using the CATEGO program on a population selected from a first screening. Point prevalence for the whole population was 13.37 percent, 16.09 percent for women, and 10.65 percent for men. The most common diagnosis was depressive illness (11.77%) followed by generalized anxiety disorders (0.9%), and phobic disorders (0.65%).

Drug dependence is one of the major health hazards, and it is on the increase in Pakistan. According to a national drug survey report in 1993 there are approximately 2.86 to 3.16 mil-lion drug abusers in Pakistan. Heroin is the major drug of abuse with approximately 1.52 million abusers (50.70%), followed by hashish, opium, alcohol, bhang, tranquilizers, and mandrax; 71.50 percent of the drug abusers were under 35 years of age.

PSYCHIATRIC MORBIDITY IN PRIMARY HEALTH CARE

Studies in developed and developing countries have shown that a substantial proportion of patients presenting to primary care physicians may have some degree of psychiatric disorders. The figures range from 15 to 56 percent (Finlay-Jones and Burvill, 1978; Ndetei and Mohangi, 1979; Mari and Williams, 1986; Gureje, 1992).

In Pakistan, the investigation of the prevalence of psychiatric morbidity among primary care attenders was carried out in two subdistricts of Rawalpindi, with one being covered by the community mental health program. This yielded a point prevalence of 30.00 and 35 percent in the two subdistricts. The rate of females is almost double that of males. Depression and anxiety were the most common diagnoses (90%). An interesting finding was that the recognition rates by primary care physicians for psychiatric morbidity in an area with a mental health training program were significantly higher than in the area without the program.

PSYCHIATRIC MORBIDITY AMONG ATTENDERS TO TRADITIONAL HEALERS

Every culture has its own methods for looking after the sick and emotionally disturbed. The decision when and whom to consult is determined by societal, systemic, and individual determinants (Andersen and Aday, 1978), Pakistan being no exception. There are a variety of traditional healers, including faith healers known locally as *peers*. Some are practicing *sufis* themselves, while others are descendants of great *sufis* and are carrying on the tradition at the *mazar* (shrine) of their forefathers. These are generally well-respected members of the community having a good knowledge of local customs and traditions. Some of them have a fair knowledge of herbs and potions. They generally do not specialize in treatment of mental illness but are considered as spiritual moral guides.

Malangs, jogis, and *amils* represent a broad spectrum of indigenous practitioners who offer their services to people suffering from various problems ranging from physical and mental illnesses to social and economic problems. They may not have a fixed abode but would rather wander from village to village relying on word of mouth for clients. Some of them claim to be practitioners of black magic.

Palmists and astrologers are generally known as "professors," and are mostly limited to urban areas. In addition to making predictions about their clients they dabble in treatments using potions and herbs.

The services of traditional healers are utilized by a number of people with emotional problems. In a study involving 11 medical centers, 1,554 patients newly referred to mental facilities were interviewed to determine the pathways to health care. It was found that in centers relatively well provided with psychiatric staff, pathways were dominated by referrals from general practitioners, while at relatively less well-staffed centers, including Rawalpindi, traditional healers constituted a significant part of the pathways to care.

Hussain, Mubbashar, Saeed, and Gater (1998) conducted a study in the subdistrict Gujarkhan of Rawalpindi, involving five traditional healer practices; it was found that 48.2 percent of the 300 consecutive attenders fulfilled ICD-10 criteria for psychiatric diagnosis. When epilepsy was included the prevalence was 52.8 percent. The male to female ratio was 1:3. More than 90 percent of the patients were suffering from depression, anxiety, and dissociative disorders. There were specific categories assigned to these emotional and psychological problems which include the following:

Saya (shadow): The patient is under the shadow of a *jinn* or a supernatural being.

Jinni: The patient is "possessed" by a *jinn* due to a misdeed on the patient's part or because the *jinn* is in love with the patient.

Spirit infestation: The patient's house is the abode of spirits and he or she has transgressed their boundaries.

Nazar: Roughly equivalent to evil eye.

Jadoo: Black magic.

Pakar: The patient has been trapped because of some wrongdoing on his or her part and it is due to *kismet* (fate).

Jhalla: Frankly psychotic patients who are generally referred to medical facilities.

Hussain et al. (1998) found that 41.2 percent of community members believe that traditional healers can help people whom physicians cannot help. There was an inverse relationship between education and this belief. Similarly females were more inclined toward this belief than males.

PRESENTATION OF PSYCHIATRIC DISORDERS

It is obvious from the foregoing discussion that depression and anxiety are the two most common psychiatric disorders at all levels. It is often assumed that anxious and depressed patients from developing countries present with somatic symptoms (Kleinman, 1987). This phenomenon has been reported in many developing countries, such as Sudan, India, Colombia, and the Philippines (Harding et al., 1980); Kenya (Ndetei and Muhangi, 1979); Ethiopia (Giel and van Luijk, 1969); and sub-Saharan Africa (German, 1987a; Lin, 1989).

There is the question of absence of equivalents for *anxiety* and *depression* in certain vocabularies and the interlinked components of emotional states such as subjective feelings, autonomic responses, expressive motor response and cognition, which are largely related to social interaction (Leff, 1988). A particular culture may choose to encourage and highlight one or more of these components at the expense of the others.

Urdu, the lingua franca of Pakistan, certainly does not lack words for *depression* and *anxiety*. Indeed these feelings are central to the cultural ethos of Pakistan. However, the culturally prescribed manner of expression varies with a particular subculture. The determining factors include sex of the individual. While it is acceptable for women to express their sense of loss publicly, it is considered unmanly for the males. Ethnic and sectarian affiliations are other important factors. The formal word for depression is *afsordgi,* but the popular term is *udasi* for depression and *bechaini/izterab* for anxiety.

Suicide is another area where cultural, and particularly religious factors, play a determining role. Javed et al. (1994) showed that suicidal ideation and intent were much less common in severely depressed patients (DSM-III-R diagnosis) presenting to psychiatric facilities in Pakistan, and the major reason cited by the patients was that suicide is expressly forbidden in Islam and the patient did not want to risk punishment in the afterlife.

Hysteria has been known since ancient times. It is now considered to be a disappearing condition in Western countries, but studies carried out in developing countries show it to be a common condition (Al-Issa, 1995). In Pakistan, however, there are no large scale studies available but anecdotal accounts abound pointing to hysteria being a common condition in psychiatric practice. Malik and Javaid (1990) found that hysteria represented about 10 percent of their diagnoses of any form of neurosis. It was mostly seen in the 15- to 20-year age range, and most common presentations included fainting fits, difficulty in breathing, and an attack of barking sounds from the throat. Hussain et al. (1998) found that dissociative disorders constituted about 15 to 16 percent of the traditional healer's practice and most common presentations were aphonia, paraplegia, and fainting fits (*dhandal*).

Eating disorders are popularly regarded as being an issue only in developed societies where Western concepts of female body shape and dieting behaviors are followed. In a survey conducted among schoolgirls in Bradford, Britain, a much higher prevalence of bulimia nervosa was found among Asian girls compared to the indigenous Caucasian girls. The majority of these girls were from immigrant families from Mirpur, Azad Kashmir (Mumford and Chaudhary, 1990; Mumford, Whitehouse, and Platts, 1990). In a follow-up study by Chaudhary and Mumford (1990) at Mirpur, Azad Kashmir, only one girl out of a sample of 271 schoolgirls was identified to be suffering from bulimia nervosa, which is comparable with findings from a survey conducted in English middle schools in Lahore, Pakistan (Mumford, Whitehouse, and Chaudhary, 1990). These findings might be reflective of high levels of stress among Asian subjects in Bradford, conflicting value systems, diverse cultural influences, and parental anxieties as compared with the subjects in Lahore and Mirpur.

TREATMENT MODALITIES

As mentioned earlier, traditional and Western-style facilities often exist side by side in Pakistan, each contributing to the development of the other. *Tahajjud* therapy for treatment of depressive illness, utilizing the principle of sleep deprivation, is an example of how religious and cultural values can be incorporated by psychiatrists into their repertoire. Hussain et al. (1998) have mentioned the use of phenobarbitone by traditional healers in the treatment of epilepsy. Hassan (1990) summarized some of the psychosocial methods employed by Muslim faith healers in Pakistan which include *Zikr* therapy and therapy through opposites. In *Zikr* therapy the name of Allah is recited in a sustained way to strengthen the inner self and subordinate one's thoughts and impulses to the moral will. *Therapy through opposites* is particularly advocated in cases of emotional disturbances caused by jealousy and envy. A person suffering from jealousy may be advised to talk lovingly and affectionately in public about the person he is jealous of. The assumption is that the desire to love and understand is latent in all human beings and has to be brought to a conscious level. Therapy through "similars" consists of pointing out to the patient that his negative experiences are not unique to him, inducing a feeling of sharing to alleviate the feeling of isolation.

Some faith healers advocate *dialogue* with God every night, confessing and verbalizing weaknesses and problems. The dialogue is held in a spirit of humility, and willingness of the learner is evoked by touching the fringes of the unconscious. In music therapy a special form of music called *qawali* has evolved over time in association with religion and mysticism. These music sessions are held on special days and are traditionally accompanied by *wird* (chanting) and dancing in ecstasy. Music therapy has been reported to be effective in cases of hysteria and anxiety. Hussain et al. (1998) have also talked about the healing practices of traditional healers including:

Tawiz (amulets): There are verses from Holy Qur'an written on a piece of paper which the person has to wear or dissolve in water and drink.

Dam: The faith healer breathes on water or sugar after saying special prayers and these are then taken by the patient.

Deinfestation: The faith healer visits the infested place and performs a *chila* for a specified number of days, during which he might fast as well. At the end of the specified period he divines the reason for infestation and the conditions laid down for deinfestation, which may take the form of animal sacrifice or alms for the poor, etc. He then declares the place deinfested by blowing in all corners of the house or giving an amulet to be buried in the house. Other methods include exorcism to drive out the *jinni,* and *pach* (cautery or trepanning the skull to drive out the evil spirits). Generally, these healers make the patient's family believe that the patient is not to be blamed as he or she is at the mercy of these spirits. The patient is put in a trance with the help of music or hypnosis. Family members and patients believe that it is the spirit talking so there is no inhibition in the patients expressing their feelings.

It can be discerned from the foregoing account that faith healers are not restricted in treatment only to ridding the affected person of fear or sorrow, but deal with the whole mosaic of human emotions. Common operative themes are therapeutic suggestions, ritual-symbolic procedures, sacrificial rites, preventive devices (amulets, charms, etc.), and catharsis (Jilek, 1993).

The traditional healers' repertoire is by no means exhausted by these psychosocial interventions. Herbs and potions form an important source for treatment of physical and psychiatric conditions. The primary importance in this form of treatment is the concept of *garm* (hot) and *sard* (cold). The environmental factors as well as different food items are endowed with hot or cold characteristics. The patient is advised to take appropriate foods depending on the underlying pathology for a specific period of time.

All the allopathic medicines are described as having hot and drying properties, which is reinforced by the anticholinergic side effects of psychotropic drugs. It is therefore essential for the patient that if he or she takes these medicines at all he or she must eat foods with cold–wet properties to counteract their action. All the traditional medicines are considered to be cold and soothing in nature and therefore beneficial for the optimal functioning of all organs of the body.

Certain systems, especially the liver and stomach, have central importance to the causation and treatment of illnesses, particularly psychosexual problems. The liver is assumed to be the organ responsible for formation and purification of blood and one drop of semen is considered to be equivalent of 70 drops of blood. Often the presentation of young males with weakness of the body means that he is having nocturnal emissions or experiencing *dhat* (loss of semen in urine) which, when seen in light of the prevalent belief, is understandable while if taken out of context risks being labeled as a delusion. Similarly, patients from a strongly religious background can experience voices or images of their Peer (spiritual guide) who might be living in another city or long dead. This is the phenomenon of *ziarat* which is considered to be a mark of distinction culturally but might be labeled as a hallucination if taken out of the cultural context (Al-Issa, 1977).

CONCLUSIONS

Modern psychiatry has evolved in the West over the last 200 years and has naturally imbibed the value system of the West as reflected in conceptualization and management strategies for psychiatric illness. Until recently these principles have been applied in developing countries with little or no modification. There are two major problems in the application of mental health delivery models evolved in the West in the context of developing countries like Pakistan. One is administrative limitations. These have been extensively reviewed (Sartorius, 1977) and the following problems have been identified:

(1) Low national priority accorded to health in general and mental health in particular resulting in severe resource constraints. (2) Limited institutional and organizational support networks. Mental health legislation and planning is often

ignored or relegated to low priority. (3) Lack of infrastructure and manpower resources.

There are also limitations of cultural relevance. There is a substantive basis for questioning the choice of mental health delivery models embodying assumptions, concepts, and methods evolved in a cultural setting profoundly different from that of the host country. This is particularly evident in the separation of the body, mind, and spirit; compartmentalization of the functioning of the mind; and considering health and disease as separate entities rather than dimensions of a single continuum. This has resulted in communication problems, stigma, diagnostic bias and treatment bias. Some innovative and indigenous approaches challenging the dogma of Western mental health care delivery have been developed in Pakistan over the last decade. The main thrust of these approaches has been to develop a community-based mental health program based on the indigenous culture, geographical continuity, informed responsibility, intersectoral collaboration, and prevention of mental illness and promotion of mental health.

PLANS FOR THE FUTURE

The Demonstration Project was started in 1985 in the Gujarkhan subdistrict of Rawalpindi (Mubbashar, Malik, Zar, and Wig, 1986) under the auspices of the Department of Psychiatry, Rawalpindi Medical College, which was designated as a WHO Collaborating Center in Mental Health Research and Training in 1986 and was designated as an Institute of Psychiatry by the Government of Pakistan in 1996. This project had four phases. The first phase aimed at the collection of sociodemographic data, evaluation of need demand for mental health services, and sensitization of the community by mass education programs at the *Juma* Congregation (Friday prayer) and local shrines. In the second phase of this project, we aimed at the development of teaching and training manuals for primary health care personnel, the development of information systems and referral mechanisms, the training of primary health care personnel, and the development of links with related sectors including education, social welfare, and traditional healers. This last point might be anathema to orthodox psychiatrists, but it is a price worth paying as the number of patients receiving medical care who would otherwise not have received it is substantial. In the third phase, the aim of the project is to set up a mechanism regarding case identification, referral, and treatment provided by the caregivers and to set up a school mental health program.

Finally, the goal of the fourth phase is to develop indicators for evaluation of community mental health programs. Maqsud (1996) has shown that indicators such as maternal and infant mortality rates, fertility rates, rates of assisted deliveries, antenatal care service utilization, immunization of children, and general attendence rates at clinics have shown gradual improvement in areas under a community mental health program as compared to areas with comparable facilities without such a program, for the last 10 years. Rahman-Syed et al. (1998) has also shown that knowledge, attitudes, and superstitions regarding community mental health in areas covered by the School Mental Health Program have shown significant positive change as compared with areas not having a program.

This program has been adopted at the national level and is now being replicated in other parts of the country after the necessary modifications. There is a great paucity of research on childhood disorders, which has been identified as one of the priority areas. Prevention of mental illness and promotion of mental health are the other areas which are the focus of attention. Some efforts in this regard are already being made, like the study of the impact of iodine supplementation on intellectual and cognitive development of children in iodine deficient areas, currently being carried out in Murree subdistrict of Rawalpindi and the Clear Vision Project of WHO which was carried out at Rawalpindi, Pakistan and Alexandria, Egypt. It was demonstrated that provision of glasses to visually handicapped children in schools resulted in substantial improvement in both their academic and social performance (Gater, Saeed, Mubbashar, Orley, and Sartorius, 1998). The course of mental illness in Pakistan and ethnopsychopharmacology also requires research.

In conclusion, psychiatric services in Pakistan have made a start in tapping traditional wisdom, and culturally integrated psychiatric services will soon be readily available to all communities.

REFERENCES

Andersen, & Aday, L. A. (1978), Access to medical care in the U.S.: Realized and potential. *Med. Care,* 16:533–546.

Chaudhary, I. Y., & Munford, D. B. (1990), A pilot study of eating disorders in mirpur (Azad Kashmir) using an Urdu version of the Eating Attitudes Test.

Finlay-Jones, R. A., & Burvill, P. W. (1978), Contrasting demographic patterns of minor psychiatric morbidity in general practice and the community. *Psychol. Med.,* 8:455–466.

Gater, R., Saeed, K., Mubbashar, M. H., Orley, M., & Sartorius, N. (1998), Clear vision: A study of the impact of correcting refractive errors on the academic and social achievements of school children in rural Rawalpindi Pakistan. Submitted to *J. Ment. Health.*

German, G. A. G. (1987a), Mental health in Africa. I: The extent of mental health problems in Africa today: An update of epidemiological knowledge. *Brit. J. Psychiatry,* 151:435–439.

————— (1987b), Mental health in Africa. II: The nature of mental disorder in Africa today: Some clinical observations. *Brit. J. Psychiatry,* 151:440–446.

Giel, R., & van Luijk, J. N. (1969), Psychiatric morbidity in a small Ethiopian town. *Brit. J. Psychiatry,* 115:149–162.

Goldberg, D. P., & Blackwell, B. (1970), Psychiatric illness in general practice: A detailed study using a new method of case identification. *Brit. Med. J.,* 2:439–443.

Gureje O., Obikoya, B., & Ikuesan, B. A. (1992), Prevalence of specific psychiatric disorder in an urban primary care setting. *Eastern African Medical Journal,* 69:282–287.

Harding, T. W., De Arango, M. V., Baltazar, J., Climent, C. E. (1980), Mental disorders in primary care: A study of their frequency and diagnosis in four developing countries. *Psychol. Med.,* 10:231–241.

Hassan, I. N. (1990), An overview of Muslim spiritual therapy and other practices in dealing with mental health problems in Pakistan. In: *Mental Health in Developing Countries*, ed. M. H. Mubbashar & A. R. Sayed.

Hussain, A., Mubbashar, M. H., Saeed, K., & Gater, R. (1998), Prevalence, treatment and classification of mental disorders among attenders of native healers in rural Pakistan. Submitted to *Acta Psychiatrica Scandinivica.*

Al-Issa, I. (1977), Social and cultural aspects of hallucinations. *Psycholog. Bull.*, 84:570–587.

——— (1995), Culture and mental illness in an international perspective. In: *Handbook of Culture and Mental Illness: An International Perspective*, ed. I. Al-Issa. Madison, CT: International Universities Press, pp. 3–49.

Jilek, W. G. (1993), Traditional medicine relevant to psychiatry. In: *Treatment of Mental Disorders: A Review of Effectiveness*, ed. N. Sartorius, G. D. Girolamo, G. Andrews, G. A. German, & L. Eisenberg. Washington, DC: London: WHO Inc.

Kleinman, A. (1987), Anthropology and psychiatry: The role of culture in cross-cultural research illness. *Brit. J. Psychiatry*, 151:447–454.

——— Sung, B. (1976), Why do indigenous practitioners successfully heal? Paper presented at the conference on the healing process. Michigan State University, East Lansing.

Leff, J. (1988), *Psychiatry Around the Globe. A Transcultural View.* (Sec. Ed.) London: Gaskell.

Lin, N. (1989), Measuring depressive symptomatology in China. *J. Nerv. Ment. Dis.*, 177:121–131.

Malik, B. A., & Javaid, M. A. (1990), Depression and neuroses in general practice. In: *Mental Health for All: All for Mental Health*, ed. M. H. Mubbashar & A. R. Syed. Rawalpindi Medical College, Pakiston: Pakistan Psychiatric Society. Institute of Psychiatry, WHO Collaboration Center for Mental Health Research and Training.

Mari, J. J., & Williams, P. (1986), A comparison of the validity of two psychiatric screening questionnaires (GHQ12 and SRQ 20) in Brazil using ROC analysis. *Psychological Med.*, 15:651–659.

Maqsud, N. (1996), Development of indicators for evaluation of community mental health programme (dissertation). College of Physicians and Surgeons Pakistan.

Mubbashar, M. H. (1992), Savage voyage—SHIFA. *J. Rawalpindi Med. College*, 2:47–54.

—— Malik, S. J., Zar, J. R., & Wig, N. N. (1986), Community based rural mental health care programme. Report on an experiment in Pakistan. *EMR Health Serv. J.,* 1:14–20.

—— et al. (1986), Reaching the unreached. Mental health care to rural masses. *Proceedings of International Seminar on Community Psychiatry.*

Mumford, D. B. (1989), Somatic sensations and psychological distress among students in Britain and Pakistan. *Soc. Psychiatry & Psychiatric Epidemiol.,* 24:321–326.

—— (1993), Somatization: A transcultural perspective. *Internat. Rev. Psychiatry,* 5:231–242.

—— (1994), Can "functional" somatic symptoms associated with anxiety and with depression be differentiated? *Internat. J. Methods in Psychiatric Res.,* 4:133–141.

—— Bavington, J. T., Bhatnagar, K. S. (1991), The Bradford Somatic Inventory: A multi-ethnic inventory of somatic symptoms reported by anxious and depressed patients in Britain and the Indo-Pakistan subcontinent. *Brit. J. Psychiatry,* 158:379–386.

—— Chaudhary, I. Y. (1990), A cross-cultural survey of eating disorders in Mirpur (Azad Kashmir) compared with Bradford (United Kingdom). In: *Mental Health for All—All for Mental Health,* ed. M. H. Mubbashar & A. R. Syed. Rawalpindi Medical College, Pakiston: Pakistan Psychiatric Society. Institute of Psychiatry, WHO Collaboration Center for Mental Health Research and Training.

—— Whitehouse, A. M., Platts, M. (1990), Eating disorders among Asian school girls in Bradford. Socio-cultural correlates. *Brit. J. Psychiatry.*

—— —— Chaudhary, I. Y. (1990), A survey of eating disorders in English Medium schools in Lahore Pakistan. *Internat. J. Eat. Disord..*

Ndetei, D. M., & Mohangi, J. (1979), The prevalence and clinical presentation of psychiatric illnesses in a rural setting in Kenya. *Brit. J. Psychiatry,* 135:269–272.

Ormel, J., Van den Brink, W., Koeter, M. W., Giel, R., van der Meer, K., van der Williegw, G., & Wilmink, F. W. (1990), Recognition, management and outcome of psychological disorders in primary care: A naturalistic follow-up study. *Psychol. Med.,* 20:909–923.

Rahman, A. Syed, Mubbashar, M. H., Gater, R., & Goldberg. D. (1998). Randomized trial of impact of school mental health programme in rural Rawalpindi, Pakistan. *Lancet,* 352:1022–1025.

Sachdev, P. S. (1985), Koro epidemic in Northeast India. *Aust. N. Z. J. Psychiat.,* 19:433–438.

Sartorius, N. (1977), Complete or Complement? *World Health,* 12:28–33.

Sharif, C. M. (1990), Islam and psychological medicine. In: *Mental Health for All—All for Mental Health,* Vol. 1, ed. M. H. Mubbashar & A. R. Syed. Rawalpindi Medical College, Pakiston: Pakistan Psychiatric Society. Institute of Psychiatry, WHO Collaboration Center for Mental Health Research and Training, pp. 33–38.

Wing, J. K., Cooper, J. E., & Sartorius, N. (1974), *The Measurement and Classification of Psychiatric Symptoms.* Cambridge, UK: Cambridge University Press.

9.

Psychiatry in Saudi Arabia

Abdullah Al-Subaie, Abdulrazzak Alhamad

HISTORICAL BACKGROUND

The modern Kingdom of Saudi Arabia was founded by King Abdulaziz ibn Saud (1882–1953) who, between 1901 and 1933, transformed warring desert factions into a single united kingdom. It occupies most of the Arabian Peninsula covering an area of 907,500 square miles. Its population is around 17 million, about 30 percent of whom are expatriates. During the long summer months, midday temperatures may reach 48°C, while winters are fairly cool, and temperatures may fall to below zero in the north and southwest. The average annual rainfall is five inches or less.

Oil was discovered in 1936 and commercial production began during World War II, and with one-third of the known oil reserves of the world, Saudi Arabia was catapulted into the modern era. Oil production forms the main source of the gross national product (GNP); however, development plans aim to encourage non-oil-producing sectors such as agriculture, industry, and minerals.

Islam is the state religion and the source of its civil and criminal legislative systems. *Shari'ah* is the comprehensive Islamic system of law that is divine in origin, religious in essence, and moral in scope. *Fiqh,* the systematic endeavor to interpret and apply the principles of *Shari'ah* derives from *Shari'ah. Shari'ah* evolved from a system that dealt with simple practical everyday issues in the early days of Islam to become the complex and inclusive social institution that it is today. It has two basic sources, the Qur'an and the prophetic traditions. *Shari'ah* also draws upon supplementary sources such as revelations to other prophets and peoples, and consensus reached by the prophet's companions, along with more rational sources such as analogy, public interest, and independent disciplined reasoning (Hammudah, 1977). *Analogy* means deriving new legislation from existing laws in order to solve new problems. This is comparable to the notion of precedence in English common law. *Public interest* implies that if new situations arise that are clearly in the public interest (e.g., new modes of transportation, medications, commercial practices) within relevant legislation in *Shari'ah,* it is considered lawful to introduce these. Whatever is clearly considered unlawful according to the two basic sources, however, cannot be superseded by other sources under any circumstance.

A central feature of Saudi religious and cultural life is of course the annual pilgrimage to Mecca (the *Hajj*). The *Hajj* is one of the five Fundamentals of Islam, and it is the duty of every able Muslim once in a lifetime. The *Hajj* is a series of rites performed in the area of Mecca, a city in the mountains west of Jeddah, and it has a great impact on the Holy City. For several weeks, the population increases markedly with the arrival of pilgrims from the Muslim world. For example, in 1995 there were some 1.2 million nonresident foreigners who participated in the *Hajj*. The *Hajj* places special stresses on the health care and public health systems, including the increased need for water supply, garbage removal, improving sanitary facilities, and public health measures (Basalamah, Rosinski, and Schumacher, 1979).

SOCIAL STRUCTURE

Although there has been a shift during the last two decades from extended families in rural areas to nuclear families in urban regions, both share a common Saudi family structure. Members of nuclear families almost always maintain both physical and emotional bonds with their extended families of origin. As a result, very few Saudi families can be regarded as nuclear in the strict sense of the term. Transformation from extended to nuclear families is creating family and marital problems and limiting social support networks (Al-Yahya, 1991). Fertility is highly valued, which, along with early marriages, accounts for the large size of the average Saudi family. Culturally, the large family enhances the sense of collective strength and influence in the community. Although polygamy is sanctioned by Islam and is legal in Saudi Arabia, only a small percentage of marriages are polygamous. Reproduction is encouraged by religious beliefs, and birth control is forbidden by some religious authorities and highly discouraged by others. The country's resources and size would also support a much larger population.

The rapid modernization and urbanization has led to conflicts between the old and the new as well as to personal insecurity and neurotic problems which are on the increase (Al-Yahya, 1991). There is a growing conflict between the traditional female role of getting married and bearing children and the new endeavors of gaining education and working outside the home. Western education, media services, and travel abroad have made women aware of their position in a conservative society where, for instance, they cannot drive.

TRADITIONAL MEDICINE

Traditional medicine in Saudi Arabia enjoys a rich heritage based on the sociocultural and religious foundation of the Arab Muslim community. In the pre-Islamic era, Arabs were reputed to be uninterested in medicine. It is reported that a pre-Islamic Arab physician (Harith ibn Kalda) studied medicine in Persia. When Kisra Anushirawan, the emperor of the Persians, came to know that Harith was a Bedouin and a physician, he said: "What on earth, are the Arabs doing studying to become physicians, when we know them to be ignorant, ill-fed and feeble-minded?" Harith then replied promptly: "Your Majesty, if these are indeed the qualities of the Arabs, then they are in the greatest need of a physician to heal their minds and feed their bodies" (Shahine, 1978).

Islamic religion, through the Qur'an, has emphasized reason and thought. It favors those who are learned over those who are ignorant, and it stresses the need to abandon traditional beliefs which are contrary to reason. How Islam emphasizes learning is illustrated by this verse from Qur'an commanding the Prophet to: "Read, in the name of God . . . read by the God who taught with the pen, who taught man what he had never known" (Sura 96:1). Arabic became the language of science throughout the Islamic empire despite the ethnic and linguistic diversity of its population. This has resulted in the establishment of reputable scientific centers in Cairo, Baghdad, and Cordova during the medieval era. Muslims of different ethnic origins contributed in translating knowledge from ancient Egyptian, Byzantine, and Persian civilizations. "Arabian medicine" is, in fact, "Muslim medicine" written in Arabic (see chapter 2, this volume).

Al-Razi (A.D. 841–926), known as Rhazes, was the first among Islamic physicians to discuss neuropsychiatric diseases and successfully treat mental disorders such as "love sickness" and lycanthropy (see chapter 2, this volume). Long before Freud, he declared that mental diseases were not due to evil spirits, but due to nervous breakdown or psychic disorders. Therefore Al-Razi might be honored as the "Father of Islamic Psychiatry" (Al-Moudodi Abu-Al'a, Muazzam, and Muazzam, 1989). Ibn Sina or Avicenna (980–1037) wrote his famous five-volume book, *The Canon of Medicine,* which contains many aphorisms which are still valid. He wrote, "If a patient makes movements with his hands as if picking things off himself, it is a sure sign of death" (Camp, 1978); he is probably referring to acute organic brain syndrome. In spite of the well-documented contributions of early Muslim physicians, Western historians of medicine have made little reference to their scientific and intellectual works in this field (Akram Bhatty, Al-Sibai, and Quorain, 1986).

Today, traditional medicine is legally one of the two major health systems in Saudi Arabia alongside modern medicine.

Some 50 to 70 percent of psychiatric outpatients have seen a traditional healer at some time for their illness and 21 to 50 percent have done so before seeking help from modern psychiatric services (Hussein, 1989; Al-Subaie, 1994). Nevertheless, no serious efforts have been made to study and make use of the concepts and practices of traditional healing in the country.

Native healers are usually middle-aged men who tend to be religious leaders or otherwise outstanding figures in society. Most of them are semi-illiterate and have no traditional or modern medical knowledge. They usually do not charge patients for their services but they expect voluntary donations.

Male native healers tend to perform their healing practices with large groups of patients of the same sex and thus enhance the effects of suggestion in treatment. Practicing traditional healing with groups popularizes the healers' success while failures and relapse of symptoms are not publicized. Female native healers, on the other hand, usually perform their healing powers on an individual basis or in small groups.

Compared to psychiatrists, who are mostly non-Saudis, native healers speak the same language as their patients and share the same beliefs and traditions. Their healing power is therefore built on a solid foundation and forms part of a whole set of social functions. This contrasts with the rigid boundaries within which Western medicine is confined. Traditional healers and even some medical practitioners believe that psychotropic drugs are addictive or at best only "tranquilizers" and should, therefore, be avoided.

Patients from all walks of life seek the help of native healers. Age, sex, social class, and education do not seem to play a great role in patients' choice between traditional healing and modern psychiatry. More women than men, however, tend to seek help from traditional healers (Al-Subaie, 1994). Patients may seek help from the same traditional healer for physical, emotional, or even social problems. The majority of those seeking help from traditional healers tend to be psychiatric patients.

Healers actually give explanations that are usually compatible with the common folklore and are therefore readily acceptable by clients. They also encourage patients to externalize and project their emotions which relieves guilt feelings and brings about some secondary gains, such as sympathy, that may not otherwise be forthcoming. The most common diagnoses for mental disorders are:

1. *Wishrah:* The word *wishrah* means a malformation or an improper healing of the skull bones leaving an opening that is discovered by the sliding hands slowly over the patient's shaved scalp. Healers look for elevations or depressions of the skull bones. Some call the elevations "male *wishrah*" and the depressions "female *wishrah.*" Others describe old *wishrah* as being cold compared to the rest of the head temperature, while the more recent *wishrah* is believed to be hot. Patients are encouraged to touch the *wishrah* in order to prove its diagnostic validity. Patients may also be sent to a hospital to obtain a skull X ray to help locate the believed abnormality. *Wishrah* is characterized by incoherence and irrelevant speech (Hussein, 1989) and appears to correspond to psychosis in current psychiatric nosology.

2. *Demonic Possession:* This disorder is characterized by abrupt emotional or physical changes or by loss of control over behavior (e.g., fainting or crying). The most common explanation of possession is that the patient had spilled something hot around sunset or at night, hurting a *jinni,* who then takes revenge by possessing the patient. Alternatively, someone may be possessed because a *jinni* falls in love with him or her. Male *jinn* (plural of *jinni*) are believed to possess women while the female *jinn* possess men. Using current psychiatric classification, these patients would mostly be diagnosed as neurotic suffering from conversion disorder but they may be organic cases such as epilepsy or psychosis. The existence of *jinn* is supported by the Holy Qur'an and the prophetic tradition (Ibn Baz, 1987) but their influence on human beings is not agreed upon by all Muslim scholars. The *jinni* is believed to enter into the possessed person and acts through parts of the body (e.g., using his or her tongue to speak). It seems, however, that over the years people have accumulated many elaborate stories and created some more beliefs that are falsely attributed to religion. Questioning these beliefs is taken to indicate poor faith.

3. *Ain* or *Nafs*: "Evil eye" is more of an explanation than a diagnosis. It is based on an Islamic principle. The evil eye occurs when an "evil person" envies another person leading to physical illnesses, injuries, or emotional disturbances. Because psychiatric diagnoses are not usually as acceptable as physical ones, many psychiatric patients attribute their suffering to the evil eye and therefore resort to faith healers, instead of seeking help from modern medicine.

4. *Sihr* or *Sabab*: Like the *jinn* and the *ain*, believing in witchcraft is another etiological factor based on an Islamic principle. Although performing witchcraft is strictly forbidden in Islam, its existence is supported by the Qur'an. How to do witchcraft and its influence on man is not well known to the public. One particular effect of witchcraft that is documented in the Qur'an is hatred between spouses which may lead to divorce. It seems that witchcraft is also an explanation that relieves the spouse from being made accountable for his or her negative emotions toward the other partner.

A specific type of witchcraft in the Saudi culture is called *rabt*. It is believed to lead to impotence in the newly married man. Believing that one's erectile problem is due to an external factor (i.e., witchcraft) is more acceptable than "sexual weakness" or doubts about masculinity or manhood.

5. *Zar*: This is a cult widespread in the Middle East and represents a special form of possession. It is a term used to describe a variety of illnesses usually suffered by women as well as a class of spirits who are believed to cause these illnesses through possession. *Zar* was first described in the Hejaz (Western part of Saudi Arabia) by Hurgronje, in 1889 (cited in Oesterreich, 1966). Hurgronje's account indicates that this trance-based healing system, which he observed in the Hejaz, is the same as that which occurs in Egypt, Iraq, Kuwait, Sudan, Somalia, and Ethiopia (Prince, 1980).

It is interesting that according to Hurgronje, *zar* possession occurred not only among Arabs but also among other cultural groups residing in Hejaz after coming for *Hajj* (pilgrimage) from different parts of the world. *Zar* is mostly seen and practiced in the western province of Saudi Arabia. A variant called *jarmah* is more prevalent among men and Black Saudis of African descent, especially in the central region.

Traditional Healing

Traditional treatment methods have been used by native healers to deal with both physical and mental problems. The following are some of the most common therapies used by these healers:

1. *Kayy or Cautery: Kayy* is used for many mental and physical disorders, though it is the main treatment for *wishrah*. This is done using iron rods of different sizes and shapes with a wooden handle. The glowing red heated iron rod is usually applied to the patient's head in various locations according to the healer's judgment and diagnosis. The size of the treated area also varies where some cauteries may be small while others as large as 4 by 20 cm. The principles of performing cautery are known only by those who perform it ("secrets of the profession" as some of them assert).

2. *Qur'an recitation:* It is a matter of faith to believe in the healing power of the Qur'an. Nevertheless, *Allah* may choose not to cure a person by the power of the Qur'an in which case he will be rewarded both for his belief in, and his attempt to use the Qur'an as well as for his endurance of suffering. Reading the Qur'an and reciting specific prayers may be performed by the patient himself or by the healer. Many rituals are carried out along with reading the Qur'an which are not related to Islamic doctrine. These include *azeemah* or *maho,* writing excerpts from the Qur'an and some prayers with saffron on a piece of paper which the patient is asked to soak in water and drink or use to wash affected areas of his body (e.g., chest in case of chest-tightness or head in case of headache). Another ritual involves touching the patient's head, chest, or massaging the affected area. Males touching females is forbidden in Islam, unless the patient is a spouse or a *mahram* (a lady that the person can never marry, e.g., first-degree relatives, aunts, etc.). One particularly unethical practice is beating the possessed

patient so as to drive the *jinni* out of the body. When patients scream from pain, the healer believes that it is the voice of the *jinni*, since patients are believed not to feel physical pain when they are possessed. Some healers may go even further and strangle the patient with their hands until he or she looses consciousness, which can be fatal. Under the pressure of beating and strangulation patients may talk in a different voice indicating a *jinni* possession. Typically, the *jinni* is first asked by the healer about the reason and circumstances of possession and then the *jinni* is asked about his or her religion and domicile. The typical answer of the *jinni* is that he or she is not a Muslim and lives far away. The *jinni* then says what he or she does to the patient and answers questions asked by the healer. Before the session ends the *jinni* is asked to convert to Islam (or else he or she will be beaten). This usually ends by acceptance of this proposal, in which case the *jinni* will be educated about Islam and asked not to possess the patient again. If the *jinni* has any requests (usually things that the patient needs) he or she will make them before agreeing to leave. It seems that some patients go through a trance state facilitated by suggestion and perhaps brain hypoxia during strangulation leading to abreaction.

3. *Zar:* Zar is a ritualistic healing process as well as a diagnosis. Treatment procedures include diagnosis of the illness as being caused by *zar* possession, the identification of the particular *zar* involved by means of a dialogue between the healer and the patient while both are in a dissociative state, and finally the determination of what the *zar* wants in the way of gifts and donations in order to alleviate the suffering of the patient (Al-Subaie, 1989).

4. *Herbs (phytotherapy):* Most of the herbs used are imported from Eastern Asia such as Rosa Damascena (red damask rose), Corlus Stations (saffron), Citrus Medica (lime), Lavandula Stocchas (Roman lavender) and Korean Schizandra (Akram Bhatty et al., 1986; Hussein, 1989). These can be used orally (boiled like tea), applied locally, or sniffed in powder form.

5. *Dietary restriction:* Usually prescribed in combination with another treatment.

6. *Seclusion and chaining:* Secluding severely disturbed and actively psychotic patients in a dark room is usually practiced along with other forms of treatment, such as Qur'an reading, beating, or cauterization. The period of seclusion varies according to treatment response.

7. *Electricity:* A few healers try electricity as a method of treatment using it in the same way that cattle prods are used, but unfortunately with little or no regard for safety.

Healers are sometimes licensed by nonmedical authorities on the basis of their professional reputation, modesty, and religious adherence. Some healers insist on stopping psychotropic medications before embarking on any form of traditional treatment. This probably accounts for problems such as noncompliance with treatment, "no show" at follow-up appointments, and discharge against medical advice. Since a common belief is that mental disturbances are due to evil spirits or demons, persons believed to be in possession of supernatural powers are likely to be consulted. The divergence in this issue between psychiatrist and faith healers leads to a poor therapeutic alliance and a strained patient–doctor relationship. Religion is a very sensitive issue in the Saudi society and psychiatrists have to be knowledgeable in Islamic matters if they are to be helpful to their patients. Because the mechanisms by which demons, witchcraft, and evil eye operate are not clearly stated in Islamic texts, and because diagnoses in psychiatry tend to be subjective, patients and even colleagues from other fields of medicine often relate psychiatric symptoms to traditional diagnoses. This is in contrast to physical symptoms which are usually believed to be "real" medical problems. One can argue that diabetes, hypertension, or even a fracture are caused by factors such as an evil eye. In this case when a physician treats these disorders, one is treating the consequences of the evil eye rather than the evil eye itself. The same argument can be used to teach patients that there is no conflict between psychiatric diagnoses and traditional concepts of causality of their symptoms. It is also quite important to educate patients about authenticated methods of therapy in Islam. *Tawheed* is a fundamental principle in Islam which means believing in the absolute oneness of God which entails believing in His absolute knowledge and power of healing. Seeking help from diviners, magicians, astrologers, or fortune-tellers is forbidden because it contradicts the principle of *tawheed*. Also, any other method that underestimates the role of mind and reasoning, such as superstition or quackery, is forbidden for the same reason. All other methods of treatment or substances are permitted unless otherwise stated in the Qur'an or the prophetic tradition, such as alcohol and pork. Even then, these are permitted if absolutely necessary. The definition of the "absolute need" is decided by religious scholars who consider each individual case on its own merits. Harmful or unethical methods are totally forbidden.

MEDICAL EDUCATION

Psychiatric Teaching

The total number of students in both general and higher education was over 4 million in 1996, of whom 50,000 were in higher education. Only two of the medical schools in the country have full psychiatric services in their participating hospitals. Medical students in university hospitals receive their psychiatric training one day a week for 12 weeks during their fifth or sixth years. The two universities that lack psychiatric facilities send their medical students to psychiatric hospitals for intensive four-week courses. One of the four existing medical colleges in Saudi Arabia awards a two-year diploma and two offer a four-year fellowship in psychiatry. In 1996 the Saudi Board of Psychiatry was established at the Saudi Council for Health Specialties to standardize the level of training in the country. Faculties of applied health sciences and health institutes train nursing and paramedical staff but specialized psychiatric training is not offered. There are several faculties of education with hundreds of psychology students in Saudi Arabia. There were, however, no provisions for clinical psychology training until 1989 when

King Saud University in Riyadh started a master's degree program in clinical psychology.

HEALTH SERVICES

The Ministry of Health (MOH) is the main provider of health services and regulates this function through 19 health directorates all over the Kingdom. Other governmental sectors that also provide health services for specific populations are the military, security, and National Guard health services for their personnel. King Faisal Specialist Hospital and King Khalid Eye Specialist Hospital are highly specialized tertiary care centers. University hospitals have no limitations of access for Saudi nationals. This is beside school health services and the private health sector. The department of mental and social health at the Ministry of Health regulates and supervises governmental and private psychiatric services throughout the country. Health services, including medications, are provided free and all but the private hospitals are fully funded by the government (Al-Subaie, 1989; Ministry of Health, 1994).

According to the 1994 Annual Health Report, the total number of beds in all health services was 41,827 with 2.4 beds for every 1,000 people; the number of doctors was 29,227 of whom 4,272 (14%) were Saudis; and the number of physicians per head of population was 1:601.

The development of various health services is shown in Table 10. (Ministry of Health, 1983, 1985, 1986a, 1990, 1994).

The Ministry of Health has made substantial progress in fulfilling the WHO General Assembly goals in 1977, namely health for all by the year 2000 (WHO, 1978). Primary health care has developed in many aspects. There was no comprehensive primary health care policy before 1980, and 889 primary health care centers were established in that year alone (Ministry of Health, 1986b). In 1994 the total number of primary health care centers was 1,719 that provide health education, mother and child care, vaccinations, and national health programs for common diseases such as asthma and diabetes (Ministry of Health, 1994). In 1995 a national committee was

Table 10.1 Development of Health Services between 1970 and 1994

	YEAR	HOSPITALS	BEDS	DOCTORS	NURSES	OTHERS
	1970	47	7165	789	2253	1452
M.O.H. Services	1990	163	25835	8194	20742	9278
	1994	173	26878	10136	26292	12604
Other	1983	23	5055	2308	4255	5052
Governmental	1990	31	6937	4658	10245	6097
Services	1994	34	8357	6176	15622	8958
	1983	52	3440	2634	4548	2150
Private	1990	64	6679	5460	8697	3705
Services	1994	72	6592	7216	9937	3884

established to integrate mental health in primary health care and a manual for the primary care team was published and other training courses were planned (MOH, 1996).

Saudization of health manpower has also increased from 460 Saudi doctors in 1979 to 4,267 in 1994 (Ministry of Health, 1994).

PSYCHIATRIC SERVICES

The first psychiatrist ever in the Kingdom of Saudi Arabia was appointed by the Ministry of Health in 1959 to take care of mentally ill patients in Taif city. In 1962 the first psychiatric hospital was established there to accommodate 240 patients, but admissions soon reached 620. In 1970, it contained 1,359 patients and in 1980, 1,522 patients. Since 1983, psychiatric services have expanded rapidly and in 1985 there were nine hospitals and two clinics in general hospitals (Ministry of Health, 1984, 1988).

Currently, services include 15 mental hospitals, three addiction treatment hospitals, four psychiatric units in general hospitals, and 57 outpatient clinics. The total number of psychiatric beds is 1,779, averaging to one bed per 8,000 people, and if the number of beds in other governmental hospitals and private facilities is included the ratio increases to one bed per 6,000 people, and this is one-third of what is recommended by world authorities; for example, the White Paper 1975 in the

United Kingdom (Ministry of Health, 1996; Royal College of Psychiatrists, 1988).

The number of psychiatric beds has only increased from 1,522 in 1980 to 1,779 in 1996 (i.e., about 15% in 16 years). Community care services is another area that has not developed enough. The first psychiatric rehabilitation day-care center was established in King Abdulaziz University Hospital in Riyadh in 1990 and two other centers were later opened for the entire Saudi psychiatric population.

MENTAL HEALTH WORKERS

The Ministry of Health had 49 psychiatrists and 33 trainee psychologists and social workers in 1981. These numbers have grown to 196 psychiatrists and 158 psychologists and social workers in 1996. All other mental health services have about 120 psychiatrists and 70 psychologists and social workers. In total there is about one psychiatrist for every 42,000 population (Ministry of Health, 1996).

Saudi psychiatrists are still few, and most of the Ministry of Health psychiatrists in the Kingdom are specialists holding a 2-year diploma or master's degree. Most of the psychiatrists are Arabic/English speaking, while most of the nursing staff speak only English, and have little previous experience in psychiatry. The lack of Arabic-speaking nurses is not limited to psychiatry; but its importance is greater for psychiatric patients where the need to communicate is much greater than in other branches of medicine.

Psychologists mostly hold a bachelor's degree in general psychology with minimal clinical psychology training, and the situation with social workers is not any better.

Psychiatric Practice

The majority of psychiatric wards are locked and physical methods of restraint are frequently used. Psychiatric treatment is medication-oriented and psychotherapy is brief and supportive. Occupational therapy is available at some centers; but for the most part patients spend their time watching television or playing cards. Patients are usually discharged to the care of their relatives with a fair percentage attending outpatient clinics. Day hospitals are very rare and halfway houses are not necessary since cultural and religious traditions emphasize strong family ties and supportive attitudes. Since there is no systematized mental health legislation to control the need for and the length of hospitalization, admission is usually negotiated between the patient, the family, and the psychiatrist. In females, utilization of community-based psychiatry, and home visits by properly trained personnel, are essential in the assessment, treatment, and prevention of psychiatric morbidity.

Professional Disputes

As reported by Al-Yahya (1991), a plan for "Saudization," which implies the replacement of non-Saudis in administration by qualified Saudis, was adopted in 1970 when psychologists who were—and still are—much more numerous than psychiatrists, received most of the administrative posts. The vast majority of them were educational or social psychologists with little administrative or clinical background. Problems such as absence of proper team work, limited drug prescribing privileges, and growing tension between members of the treating team then arose.

Official literature seldom distinguishes between a clinical psychologist and other psychologists or psychiatrists. Definitions adopted according to Al-Yahya (1991) are: "The psychiatrist is a doctor specialized in [treating] symptoms that the patient complains [of] from [the patient] as well as his relatives' accounts, and by [the] aid of medical and social reports he will examine all contributing factors in a psychiatric case, and accordingly he will provide a preliminary diagnosis and will prescribe the proper medication. . . ."

"The psychologist is a person who is specialized in the diagnosis and treatment of psychiatric diseases, providing psychotherapy sessions and utilizing different schools of psychotherapy, psychoanalysis, behavioral and humanitarian. . . ."

EPIDEMIOLOGY OF MENTAL ILLNESS

There is a serious lack of original epidemiological work addressing the incidence and prevalence of mental disorders in Saudi Arabia. However, in recent service utilization studies of psychiatric outpatient departments (El-Sayed, Mahgraby, Hafeiz, and Buckley, 1986), general hospital emergency rooms (El-Gaaly, 1987; Al-Subaie, Marwah, Hawari, & Rahim, 1996), psychiatric inpatient wards (El-Esra and Amin, 1988), and primary care psychiatric clinic settings (El-Rufaie, 1988), a number of striking findings have emerged. In all of these studies, men seeking psychiatric help outnumbered women. This is contrary to the findings of similar studies in the Western world. These results may not reflect the true prevalence of psychiatric disorders of course, since Saudi women seem to use faith healing more often than men. Also, women may not attend hospitals as frequently as men since, for cultural reasons, they are totally dependent on men to take them there. Furthermore, according to El-Sayed et al. (1986) women in "Eastern societies" are thought to be tolerant of both physical and psychological pain which may be considered culturally normative for them. As an alternative explanation, El-Islam (1976) and El-Sendiony (1981) have suggested that the extended family may play a protective role and reduce morbidity among Saudi women.

A second finding is that the majority of users of psychiatric services were in the second and third decades of life. This pattern has been attributed to the multiple stresses and conflicts between traditional and modern values brought about by rapid urbanization and changes in life-style in this region of the world (El-Sayed et al., 1986; El-Gaaly, 1987). There have been similar findings in other Arab Gulf states (El-Islam, 1976, 1982, 1983; El-Islam, Abu-Dagga, Malasi, and Moussa, 1986) and these have been attributed to intergenerational conflicts which affect young people in three major areas: patterns of family relations, forms of marriage, and the role of women in society. Instead of the traditional arranged marriage and patrilocal residence pattern, young people prefer to choose their own spouses and live on their own. Instead of working on the family's farm or in the family store, for example, children now pursue individual goals, interests, and concerns which may not be approved by their parents. Improved transportation and communication facilities undoubtedly play a role in promoting individualism and lead to the breakdown of the extended family system. As to the roles of women in Saudi society, women are now more reluctant to marry at an early age, choosing to pursue higher education and careers. Women are also less accepting of having their role restricted to motherhood. This assertiveness is not always welcomed by men who may feel threatened by educated, self-determined women. The small representation of elderly in these studies can be explained by their shorter life span in underdeveloped countries; and by the fundamental, ingrained Islamic teaching that the young should have absolute respect for old people and have a duty to provide for them. The elderly may even be considered a blessing for the family (El-Sendiony, 1981).

Hysterical conversion appears to be quite prevalent in Saudi Arabia, in keeping with the general finding that this disorder has a higher prevalence in developing than in industrialized societies (Neki, 1973; Chandrasena, 1979; Hafeiz, 1980; Okasha, 1986). It is seen mainly in general hospital emergency rooms and on medical wards. The presentation is usually that of a dramatic and acute loss of sensorimotor function. Aphonia, paralyses, blindness, fainting attacks, epileptic-like fits, or excitement are not uncommon. Patients are usually accompanied by concerned family members who are also in a highly emotional state. The management (kind reassurance of the patient and relatives, suggestion, and administration of parenteral anxiolytics) often leads to a cure as dramatic as the onset of the disorder.

Several papers have called attention to the high prevalence of social phobias in Saudis (Chaleby, 1987a; Chaleby and Raslan, 1990; Al-Khani and Arafah, 1990; Al-Khodair, 1992). According to Chaleby (1987a) social phobia constituted 13 percent of the neurotic disorders in his clinical population (compared to 2% in Western literature). These studies found the disorder to be most prevalent among young, unmarried males with relatively high educational and occupational levels. The presentation was usually of complaints of shyness, fear, and high sympathetic arousal, accompanied by excessive avoidance of certain situations where the person felt under scrutiny (e.g., speaking, eating, or performing in public). Overt criticism, limited privacy, and the attribution of exaggerated importance to appearance and judgment on first impression are all highly characteristic social features of Saudi Arabian culture. Deviation from rigid social codes and highly valued customs can be detrimental to vulnerable individuals. These social rules are applicable even to everyday situations such as talking to others (where one has to choose words according to the interlocutor's age, sex, and social status) or merely greeting people (asking about the health of every member of the family, naming males and referring to females using symbolic language) (Chaleby, 1987a). The low incidence of social phobia in women was felt to be due to the fact that Saudi women are protected from exposure to these anxiety-inducing male social situations; women's gatherings are largely recreational with a minimum of rituals.

Obsessive–compulsive disorder commonly presents with religious themes and compulsions in Saudi Arabia (Mahgoub and Abdel-Hafeiz, 1991; Al-Subaie et al., 1992). There were no reports of panic disorder and agoraphobia although they are often seen in practice.

Schizophrenia tends to cluster in families in Saudi Arabia (due to consanguinity according to Chaleby [1987b]) supporting the genetic hypothesis of this disorder. As expected in developing countries, catatonic states are quite common. This increased prevalence has been explained on the basis of culture, the small number of psychiatrists, or public ignorance which leads to delay in seeking help until the disorder becomes severe or life threatening (Chandrasena, 1986). Mutism, stupor, and psychomotor retardation are more common than excitement. Psychomotor retardation may not be recognized as a mental illness, thus delaying treatment, whereas excitement may be interpreted in cultural terms as demonic possession, to be treated by traditional healers. This is similar to a pattern noted in India (Govindasamy, 1958).

Until recently there has been no mention of eating disorders in published literature about psychiatric epidemiology in Saudi Arabia. This most likely reflects their true rarity. Saudi culture does not draw attention to the female figure and discourages public display of the female body. Thinness has been traditionally equated with poverty or ill health and people continue to consider mild obesity as a sign of wealth and health. Among primary care patients, 36.4 percent of Saudis were overweight and most of them were females (Al-Shammari, Khojah, and Al-Subaie, 1994). Al-Subaie (Al-Subaie, Bamgboye, Al-Shammari, Al-Sabhan, Al-Shehri, and Bannah, 1996a,b) surveyed female students between the ages of 11 and 20 in Riyadh (the capital of Saudi Arabia) using the Eating Attitudes Test (EAT-26) and the Eating Disorders Inventory (EDI) and found the proportion of positive cases of eating disorders to be 1 percent.

Guilt feelings are uncommon in Saudi Arabia. Like Christianity and Judaism (but unlike Buddhism, Hinduism, and the African religions), Islam stresses the idea of sin, and therefore, contrary to transcultural interpretations such as the one by Murphy, Wittkower, and Chance (1967), the lower incidence of guilt feelings in Saudi Arabia cannot be attributed to such global religious differences. Nevertheless, Islam has a somewhat different view of sin, penitence, and forgiveness than Christianity and Judaism. In Islam sin is any act, thought, or desire that is deliberate, defies the unequivocal law of God, violates the rights of God or the rights of other people, is harmful to the soul or the body, is committed repeatedly, and is normally avoidable. Sin is neither innate nor hereditary, since according to the Qur'an and the prophetic tradition, man is born in a natural state of purity. Whatever occurs after birth is the result of external influences. Penitence therefore demands complete abstinence from sinful behavior and asking God's forgiveness, which is believed to be always available if these conditions are met (Hammudah, 1975).

Affective psychosis was the most common diagnosis among inpatients and depression was most prevalent in middle-aged housewives (El-Esra, and Amin, 1988). Also affective disorders were about 66 percent of the postpartum psychosis according to Shoeb and Hassan (1990) and 77 percent according to Rahim and Al-Subaie (1991). Compared to a similar British sample, more Saudi patients in this study were multiparous, sought help later, and presented with motility disorders (Rahim and Al-Subaie, 1991). Among primary care patients, depression was more common among divorced or widowed females under 25 years of age (Al-Shammari, Khojah, and Al-Subaie, 1993). Suicidal behavior and deliberate self-harm are rare in Saudi Arabia. Mahgoub, Al-Freihi, Al-Myhaya, and Al-Nahdi (1988) and Malik, Bilal, Mekki, and Kinani (1996) found the majority of parasuicidal patients to be young single females who impulsively overdosed after an interpersonal conflict. These findings were replicated by Daradkeh and Al-Zayer (1988) despite the fact the study sample was drawn from an industrial community which may not be representative of the Saudi population. Since suicide is considered an unforgivable sin, asking about death wishes is about the only way to assess a potentially suicidal patient without offending him.

Alcohol and drug abuse are relatively uncommon. This may be explained by strict recent Saudi legislation which made smuggling or trafficking in drugs punishable by death, and also by the strong Islamic attitude which forbids all mind-altering substances. This stricture, of course, does not include psychotropic medications used to treat "disturbed minds." Islam in its early days dealt with alcohol in four stages over a few years. The first revelation of the Holy Qur'an in this regard addressed itself to the sense and good judgment of people in Mecca, making a distinction between strong drink and good nourishment. After this alerting verse and in response to a question put to the Prophet, came the second revelation that there was more sin than benefit in using alcohol. At this stage, the decision to abstain was left to the individual. The third verse of the Qur'an partially forbidding alcohol and demanding sobriety during prayers (the second pillar of Islam) was revealed in Medina. Since prayers are performed by Muslims five times a day, many had to substantially reduce or give up their drinking. Finally came the fourth verse, calling upon people to completely abstain from alcohol. According to the tradition of the Prophet, it is not only the drinker of alcohol who is cursed but also whoever brews its, carries it, sells it, buys it, and to whom it is brought (Baasher, 1981). The most commonly abused substances are opiates and alcohol, and the typical abuser is a young male (Osman, 1992).

Violent destructive behavior, adultery, and paraphilia are forbidden by Islamic law and are highly stigmatized in Saudi society. These behaviors are dealt with by the criminal code, which may partly explain their underrepresentation in psychiatric practice. Male homosexuality is said to be common (Dubovsky, 1983). However, Western observers may be likely to mistake the socially acceptable modes of physical expression of warmth and friendship (e.g., males holding hands and kissing in public) as homosexuality (Racy, 1970; El-Gaaly, 1984). Acknowledging that homosexuality exists in many cultures, in Saudi Arabia it is stigmatized by people, forbidden by religion, and punishable by law. Nevertheless, it is recognized by mental health workers as an illness and treatment is offered to motivated individuals with ego-dystonic homosexuality.

Psychosomatic disorders, although fairly common, are considered by both patients and physicians as purely physical, ignoring their sometimes clear psychosocial basis. Somatization disorder is fairly common, especially in lower social class patients and women (Racy, 1980). The most common systems involved are the gastrointestinal, cardiovascular, and central nervous systems. Psychiatric consultations are sought mostly to help in the differential diagnosis of cases lacking organic physical etiology.

The Saudi family is a closed system with rigid boundaries, rendering any form of family or group therapy (except perhaps educative types) extremely difficult. However, if these treatment modalities can be presented in a way that is perceived as supportive of the traditional Saudi family's worldview, it may become more acceptable (Di Nicola, 1985). The extended family has lost some of its functions through the transformation of the society. Some researchers have suggested that while offering the advantage of protection to its members, the cohesion and closeness of the extended family increases the individual's sensitivity to the discord which is endemic in large family systems (Chaleby, 1986). This is especially true for women who, while becoming more educated and cognizant of their rights and roles, more often report marital and family stresses as contributing to their symptoms (Chaleby, 1986). Al-Khani, Bebbington, Watson, and House (1986) found the rate of life events among Saudi married schizophrenic females to be significantly higher than for female controls or any other group in his study.

Current Problems and Future Trends

There are very few native Saudi consultant psychiatrists in the country. However, the importance of this field has tempted new graduates to choose psychiatry as a career, either taking the local programs or studying abroad. With the number of medical school graduates expected to increase to just over 600 in the next few years, more will be selecting psychiatry as their career choice. Unfortunately, the implications of Saudi doctors training in other cultures and then returning home to practice medicine in general and psychiatry in particular have not been studied. Chaleby (1992) called attention to the problems of applying psychotherapeutic concepts derived from Western models of thinking to Arab patients and illustrated the need to modify it to fit the Arab cultural model (see chapter 12). Such modification was suggested by Al-Subaie and Al-Hajjaj (1995) with regard to treatment of substance abuse and dependence. Despite financial incentives and availability of appropriate equipment, there is still a severe shortage of paramedical mental health workers such as clinical psychologists, psychiatric social workers, and specialized nurses.

Child psychiatry services are poorly developed in Saudi Arabia and there are only two or three child psychiatrists in the country. Children are seldom seen at psychiatric facilities, due in part to the public's (including teachers') ignorance of children's feelings and deviant behavior (especially in younger age groups) and the complete separation of the educational and health systems. Only severe types of children's mental illnesses are recognized, treated, and followed up by special educators in specialized schools. Otherwise, mildly or moderately disturbed children may have to suffer repeated failure and humiliation within the regular school system. According to Abdul-Rahim, Al-Hamad, Chaleby, and Al-Subaie (1996), conduct disorders were underrepresented in the clinic population whereas mental retardation, attention deficit hyperactivity disorder, conversion, and obsessive–compulsive disorders were overrepresented. Forty-six percent of the subjects were first referred to faith healers, and the referral rate from pediatricians was only 0.6 percent compared to 22 percent in Western literature.

El-Ghamdi (1984) found that 88 percent of the institutionalized juvenile delinquents in his study (29 boys) came from Saudi cities, compared to a much smaller proportion of nomads or rural inhabitants. Twenty-four percent of his total sample were institutionalized for "drunkenness," many of whom were likely to be "young people who were merely on a brief drinking spree and had fallen foul of the police in a culture highly intolerant of inebriety" (El-Sendiony, 1986). Although parents infrequently use physical discipline, it is sometimes hard to draw a line between it and the rarely reported child abuse, which is considered a punishable crime under Saudi Arabian law (Al-Eissa, 1991).

Individual efforts in the standardization of psychological measurements have been carried out in Saudi Arabia (West, and Al-Kaisi, 1982; El-Rufaie and Absood, 1987; Al-Subaie et al., 1996a,b). In order to conduct culturally valid research using Western research instruments, careful translations must be made with recognition of the grave difficulties in arriving at meaning equivalence. Further studies on pharmacotherapy and the dose-response profiles of psychoactive drugs are needed as suggested by Conacher, Marazki, and Evans (1987), who found that Saudi schizophrenic patients treated with haloperidol tended to have a higher incidence of acute dystonic reactions compared to Western patients.

Public awareness of mental health is of paramount importance in reducing the stigma associated with it, especially in this impressionistic, judgmental society. Mental health education should be conducted by knowledgeable staff using the media to introduce available services and to educate the public. Although there is no antipsychiatry movement, there are occasional articles about the harmful effects of medications and electroconvulsive therapy (ECT) (even though this later is administered by the most modern methods and equipment). This is a very sensitive area for Saudi patients who consider any self-inflicted or voluntarily accepted self-harm as sinful. For the overwhelming majority of patients, the therapist needs to demonstrate both knowledge of and respect for their religious beliefs and values to be therapeutically effective. An example of this kind of problem is a patient insisting on fasting during the month of Ramadan (the fasting month for Muslims) and discontinuing his lithium as part of the fast. The psychiatrist must be knowledgeable about general medicine and able to provide concrete, practical discussions which are applicable to the kind of short-term treatment of patients that is familiar to the nonpsychiatric physician (Dubovsky, 1983).

Some liaison between physicians in private practice and health services in general is still lacking in Saudi Arabia, which increases the load on the few already busy psychiatrists and hence reduces the quality of follow-up. The important role of the extended family in providing support to their mentally ill members is made obvious by the high percentage of patients brought to the emergency room by their relatives (El-Gaaly, 1987; Al-Subaie, Marwah, Hawari, and Rahim, 1996), and the reliance of the mental health system of postdischarge care by the family.

Pasnau and Hartmann (1983) posed several questions regarding the implications for potential abuse of psychiatry inherent in the absence of mental health laws and suggested the possibility of finding ways to help in the development of new legal guidelines in the context of traditional Islamic law and customs in Saudi Arabia. This could be possible in the foreseeable future under the current Islamic resurgence movements and concurrent trends toward the Islamization of science. The concept of Islamization refers to basing knowledge on an Islamic foundation and purging it of any atheistic, materialistic philosophy and abiding by Islamic values in the search for knowledge, choice of fields of research and the use to be made of the purified knowledge generated thereby (Sheikh Idris, 1987). As suggested by Ba-Yunus (1988), these efforts have to include three areas: Islamization of the educational system at all levels; mobilizing parents in order to mobilize students; constructing research projects aimed at analyzing community problems and seeking their solutions; and involving non-Muslims in these endeavors to propagate Islam and share knowledge with the rest of the world.

REFERENCES

Abdul-Rahim, F. E., Al-Hamad, A., Chaleby, K., & Al-Subaie, A. (1996), A survey of a child psychiatric clinic in a teaching hospital in Saudi Arabia: Clinical profile and cross-cultural comparison. *Saudi Med. J.*, 17:36–41.

Akram Bhatty, M., Al-Sibai, H., & Quorain, A. (1986), The promotion and development of Islamic traditional medicine. *Saudi Med. J.*, 24:41–46.

Baasher, T. (1981), The use of drugs in the Islamic world. *Brit. J. Addiction*, 76:233–243.

Basalamah, A., Rosinski, E., & Schumacher, H. (1979), Developing the medical curriculum at King Abdulaziz University. *J. Med. Ed.*, 54:96–100.

Ba-Yunus, I. (1988), Al-Faruqi and beyond: Future directions in Islamization of knowledge. *Amer. J. Islamic Soc. Sci.*, 5:13–28.

Camp, J. (1978), *The Healer's Art. The Doctor Through History.* London: Frederick Muller.

Chaleby, K. (1986), Psychosocial stresses and psychiatric disorders in an outpatient population of Saudis. *Acta Psychiatr. Scand.*, 73:147–151.

——— (1987a), Social phobia in Saudis. *Soc. Psychiatry*, 22:167–170.

——— (1987b), Cousin marriages and schizophrenia in Saudi Arabia. *Brit. J. Psychiatry*, 150:547–549.

——— (1992), Psychotherapy with Arab patients: Toward a culturally oriented technique. *Arab J. Psychiatry*, 3:10–27.

—————— Raslan, A. (1990), Delineation of social phobia in Saudi Arabians. *Soc. Psychiatry & Psychiatr. Epidemiol.*, 25:324–327.

Chandrasena, R. (1979), Psychiatry in Sri Lanka: An overview. *Brit. J. Psychiatry Bull.*, July:119–121.

—————— (1986), Catatonic schizophrenia: An international comparative study. *Can. J. Psychiatry*, 31:249–252.

Conacher, G., Marazki, M., & Evans, D. (1987), Acute dystonic reactions in Saudi Arabian psychiatric patients treated with Haloperidol. *Acta Psychiatr. Scand.*, 75:333–334.

Daradkeh, K., & Al-Zayer, N. (1988), Parasuicide in an Arab industrial community: The Arabian American Oil Company experience. *Acta Psychiatr. Scand.*, 77:707–711.

Di Nicola, V. F. (1985), Family therapy and transcultural psychiatry: An emerging synthesis, Part II: Portability and culture change. *Transcult. Psychiatric Res. Rev.*, 22:151–180.

Dubovsky, S. (1983), Psychiatry in Saudi Arabia. *Amer. J. Psychiatry*, 140:1455–1459.

Al-Eissa, Y. (1991), Battered child syndrome: Does it exist in Saudi Arabia? *Saudi Med. J.*, 12:129–133.

El-Esra, A., & Amin, A. (1988), Hospital admissions in a psychiatric division in Saudi Arabia. *Saudi Med. J.*, 9:25–30.

El-Gaaly, A. (1984), More on psychiatry in Saudi Arabia. *Amer. J. Psychiatry*, 141:1020.

—————— (1987), Psychiatric emergencies at King Khalid University Hospital. *Saudi Med. J.*, 8:382–386.

El-Ghamdi, H. (1984), *The Dynamic Forces in Personality of Juvenile Delinquents in the Saudi Arabian Environment.* M. A. Thesis, Department of Psychology, University of Ummal-Qura, Mecca, Saudi Arabia (in Arabic).

Govindasamy, G. (1958), Cultural aspects of psychiatric illness. *All India Instit. Ment. Health*, 1:2.

Hafeiz, H. (1980), Hysterical conversion: A prognostic study. *Brit. J. Psychiatry*, 136:548–551.

Hammudah, A. (1975), *Islam in Focus.* Washington, DC: American Trust Publication.

—————— (1977), *The Family Structure in Islam.* Washington, DC: American Trust Publication.

Hussein, F. (1989), A study of the role of unorthodox treatments of psychiatric illnesses. *Arab J. Psychiatry*, 2:170–184.

Ibn-Baz, A. (1987), Iydah Al-Hak. *Al-Mujtama'a Mag.*, 8:39–41 (in Arabic).

El-Islam, M. F. (1976), Inter-generational conflict and young Qatari neurotics. *Ethos*, 76:45–56.

—————— (1982), Arab cultural psychiatry. *Transcul. Psychiatric Res. Rev.*, 19:15–24.

—————— (1983), Cultural changes and inter-generational relationships in Arabian families. *Internat. J. Fam. Psychiatry*, 4:321–329.

—————— Abu-Dagga, S., Malasi, T., & Moussa, M. (1986), Inter-generational conflict and psychiatric syndromes. *Brit. J. Psychiatry*, 149:300–306.

Al-Khani, M., & Arafah, M. (1990), Social phobia in Saudi patients: A preliminary assessment of prevalence and demographic characteristics. *Annals Saudi Med.*, 10:615–619.

—————— Bebbington, P., Watson, J., & House, F. (1986), Life events and schizophrenia: A Saudi Arabian study. *Brit. J. Psychiatry*, 148:12–22.

Al-Khodair, I. (1992), *Cross-cultural Study of Social Phobia in Saudi Arabia and Scotland.* Edinburgh, Scotland: University of Edinburgh.

Al-Moudodi Abul-Al'a, Muazzam, M. G., & Muazzam, N. (1989), Important contributions of early Moslem period of medical sciences: II Clinical sciences. *J. Islamic Med. Assn.*, 21:64–79.

Mahgoub, O. M. & Abdel-Hafeiz, H. B. (1991), Pattern of obsessive–compulsive disorder in Eastern Saudi Arabia. *Brit. J. Psychiatry*, 158:846–842.

—————— Al-Freihi, H., Al-Myhaya, S., & Al-Nahdi, M. (1988), Deliberate self-harm in the Eastern region of Saudi Arabia: A hospital based study. *Ann. Saudi Med.*, 8:126–130.

Malik, G., Bilal, A., Mekki, T., & Kinani, H. (1996), Drug overdose in the Assir region of Saudi Arabia. *Ann. Saudi Med.*, 16:33–36.

Ministry of Health, Saudi Arabia. (1983), *Annual Health Report.* Riyadh, Saudi Arabia: Al-Farazdak Press.

—————— (1984), *Taif Mental Hospital.* Jeddah, Saudi Arabia: Al-Asfahani Press.

—————— (1985), *Annual Health Report.* Riyadh, Saudi Arabia: Al-Farazdak Press.

—————— (1986a), *Annual Health Report.* Riyadh, Saudi Arabia: Al-Farazdak Press.

—————— (1986b), *Primary Health Care: Manual for Health Centers Personnel.* Riyadh, Saudi Arabia: Addereyah Press.

—————— (1988), *Riyadh Mental Hospital.* Riyadh, Saudi Arabia: The National Guard Press.

—————— (1990), *Annual Health Report.* Riyadh, Saudi Arabia: Al-Farazdak Press.

—————— (1994), *Annual Health Report.* Riyadh, Saudi Arabia: Al-Farazdak Press.

—— (1996), *National Manual For Primary Mental Health Care. General Directorate of Health Centers*. Riyadh, Saudi Arabia: MOH.

Murphy, H. B. M., Wittkower, E., & Chance, N. (1967), A cross-cultural inquiry into the symptomatology of depression. *Internat. J. Psychiatry*, 3:6–15.

Neki, J. (1973), Psychiatry in South East Asia. *Brit. J. Psychiatry*, 123:257–269.

Oesterreich, T. K. (1966), *Possession: Demoniacal and Other among Primitive Races, in Antiquity, the Middle Ages and Modern Times*. New York: University Books.

Okasha, A. (1986), Preliminary psychiatric observations in Egypt. *Brit. J. Psychiatry*, 114:629–637.

Osman, A. (1992), Substance abuse among patients attending a psychiatric hospital in Jeddah: A descriptive study. *Ann. Saudi Med.*, 12:289–293.

Pasnau, R., & Hartmann, L. (1983), Psychiatry in the Kingdom of Saudi Arabia. *Amer. J. Psychiatry*, 140:1493–1494.

Prince, R. (1980), Variations in psychotherapeutic procedures. In: *Handbook of Cross-Cultural Psychology*, Vol. 6, ed. H. C. Triandis & J. G. Draguns. Boston: Allyn & Bacon, pp. 291–349.

Racy, J. (1970), Psychiatry in the Arab East. *Acta Psychiatr. Scand.*, (Suppl.) 211.

—— (1980), Somatization in Saudi women: A therapeutic challenge. *Brit. J. Psychiatry*, 137:212–216.

Rahim, F. E., & Al-Subaie, A. (1991), Puerperal psychosis in a teaching hospital in Saudi Arabia: Clinical profile and cross-cultural comparison. *Acta Psychiat. Scand.*, 84:508–511.

Royal College of Psychiatrists. (1988), *Psychiatric Beds and Resources: Report of a Working Party of the Section for Social and Community Psychiatry*. Gaskell, U.K.

El-Rufaie, O. (1988), A psychiatric clinic in a primary care setting: Evaluating the experience. *Saudi Med. J.*, 9:20–24.

—— Absood, G. (1987), Validity study of the hospital anxiety and depression scale among a group of Saudi patients. *Brit. J. Psychiatry*, 151:687–688.

El-Sayed, S., Maghraby, H., Hafeiz, H., & Buckley, M. (1986), Psychiatric diagnosis categories in Saudi Arabia. *Acta Psychiatr. Scand.*, 74:553–554.

El-Sendiony, M. (1981), The effect of Islamic Sharia on behavioral disturbance in the Kingdom of Saudi Arabia. Mecca (Saudi Arabia): Mecca Printing and Publishing.

——— (1986), Book review: *The Dynamic Forces in the Personalities of Juvenile Delinquents in the Saudi Arabia Environment*, by H. A. Al-Ghamdi. *Transcult. Psychiatric Res. Rev.*, 23:248–150.

Shahine, Y. A. (1978), *The Arab Contribution to Medicine*. London: Longman for the University of Essex, pp. 1–4.

Al-Shammari, S., Khojah, T., & Al-Subaie, A. (1993), Anxiety and depression among primary care patients in Riyadh. *Internat. J. Ment. Health*, 22:53–64.

——— ——— ——— (1994), Transcultural attitudes towards being overweight in patients attending health centers in Riyadh, Saudi Arabia. *Fam. Pract. Res. J.*, 14:149–156.

Sheikh Idris, J. (1987), Islamization of sciences, its philosophy and methodology. *Amer. J. Islamic Soc. Sci.*, 4:201–208.

Shoeb, I., & Hassan, G. (1990), Postpartum psychosis in the Assir region of Saudi Arabia. *Brit. J. Psychiatry*, 157:427–430.

Al-Subaie, A. (1989), Psychiatry in Saudi Arabia: Cultural perspectives. *Transcult. Psychiatric Res. Rev.*, 26:245–262.

——— (1994), Traditional healing experiences in patients attending a university outpatient clinic. *Arab J. Psychiatry*, 5:83–91.

——— Al-Hajjaj, M. (1995), Awareness and knowledge of Saudi university students about drug dependence. *Saudi Med. J.*, 16:326–329.

——— Marwah, M. K., Hawari, R., & Rahim, F. E. (1996), Psychiatric emergencies in a university hospital in Riyadh, Saudi Arabia. *Inter. J. Ment. Health*, 25:59–68.

——— Bamgboye, E., Al-Shammari, S., Al-Sabhan, K., Al-Shehri, S., & Bannah, A. (1996a), Validity of the Arabic version of the eating disorders inventory (EDI). *Brit. J. Psychiatry*, 168:636–640.

——— ——— ——— ——— ——— (1996b), Validity of the Eating Attitudes Test (EAT-26) in Arabic. *Internat. J. Eat. Disord.*, 22:53–64.

West, J., & Al-Kaisi, H. (1982), Depression Scale for Arabs. *Proceedings for the Seventh Saudi Medical Meeting. Dammam* (Saudi Arabia): College of Medicine and Medical Sciences, King Faisal University.

World Health Organization. (1978), *Primary Health Care*. Joint report of the WHO & UN in Alma Ata, USSR. Geneva: WHO.

Al-Yahya, F. (1991), Saudi Arabia: Acknowledging problems in a transitional culture. In: *Mental Health Services in the Global Village*, ed. A. Appleby & A. Arya. Royal College of Psychiatrists, Gaskell, London.

10.

Anxiety Disorders and Treatment in Arab–Muslim Culture

Adnan Takriti, Tayseer Ahmad

Anxiety is a universal human experience, but its content and meaning tend to vary from one culture to another (Al-Issa and Oudji, 1998). Muslim societies are not immune from anxiety disorders, but as Marks (1978) pointed out, belief systems may play a vital role in determining how people view these disorders and their treatment. The Arab–Islamic culture with its concepts, beliefs, and practices may have both positive and negative effects on the development, perpetuation, and outcome of the illness.

Similar to people in other cultures, Muslim populations are influenced by many factors such as child rearing practices, intergenerational conflicts, and Westernization, and thus, anxiety disorders in Muslim societies are expected to be influenced by these factors as well as by Muslim religious beliefs.

This chapter discusses the influence of the Arab–Muslim culture on the main types of anxiety disorders, including their development and treatment. Since psychiatrists in the Arab–Muslim countries use the American (DSM-IV, APA, 1994) and the international (ICD-10, WHO, 1992) classification of mental disorders, we will follow the same systems in the organization of this chapter. Thus, we deal with the influence of Islamic culture on different types of anxiety disorders including panic disorder, agoraphobia, social phobia, specific phobia, obsessive–compulsive disorder, and generalized anxiety disorder. We also discuss the use of drug treatment and group therapy with Muslim patients for anxiety disorders as well as other types of mental illness.

THE PREVALENCE OF ANXIETY DISORDERS IN ARAB–MUSLIM COUNTRIES

Few epidemiological studies have been conducted in Arab countries using proper methodology in patient or nonpatient groups representing specific populations. This could be due to many limitations such as lack of awareness of the problem, poor psychosocial education of population, uncooperative subjects who avoid participation in such studies so as to avoid social stigma, and lack of collaboration among Arab–Muslim psychiatrists and psychologists. Most of the studies that have been conducted are based on data either from psychiatric hospitals or outpatient clinics, in addition to fewer studies from primary health sources. These data cannot accurately represent the whole psychiatric population, since no community studies have been available. A parallel population has been cared for by native healers due to reluctance of the family to refer their patients to a psychiatrist. Furthermore, many anxiety disorder patients have been cared for in primary health care (Suleiman and Ahmad, 1993; Al-Subaie, 1994) and by medical specialists. Yet, a few studies of anxiety disorders may provide some indication about the rates of anxiety disorders. In Egypt a survey of 1,000 psychiatric outpatients (Okasha, Kamel, and Hassan, 1968) found that anxiety disorder patients totaled 25.2 percent, with obsessive patients representing 2.6 percent. In Jordan, Takriti and Ahmad (1992) studied 570 patients diagnosed with anxiety disorders according to DSM-III-R. These diagnoses comprised of panic disorder 132 (23%); panic with agoraphobia 18 (3%); social phobia 29 (5%); simple phobia 58 (10%);

OCD patients 75 (13%); and a majority with generalized anxiety disorder 258 (45%). These results are consistent with Western studies. Arafa, Al-Khani, Hamdi, Amean, El Defrawi, and Moussa (1988) in a study of the prevalence of anxiety disorders among a group of psychiatric patients in Saudi Arabia, found that social phobia comprised about 80 percent of phobic disorders, 20 percent of neurotic disorders, and 9 percent of all psychiatric disorders. Chaleby (1987) found that social phobias represented 13 percent among a Saudi outpatient population. In contrast, Takriti and Ahmad (1992) found that social phobia represented only 5 percent of the anxiety disorders in Jordan. Al-Issa and Oudji (1998) reviewed studies in non-Western countries which supported the universality of anxiety. For example, Good and Kleinman (1985) and Murphy (1982) reported population surveys of anxiety in urban and rural settings in different countries such as Ethiopia, Iran, and India in the 1960s and 1970s indicating rates ranging between 1 and 3 percent. Although some studies conducted in the West and the United States as in other cultures showed various rates of prevalence of anxiety disorders, they tended to agree on the universality of anxiety disorders.

OBSESSIVE–COMPULSIVE DISORDER (OCD) IN ARAB–ISLAMIC CULTURE

Obsessive–compulsive disorder in Islamic and Arab culture is not different in form but in content from the West; obsessional thoughts and rituals are modified by the Islamic culture.

The word *waswās, obsession* in English, is mentioned in Qur'anic verses as equivalent to *sheytan* (devil) which bears a negative connotation. Thus, *waswās* may create anxiety in patients based on the belief that they might be haunted by an evil spirit. This idea may be suggested to the patient by the faith healer. Moreover, a belief in *waswās* and its meaning is common knowledge to all Muslims. In Saudi Arabia Mahgoub and Abdel-Hafeiz (1991) studied 32 obsessive–compulsive disorder patients and found that religious themes were predominant in 50 percent of compulsive acts and obsessive thoughts.

In Egypt, Okasha, Saad, Khalil, El-Dawla, and Yehia (1994) found that the most common obsessions were religious and associated with contamination (60%). Religious rituals represented 68 percent of the symptoms of females in Qatar (El-Islam, 1994). Among these female patients, El-Islam found that obsessional fears revolved around failure to control devil-induced impulses to harm the self or others. These religious themes seem to be more frequent among Muslim OCD patients than among Hindu patients studied by Akhtar, Wig, Varma, Pershad, and Verma (1975) and are almost absent among Western patients (chapter 14, this volume). Takriti and Ahmad (in press) studied 90 OCD patients and found that 30 percent of the content of their ideas are of a religious nature related to God, the Prophet, and other Islamic themes. Obsessional ideations are usually incompatible with their Islamic belief system (e.g., abusive, disbelieving, scorning, and belittling) which creates severe guilt feelings. For instance casting tremendous doubts about the presence of God, and obscene ideas (e.g., religious beliefs associated with inappropriate sexual themes) are expressed whenever religious practices are performed (reading or listening to the Qur'an or praying). In the studies by Okasha, Rafat, Al-Dawla, and Effat (1991) and Takriti and Ahmad (1996), it was found that young single females show obsessional fear of losing their virginity. Females who touch or use objects related to males develop fear of pregnancy and fear of contamination with sperm. This group constitutes 10 percent of a sample of 62 OCD patients in this study. In Arab–Muslim culture virginity is valued and intersex mixing is not socially acceptable. Unmarried girls are expected to be virgins in this culture even among non-Muslim females.

Okasha et al. (1991) studied 84 Egyptian obsessional patients who were followed up for five years. They found urban–rural differences in symptomatology, with ideas, ruminations, and fears more common in urban populations, and impulses predominating in patients coming from rural areas. Also, the study supports the idea that obsessional patients tended to receive a strict and puritannical upbringing with much emphasis on obedience and cleanliness among those patients with predominantly religious impulses and cleaning rituals. Fundamental Muslims consider repeating the ablution or *wadoow* rituals necessary after touching or shaking hands with the opposite sex or being in contact with a dog. The female is considered unclean during and after menstruation and therefore cannot pray or read the Qur'an or have marital relationships except after having a bath (see also Chapter 5, this volume). These represent a source of obsessional rituals. Because of fear of sin, some patients develop compulsions during the performance of *wadoow* and prayer. This leads them to doubt that they have carried out the assigned *wadoow* and performed the prayer accurately. Such doubts might have different interpretations in different patients; for example, some fear contamination with urine, impure water, or dirt. Islamic teaching tells not to repeat more than the assigned number of washings; consequently such rituals with religious content are necessarily considered morbid behavior. The aim behind *wadoow* is to be physically clean and to monitor and control yourself, therefore the therapist should have a good knowledge of Islamic teaching related to worship. Ignorance about Islamic teaching will lead the therapist to misinterpret the behavior of OCD patients and thus interfere with their evaluation and management. Although the thought content of patients who develop the disorder are related to religious practices, this does not imply that Islamic beliefs reinforce the evolution of OCD. The effects of religion on OCD seem to be pathoplastic rather than causative.

SOCIAL PHOBIA IN ARAB–ISLAMIC CULTURE

Studies cited earlier show that social phobia is one of the most common phobic disorders in many Islamic countries. Social phobia requires management, since other types of phobias such as agoraphobia are not considered seriously by the population. Arafa et al. (1992) attempted to explain the prevalence of social phobia in terms of various sociocultural factors such as strict rearing with a strong demand for conformity to general rules, that extends to minor social activities, including how to address others and how to behave (standing and sitting) according to social status, age, and sex. Chaleby (1990) found that 53 percent of socially phobic patients had a distant and abusive father who humiliated them. El-Islam (1982) suggested that the socialization of patients with social phobia is characterized by the cultivation of shame rather than guilt, and the enhancement of conformity and fear of others' criticism rather than individuality and self-criticism, resulting in sensitivity to disapproval and criticism. This will reduce the social learning process and thus the child will become socially inhibited. Both the cognitive and behavioral aspects of social learning are negatively influenced by strict socialization.

Also in Saudi society and other Arab or Muslim countries rapid socioeconomic and developmental changes have resulted in urbanization and upward social mobility. A large sector of the population has moved from Bedouin and rural areas to cities, with families being subjected to higher sociocultural stressors. Other cultural influences are related to social relationships with the opposite sex. In Islam mixing of the sexes is prohibited between those adult males and females who are not *mahram*, or not close relatives but strangers. Sex is only allowed between males and the females after marriage. For females mixing results in stigmatization and feelings of guilt because the woman has broken a taboo. Westernization in Muslim countries and exposure to Western values of integration of the sexes cause intergenerational conflicts between parents who are committed to their religious beliefs and their children who are under Western influences. The disciplinary measures by parents and the attitudinal differences between parents and children create an anxiety reaction, possibly social phobia, related to the opposite sex. Social phobia in Islamic culture is highlighted by male–female isolation. Islamic teachings prohibit free social contact between the sexes, favoring the shy, obedient, and reticent female in social settings. Since Islamic intersex mixing is not advised before marriage, young people are urged to marry as early as possible. Young adults who stay single might be subjected to long-term social stressors. Nonassertive behavior may be the result of a conflict related to the integration of the sexes, where both males and females are challenged to express themselves in the presence of the opposite sex.

A study of Takriti (1987) of 35 socially phobic patients (8 females and 27 males) found two distinct prototypes. The first prototype consisted of two subgroups. One group is of young patients who have been raised by an authoritarian parent, mainly the father, who could not let them express themselves and punished them for any effort to do so. The other subgroup have parents who absent themselves from family life and children who are left with an inadequate behavior repertoire. Both subgroups usually grow up to be shy and nonassertive with poor self-image, and thus develop social phobia more intensely as they grow up to meet the challenges of social and professional life. This group usually develops a poor verbal behavior repertoire, lack of self-confidence, poor self-image, and a negative expectation in social encounters with the opposite sex, due to lack of social skills. The other prototype of social phobics are those who have an adequate psychosocial background, grew up expressive and assertive, and have remained so even after they develop their phobia. Their phobia is usually a response to an experience of a traumatic social event leading to social avoidance. Cognitive behavior therapy tends to help the first type while gradual exposure therapy helps the second.

AGORAPHOBIA IN ARAB–ISLAMIC CULTURE

Agoraphobia is also influenced by cultural factors in Islamic society. Women are not encouraged to go outside the home but remain at home to raise children and run the household. In traditional Islamic society women are also not expected to go outside unescorted.

This type of behavior may mimic agoraphobic features in which the female becomes housebound. Leaving the home provokes anxiety, requiring an escort if she is forced to do so. However, in a traditional Islamic culture, the female is stigmatized and rebuked if she leaves the home frequently to visit neighbors or the market. The family may fear the stigma that a female outside of her home might be subjected to humiliation or to promiscuous behavior, as well being at the mercy of other unwanted events (Takriti, 1987).

CULTURE AND GENERALIZED ANXIETY

It is well known that generalized anxiety disorders may present themselves with somatic complaints (autonomic nervous system reactivity), and focus on one or more parts of the body such as backache, chest pain, and headache. Research in some Islamic countries confirms that these somatic features are more prevalent than in the West (Ahmad and Takriti, 1993; Suleiman and Ahmad, 1993). It is quite rare that a patient with GAD complains of psychological symptoms. The presentation of somatic symptoms may explain the tendency of patients to keep visiting their primary care physicians for physical investigations of their complaints, overlooking psychological disorders. Furthermore, such patients may have comorbidity with panic disorder and phobias, or mood disorder; yet they still visit their GP or other specialists, avoiding the stigma of mental illness. This trend is usually reinforced by doctors who serve to reduce their patients' anxiety related to psychiatric disorders. Visiting a psychiatrist is equated with madness and patients are hesitant to obtain psychiatric treatment (Ahmad and Takriti, 1993; Suleiman and Ahmad, 1993).

SPECIFIC PHOBIA IN ARAB–ISLAMIC CULTURE

Simple phobia is influenced by culture. Clinical observation suggests that different cultures have their own different kinds of phobia (spider phobia is more common in Western culture while in Arab–Muslim culture, dog phobia is more common). However, Marks reported that some specific phobias run in families and are especially associated with mothers and daughters by modeling within the family context. Some phobias are found to be common across different cultures such as fears of heights, death, and insanity (Marks, 1969). Clinical observation indicates that Arab–Muslim patients tend to suffer from the same common phobias known in other societies. However, it was noted that cat and dog phobias are common because the majority of cats and dogs are not domesticated and dogs are considered dirty animals. Also, death phobia is quite common due to strong bonds and family attachment which create more intense reactions to death and tend to exaggerate grief reactions. It was reported by Ahmad (1994) that about 10 percent of the patients referred for behavior therapy were diagnosed as having necrophobia as a result of accidents. During childhood some children develop a fear of dead bodies and generalize their fears to anything related to death or dead bodies such as coffins, funerals, and death ceremonies. Mothers may induce phobias in their children by telling them that the soul of a dead person who was the victim of injustice was still wandering and mourning in their house. This belief is known in rural Jordan as *Almfoul.* The impact of cultural influences on fear of dead bodies is also suggested by Hashim (1974). In Lebanese and Syrian culture it is common for people to exaggerate their responses to the death of a loved one or a friend. Such behavior is accepted and even respected in mourning the dead. El-Islam (1994) observed that many Muslims have a fear of death because in Islamic teaching we believe that the dead person will be judged by angels in the grave (grave torture) and subjected to hell-fire in their later postmortal life (see chapter 5, this volume). Fear of death is usually more severe at bedtime when sleep is actually regarded as a "micro" form of death that might extend into real death.

MANAGEMENT OF ANXIETY DISORDERS

The treatment modalities used in the Western culture, namely drug therapy and psychotherapeutic procedures, could be applied in Islamic societies. However, there are many sociocultural factors that might affect the selection, process and outcome of therapy.

Drug Therapy

Our clinical experience suggests that the recent advances in the drug treatment of anxiety disorders have contributed positively to their outcome in Muslim culture as they have in the

Western. However, there are many negative factors that may interfere with patient management. Patients are most commonly self-referred to the psychiatrist at a later stage of their disorder after being seen by faith healers. Al-Subaie (1994) found that 49 percent of the patients, mostly women, have been seen by native healers.

The cause of psychiatric problems including anxiety disorder is perceived to be related to supernatural events. Alsughayir (1996) studied 285 individuals from five areas of Riyadh City in Saudi Arabia, who mostly suffered from anxiety and mood disorders, and found that most people attributed their disorder to the evil eye or *jinni* (spirit) possession. Judgment of patients and faith healers with the absence of clear physical causes and a poor response to medical treatment were the main reasons to attribute certain psychiatric disorders to the evil eye. Most symptoms attributed to the evil eye were depression and anxiety. More males attributed injuries and sexual dysfunction to the evil eye, whereas more females attributed dermatological and menstrual disturbances to it. Similarly, in Egypt, Abdel-Gawad, Loutfi, and Rahman (1989) found that envy and the evil eye were reported as causes of mental illness by approximately 55 percent of patients' relatives. These beliefs among traditional Muslim populations tend to make them less willing to contact psychiatrists or comply with their prescribed medication.

Another major problem with drug treatment is the belief related to the stigma of taking psychotropics by the population at large regardless of social class. Also, the idea that all drugs which are used by psychiatrists are addictive and habit forming may impede treatment. Besides the concept that all psychotropics are sedating and cause diminished awareness, and even render the person abnormal in social and occupational settings, people also firmly believe that drugs have lasting negative side effects on physical well-being.

Drug treatment is further hindered by patient noncompliance. In addition to misconceptions about drugs (Zubie, Suleiman, Ahmad, Shobaki, and Shnaigat, 1996), patients tend to discontinue medications due to either initial improvement or the presence of initial side effects, which are exaggerated by the patient or the family. In conclusion, sociocultural factors have an impact on drug management of anxiety disorders by either utter refusal to take vital drugs that can assist in curing or mitigating the symptoms, or premature disruption of drug therapy. Psychological education to enhance compliance and to correct misconceptions is mandatory. Explanatory procedures and knowledge concerning the biological nature of the disorder and the ways that drugs work in the body may help. The interface between biological and psychological mechanisms in producing anxiety disorders must be explained to the patient.

INDIVIDUAL AND GROUP PSYCHOTHERAPY

Psychotherapy is a new concept in the Arab–Islamic culture (chapter 12, this volume; Mutlaq and Chaleby, 1995). Psychotherapy has been used by some Arab and Muslim psychiatrists and psychologists, but there has been a paucity of published literature regarding psychotherapy, especially for anxiety disorders. However, we observed that in the Arab–Muslim culture families have a positive impact upon patients by their encouragement and support during therapy. Family members might be taken into treatment by working as cotherapists in the treatment of anxiety disorders. For example, in cases of agoraphobia, exposure in vivo might involve a female family member for female patients to escort patients outdoors, so as to fulfill the cultural demand since they are not allowed to be accompanied by male therapists. A female cotherapist might also be a substitute therapist in situations where mixing with male therapists is completely forbidden. The same kind of modifications in the behavioral procedures and techniques do apply in the management of OCD where a female therapist can carry out the exposure treatments. Family members can act as cotherapists in the follow-up management and rehabilitation. Imaginal techniques can also be utilized, such as implosive therapy as a preparatory procedure, which proved to be suitable in Jordanian culture (Takriti, 1992).

Early attempts to use group psychotherapy within Arab cultures were made in the mid-1970s in Egypt by Rakhawi (1978) and Shaalan (1987) who were the first to use Western group psychotherapy. The Egyptian experience proved to be successful only after modification of their approach and recognition of the limitations of certain techniques. Rakhawi (1978) used an authoritarian directive approach similar to one used in individual psychotherapy with Muslims (see chapter 12, this volume). Issues are dealt with immediately on a here-and-now basis. Therapist personal opinion is usually a predominant factor in the therapy setting. The success of this approach is believed to result in its acceptance by patients and becomes more compatible with cultural norms. As noted by Al-Abdul-Jabbar and Al-Issa (chapter 12, this volume) the patriarchal structure model of interaction is emphasized and reenacted in the therapy. Similar to individual psychotherapy, using the nondirective approach and a permissive attitude toward having emotions expressed freely in the group is expected to lead to conflicts between patients in the group. These conflicts are difficult to resolve, and may end with angry withdrawal of some patients or may result in family problems such as a divorce. Nevertheless, group psychotherapy continues to be practiced with success with a careful selection of patient groups especially among the highly educated and students.

Mutlaq and Chaleby (1995) summarized the main problems related to Arab cultures in group psychotherapy.

Personal and intergroup conflicts. Most patients have difficulty in handling abstract ideas and differentiating between these ideas and the person who expresses them. That is, they tend to look for the personal motivation behind ideas expressed during the session. There is also a concern about the personality of the speaker.

Sensitivity to insight. As in individual psychotherapy, patients cannot cope with sudden insights into their inner conflict. At the same time they are acutely aware of and sensitive to other group members' opinions concerning themselves. Therapists therefore need to be extra sensitive to group members' interactions.

The tribal status in the Arab world. The tribal world culture has maintained its role and effect at different levels of society. Islam has a strong position against tribal attitudes. Nevertheless, these attitudes do still exist and exert their effect. An individual may not communicate on a deep or intimate personal level with an individual of different tribal status. With the recent modernization of Arab culture this issue is diminishing and does not constitute much of a problem in therapeutic groups. However, the therapist needs to be aware of the possibility that this conflict may arise.

Group stability. Group therapy is a new concept in Arab–Muslim culture, and thus its aims are still unclear for patients who often withdraw spontaneously, without notice from the group and are usually replaced by a continuous flow of new patients. Thus, the group is usually open to changes in its membership by necessity and not by choice.

Understanding the group setting. It is still difficult for many Arab–Muslim patients to perceive the group setting as therapeutic. Instead it is often viewed as a social activity, and this creates confusion and a low level of compliance with therapy. Also it represents a source of dissatisfaction for some patients, who may feel that they are not being well looked after or not being given proper treatment. Since the distinction between socialization and therapy is not very clear, patients frequently engage in social relations outside of the group. This is a common occurrence and tends to take place in spite of repeated instructions from the therapist to the contrary.

Privacy issues. Patients have little commitment to keep secrets concerning each other which results in personal gossip.

Society's view. Arab society in general views group therapy with caution. The concept of group therapy is not well understood within Arabic–Muslim culture, especially mixed sex groups may face much criticism.

CONCLUSION

Arab–Muslim culture has a certain impact on some aspects of anxiety disorders, particularly on its symptoms. There is a lack of epidemiological data that can be compared with those of other cultures. Studies have firmly established that culture influences the evolution, the content, and the management of anxiety disorders. However, many preliminary findings await more empirical data based on nationwide epidemiological studies and controlled evaluations related to the prevalence of anxiety disorders and their management in the Arab–Islamic cultural setting.

REFERENCES

Abdel-Gawad, M. S., Loutfi, Z., & Rahman, A. (1989), Knowledge of relatives of psychiatric patients about mental illness. *Arab J. Psychiatry*, 1:22–29.

Al-Abdul-Jabbar, J., & Al-Hamad, A. (1992), Psychotherapy with Arab patients. *Arab J. Psychiatry*, 3:16–27.

Ahmad, T. F. E. (1994), Management of necrophobia: Some cultural considerations. *J. Roy. Med. Serv.*, 2:20–22.

——— Takriti, A. (1993), Panic disorder and hypochondriasis. *Arab J. Psychiatry*, 4:24–35.

Akhtar, S., Wig, N. N., Varma, V. K., Pershad, D., & Verma, S. K. (1975), A phenomenological analysis of symptoms in obsessive compulsive neurosis. *Brit. J. Psychiatry*, 127:342–348.

Alsughayir, M. A. (1996), Public view of the evil eye and its role in psychiatry. A study in Saudi society. *Arab J. Psychiatry*, 7:152–160.

American Psychiatric Association (1994), *Diagnostic and Statistical Manual of Mental Disorders*, 4th ed. (DSM-IV). Washington, DC: American Psychiatric Press.

Arafa, M., Al-Khani, M., Hamdi, E., Amean, El Defrawi, M. H., & Moussa, F. A. (1992), Social phobia in an Arab culture: The impact of sociocultural factors. *Egypt. J. Psychiatry*, 15:102–112.

Chaleby, K. (1987), Social phobia in Saudis. *Social Psychiatry*, 22:167–170.

——— (1990), Perceived parental attitude in social phobia patients. *Arab J. Psychiatry*, 2:112–117.

Good, B. J., & Kleinman, A. M. (1985), Culture and anxiety: Cross-cultural evidence for the patterning of anxiety disorders. In: *Anxiety and the Anxiety Disorders*, ed. A. H. Tuma & J. D. Maser. Hillsdale, NJ: Lawrence Erlbaum, pp. 297–323.

Hashim, N. (1974), *Comparison of Attitudes Toward Death between Nursing Students in the Middle East and the United States.* Unpublished MS thesis. Beirut, Lebanon.

El-Islam, M. F. (1982), Arabic cultural psychiatry. *Transcult. Psychiatr. Res. Rev.,* 19:5–24.

—— (1994), Cultural aspects of morbid fear of Qatari women. *Soc. Psychiatric Epidemiol.,* 29:137–140.

Al-Issa, I., & Oudji, S. (1998), Culture and anxiety disorders. In: *Cultural Clinical Psychology: Theory, Research and Practice,* ed. S. Shahe, S. S. Kazarian, & D. R. Evans. New York: Oxford University Press, pp. 127–151.

Mahgoub, O. M., & Abdel-Hafeiz, H. B. (1991), Pattern of obsessive-compulsive disorder in Eastern Saudi Arabia. *Brit. J. Psychiatry,* 158:840–842.

Marks, I. (1969), *Fears and Phobias.* New York: Academic Press.

—— (1978), *Living with Fear, Understanding and Coping with Anxiety.* New York: McGraw-Hill.

Murphy, H. B. M. (1982), *Comparative Psychiatry: The International and Intercultural Distribution of Mental Illness.* Nerlin, Germany: Springer-Verlag.

Mutlaq, H., & Chaleby, K. (1995), Group psychotherapy with Arab patients. *Arab J. Psychiatry,* 6:125–136.

Okasha, A., Kamel, M., & Hassan, H. (1968), Preliminary psychiatric observation in Egypt. *Brit. J. Psychiatry,* 114:949–955.

—— Rafat, M., Al-Dawla, A. S., & Effat, S. (1991), Obsessive compulsive disorder in different cultures. An Egyptian perspective. *Egypt. J. Psychiatry,* 14:15–30.

—— Saad, A., Khalil, A. H., El-Dawla, A. S., & Yehia, N. (1994), Phenomenology of obsessive–compulsive disorder: A transcultural study. *Compreh. Psychiatry,* 35:191–197.

Rakhawi, Y. (1978), *Introduction to Group Psychotherapy, on Search for Self and Life.* Cairo, Egypt: Al Gad Publishing.

Shaalan, M., Rakhawi, Y., Gauad, M. S., & Loutfi, Z. (1987), Experience with group psychotherapy in the Egyptian culture. *Egyptian J. Psychiatry,* 16:69–78.

Al-Subaie, A. (1994), Traditional healing experiences in patients attending a university outpatient clinic. *Arab J. Psychiatry,* 5:83–91.

Suleiman, R., & Ahmad, T. (1993), Presence of panic disorder among medical patients referred to psychiatry. *Arab J. Psychiatry,* 2:84–92.

Takriti, A. (1987), The influence of cognitive events in the management of social phobia. Paper presented at Third Pan-Arab Congress on Psychiatry, Amman, Jordan.

———— (1992), Some aspects of anxiety disorders in Jordan. Paper presented at the annual meeting of the Royal College of Psychiatrists, Dublin.

———— Ahmad, T. (1992), Panic disorder: A clinical study. *Arab J. Psychiatry*, 3:28–44.

———— ———— (1996), Cognitions and ideations of obsessive–compulsive patients in Jordan.

World Health Organization (1992), *International Classification of Mental and Behavioral Disorders* (ICD-10). Geneva, Switzerland: WHO.

Zubi, M., Suleiman, R., Ahmad, T., Shobaki, M., & Shnaigat, W. (1996), Non-compliance among psychiatric patients. Paper presented at the Seventh Pan-Arab Congress of Psychiatry, Beirut. Lebanon.

III.

Muslims in the Diaspora

11.

The Mental Health of Muslim Immigrants in Europe

Ihsan Al-Issa

Migration (*hijra*) and travel (*safar*) are part of the socialization of all Muslim children. For Muslims *hijra* refers primarily to the prophet Muhammad's migration in A.D. 622 when almost all the Muslim community moved from Mecca to Medina. The word *hijra* and its derivative verb *hajara* (to migrate) or *muhajir* (immigrant) is encountered in many verses of the Qur'an (e.g., Suras 59:9; 2:218; 3:195; 9:100, 117; 33:6; 59:8; 60:10; 8:72). For Muslims everywhere, travel has religious connotations because of the pilgrimage (*Hajj*) to Mecca, which is one of the pillars of Islam. If affordable, the *hajj* is a religious duty of all Muslims. Visits to holy shrines (*ziyara*) are also widespread in the Muslim world (see chapter 2, this volume). Apart from the religious aspects of travel, it has been encouraged by both the Qur'an and the prophet tradition (*Hadith*) for other reasons such as the search for knowledge.

A Muslim scholar, Al-Shafii, listed five benefits of travels (*asfār*): "the relief of sorrow (*hem*), earning a living (*iktisabū ma'ishatin*), knowledge of science and arts (*'ilm wa ādāb*), and the company of a person with a good character (*majid*). Thus, travel is conceived by Muslims as beneficial for depression and sorrow as it provides different reinforcements and pleasurable

253

activities. Concerning the association between travel and the search of knowledge (*talab al-'ilm*), Gellens (1990) cites Anas Bin Malik who reported that the prophet said, "Those who go out in search of knowledge will be in the path of God until they return" (p. 50). The Qur'an (106:2) also mentions the journey (*rihla*) of Quraysh, the tribe of the prophet, to Yemen in the south in winter and to Syria in the north in summer. The *rihla* for trade and earning a living is conceived as a pious activity which receives God's approval (Gellens, 1990). The association between travel and the company of a reputable person shows a positive and accepting attitude toward strangers in foreign lands.

In medieval Islamic society, travel was valued not only for religious reasons and the search for knowledge but also for its integrating effects on Muslim communities. As El-Moudden (1990) pointed out: "pilgrimage (*hajj*) leads the pilgrim to Mecca and Medina, and the search for knowledge (*talab al 'ilm*) leads the student to one of the esteemed places of Islamic teaching, such as Medina, Cairo, or Fez. In all these cases, travel brings individuals and groups to centres and unites them with the wider community of the faithful (*umma*)" (p. 69).

All travels and migrations of Muslims during the medieval era took place in the land of Islam (*dar al-Islam*) where they shared the Islamic culture with populations of different ethnic and linguistic background and therefore felt at home (Dunn, 1986). The nineteenth century brought about movement of Muslims to the West, lands of infidels (*dar al-kufr*). They emigrated for reasons of higher education, training, employment, or to settle in these countries. According to Islamic law, emigration to *dar al-kufr* is prohibited only when the person, the property, and/or the religion of a Muslim are not safe in these countries (Masud, 1990). Although Muslims in the West enjoy religious freedom and relative safety of life and property, they face many problems in non-Muslim countries. They face linguistic difficulties and feel cultural alienation despite the material rewards and comforts provided by Western technology. Conflicts between the indigenous population and Muslim immigrants have recently intensified because of high rates of unemployment and the rise in Western countries of right wing movements based on racial and religious hatred. This chapter discusses the mental health of Muslim immigrants in Western European countries, particularly Belgium, France, Germany, and the United Kingdom. North Africans, Pakistanis, and Turks constitute the main Muslim immigrant groups in the West.

PATTERN OF MUSLIM MIGRATION

Most Muslims migrated to the West for economic reasons. They were initially invited by European countries to meet their need for labor during economic expansion after World War II. These guest workers in European countries are given permission to take up jobs for a limited period of time, but they have to leave these countries immediately after the termination of their jobs. France, Germany, Belgium, and other European countries attracted workers from the Mediterranean countries including Muslim countries (Algeria, Morocco, and Turkey). Britain, on the other hand, attracted Pakistanis and other immigrants from the Indian subcontinent because of its colonial history.

The pattern of migration of Muslims to Europe was that they were almost entirely young men who were single or migrated without their families, but were joined by other male workers from the same family or village. They were willing to take up jobs rejected by the indigenous population. They also did not intend to stay, and kept emotional ties with their countries. They sent money back home with the hope that soon they would be returning to their country for good. In contrast, most migrants to North America are settlers who intend to stay permanently in the new country. They come to look for better opportunities and a better new life.

The largest number of Muslims are in France between 3 and 5 million North Africans and Turks (Stein, Kerchouche, Pasquire, and Amine, 1995), followed by Germany with 2 million Turks (Mandel, 1990), and Britain with 397,000 Pakistanis in 1989 (Richmond, 1994). There are Muslim immigrants scattered in almost all other European countries (e.g., there are

90,000 Turks as well as a substantial number of Moroccans in Belgium) (Gailly, 1997). Some of these immigrants are now second or third generation citizens of Western countries and the probability that they will go back to the countries of their ancestors is rather slim.

SOCIOCULTURAL BACKGROUND

The majority of Muslim immigrants to Europe are poor with little education and come from a rural background. They lack the experience of urban living and are strongly committed to Islamic religious practices and the extended family. Individualism, independence, and other social values in the West are considered selfish and irresponsible in contrast to dependence on and loyalty to family and relatives (Saifulla Khan, 1979).

Cultural differences may create less problems in a multicultural society where the values of ethnic groups can be preserved and respected. However, with the European immigration policies of assimilation such as in France, cultural differences between Muslims and the indigenous population have become a source of constant conflict. For example, in 1989, the French Ministry of Education supported the dismissal of Muslim girls from school because they were wearing headscarves. Since the headscarf is part of the cultural identity of Muslims and reflects the Islamic concept of modesty, the French legislation against it has deprived a large proportion of citizens of the right to be different. The exclusion of Muslim female students who wear the headscarf from public schools has sharpened the division between Muslims and the rest of the population. The rebirth of a strong national right wing movement in France and the support of some Algerians in France of the Islamic fundamentalists have intensified tension between North Africans and the French population. A recent opinion poll (Tinco, 1994) reveals that the French tend to identify Islam with fanaticism, submissiveness, and rejection of Western values. On the other hand, Muslims in France consider Islam as the religion of democracy, justice, and liberty. These contrasting views between Muslims and the indigenous population may be a major source of social conflicts. In the same opinion poll by Tinco, the young, the educated, and recent immigrants among Muslims expressed worry about their ethnic identity.

Anti-Muslim sentiment and negative reactions against Islamic traditions were also strong in Germany (Mandel, 1990).

> [It varied] from the forcible removal of girls' headscarves by public-school teachers, to public mockery or ridicule, to the various strategies employed to oppose and undermine Qur'anic schools. The *kopftuch* (headscarf) debate continues as a heated issue, more among Germans than Turks. Many Germans feel offended by seeing Turkish women and girls with their heads covered. Ironically, the left (particularly feminists) and the right have united in their categorical opposition to the wearing of scarves. Though articulated and rationalised differently—it is variously described as "ugly," "backward," "un-German," "sticking out," or symbolic of sexist, patriarchal dominance and repression—the message is the same. In a self-consciously blatant Christian society, albeit dually denominational, it is not surprising that non-Christians may react by feeling unaccepted and marginalised [Mandel, 1990, p. 164].

The wearing of the headdress and other Muslim customs such as the avoidance of pork in the Muslim diet are interpreted negatively by the indigenous population as a type of social rejection and a refusal to accept the country's norms (Mandel, 1990). Indeed, in France, some Muslim beliefs are not considered compatible with the prevailing republican norms in French society (Begag, 1990).

CHILDREN OF MUSLIM IMMIGRANTS

Two major issues of concern for Muslim immigrants are acculturation and identity (Esmail, 1996). This is particularly true for children who, in the process of acculturation, acquire values which are inconsistent with what they learn at home. Acculturation may result in alienation between children and their parents. Since the children are better educated and have better knowledge of the foreign language, the parents may become dependent on them, something that is humiliating in their patriarchal culture. For Muslim communities in the West, behavior such as consumption of alcohol, codes of dress, and intimacy between the sexes may represent "loaded symbols" that may result in intergenerational conflicts (Esmail, 1996). Esmail illustrates such conflict in the case of a middle-aged Pakistani father whose:

> [R]elationship to his son was . . . a mixture of pride, dependence, anxiety, and resentment. He said his son was "very clever." He was clever at English. The man bought lotteries, and relied on his son to listen to TV news for winning numbers. He relied on his son to explain changes in immigration laws. His son was clever enough to understand the "difficult English" spoken by politicians. Yet he had grown "cheeky." He had been refusing to come to the mosque. He was in the habit of berating his mother's cooking, asking instead for American food. And he had lately developed an appetite for designer's clothes. Who was the ruler of the household—his parents or him?
>
> His son joined us. He reproached his father, rather strongly, for asking me about his career. It was none of his father's concern, he implied. He would figure it out himself. His father responded by accusing him of not being "serious"—of wanting to waste away his life going to parties. His son left. His father declared he would "send" his son to me at my hotel—could I impress upon him his religious obligation to defer to his parents? I did not, of course, expect a visit [p. 148].

A large proportion of Muslim immigrants are failing in the educational system and their opportunities are reduced, for example, in France (Begag, 1990) as well as in Germany and Britain (Castles, Booth, and Wallace, 1984). In France 70 percent of children of immigrants aged between 16 and 25 are unemployed and without vocational training. High unemployment and exclusion in certain neighborhoods has resulted in juvenile delinquency, drug addiction problems, racism, and fights against police in low-income areas in the major cities of Paris, Lyon, and Marseilles where most of them live (Begag, 1990).

It is not that these children are not motivated to achieve in school. A study by Kastoryano (1986) shows that Turkish children frequently have higher expectations in terms of professional mobility through increased schooling than do children of similar socioeconomic backgrounds among nationals. Nonetheless, their aspirations rarely lead to better jobs and in the case of most families, parents are unable or reticent to provide the home support necessary for scholastic success.

Hubain (1987) pointed out that in Germany there is discrimination against foreign children during the school years and training such as creating special classes for foreign children and giving priority to German and EEC citizens for apprentices' and workers' jobs. The bad quality of housing adds to the school handicaps. In Belgium most Turkish children go to "immigrant" or "black" schools which are usually of low quality and where most of the children are Turkish or Moroccan (Gailly, 1997). The system seems to duplicate the lower status of the parents and perpetuate the isolation of the Muslim community from participating in the mainstream of society.

The difficulties of integration of Muslims in the host cultures are complicated by widespread discrimination against Muslim immigrants relative to other Christian immigrants from Europe. For example, North Africans in France are regarded as more different from the native population and more "inferior" and are discriminated against more than Portuguese immigrants in France. Similarly, Turkish immigrants in Germany with their different religious outlook and life-style are more often targets of discrimination than Southern European immigrants (Kagitcibasi, 1987). Even in Canada where multiculturalism is encouraged, a national sample felt the least comfortable being with Arabs, Muslims, and Indo-Pakistanis as compared with other groups (Berry and Kalin, 1995). Typical responses of North Africans during recent interviews concerning their adaptation to French society are the following:

"Anyway, it is difficult to be completely integrated, people will never consider you as their equal" [Stein et al., 1995, p. 23].

"Integration. I am fed up with talking about integration. I arrived here at the age of 3. I studied child care at the university.

I live and work here. My family and friends are here. Explain
to me how I can be integrated any more. It is not integration
that one should talk about. It is acceptance. Acceptance by others is when they stop blaming us for our name, our skin and
our face, and stop confining us in rotten neighbourhoods far
from everybody else. When people become less racist, things
will get better" [Backmann and Aichoune, 1994, p. 4].

North Africans in France are not only reacted to as French by
the native population but they are also considered as Arabs,
Muslims, Algerians, *Beurs* (North Africans born in France), and
Harkis (children of North African army veterans), as well as
pejoratively called *bicots* (little goats) and *ratons* (little rats). As
Stein et al. (1995) pointed out, these multiple identities are
too much for one person to bear. The stereotype of North
Africans as fanatics seems incompatible with the findings that
three-quarters of Muslims in France do not object to a member
of their family having a non-Muslim spouse (Tinco, 1994).
Many North Africans in France do not define themselves as
Muslims, yet they are perceived as such by French society
(Solé, 1994).

Those with North African racial traits have to face strong
prejudices as well as frequent police harassment. A study of a
sample of 128 young French Muslims, between ages 16 and 25,
has shown that their psychological problems as well as their
experience of rejection by the native French white society was
associated with the color of their skin (Bouneb, 1985). Children
also suffer in school from prejudice and discrimination as indicated in the following statement of a 7-year-old Turkish boy to
a social worker in Britain: "at school sometimes they call me
'paki'—he looked down at his hands (he was a dark boy) and
he shouted at them that he is not a 'paki'; those boys are nasty
to 'pakis'; they hurt them" (Andreou, 1992, p. 149). Despite
the rejection of Muslim adults and children by the indigenous
population, the tendency is to blame the victim. In a survey in
France reported by Amar and Milza (1990), 55 percent of a
national sample blamed Algerians by considering them as the
most difficult nationality to integrate into French society.

PSYCHIATRIC DISORDERS AMONG MUSLIM IMMIGRANTS

Pakistani and Turkish Immigrants

One consistent finding is that Muslim immigrants from Pakistan and Turkey manifest less psychiatric disorders than the indigenous population. Admissions to mental hospitals for all diagnoses in England in 1981 show that Pakistanis (and those from Bangladesh) have lower rates of mental illness than the indigenous population (Cochrane and Bal, 1989; Cochrane, 1995). This trend is found in schizophrenia and paranoia (females only), depression, neuroses, and alcohol abuse (see Table 11.1). Data from community surveys of mental illness confirm the relative low rate of mental illness among those from Pakistan and Bangladesh (Cochrane and Stopes-Roe, 1977). Cochrane (1979) used the Rutter Questionnaire and found that children of Pakistani parents have a lower rate of deviant behavior than the indigenous population. The same lower rates among children were found in psychiatric admission.

Similar to Pakistanis in Britain, Turkish guest workers tend to show better mental health than the indigenous population.

TABLE 11.1 Rates of All Mental Hospital Admissions for Selected Diagnosis per 100,000 Population in England, 1981, Country of Birth (adapted from Cochrane and Bal, 1989)

Country of birth	Schizophrenia and Paranoia		Depression[1]		Neuroses[2]		Alcohol Abuse[3]	
	Male	Female	Male	Female	Male	Female	Male	Female
England	61	58	79	166	28	56	38	18
Ireland	158	174	197	410	62	111	332	133
India	77	89	68	118	22	27	73	8
Pakistan[4]	94	32	68	96	15	47	6	1
Caribbean	359	235	65	152	6	25	27	9
Hong Kong	65	50	12	75	16	29	4	8

[1] Affective psychoses and depressive disorders
[2] Includes "neurotic depression"
[3] Alcohol psychosis, alcohol dependence, and nondependent abuse of alcohol
[4] Includes Bangladesh
From Cochrane, R. (1975), *Mental Health Among Minorities and Immigrants in Britain.* In I. Al-Issa, Ed. (1997), *Handbook of Culture and Mental Illness. An International Perspective.* Madison, CT: International Universities Press.

For example, in the city of Mannheim, the rates of schizophrenia, alcohol-related problems, and organic brain syndromes were lower among guest workers than the German population. Psychoneurotic and psychosomatic disorders show no significant difference among the two populations (Krahl, 1995). It was also found that guest workers develop schizophreniclike psychosis and affective illness requiring hospital admission mainly during their first year of stay. Typical syndromes of guest workers are hypochondriacal depressive syndromes, paranoid reactions, psychosomatic conditions such as those related to the gastrointestinal tract, sexual dysfunctions, and sleep disorders (Krahl, 1995). Gailly (1997) also reported that Turkish guest workers in Belgium have less mental illness than the indigenous population except that they are slightly more inclined to seek medical advice for infections and problems with the digestive system, tuberculosis, diabetes, and diet related disorders (obesity, hypertension). The symptoms and the outcome of disorders among guest workers in Germany described by Tanaka-Matsumi and Draguns (1997) seem to reflect their cultural background and interaction with the host culture. The prevalence of acute paranoid reaction with dramatic emotional features among this group was attributed to misunderstanding of the host culture and its customs and language. Tanaka-Matsumi and Draguns (1997) also noted that

> . . . anxiety tends to be expressed in its raw, pure and intense form resulting in dramatic, but relatively benign, states of acute distress. The common denominator of these syndromes is their relatively favorable prognosis, provided that the therapists take into account the cultural context of symptom presentation. Prognosis is worse if the symptoms are mistaken for more serious pathology [p. 471].

The low rates of mental illness among Muslims in Europe may be partly explained by the selection prior to migration whereby only those who are physically fit can get a work permit (Krahl, 1995). Since a large number of Pakistanis in Britain and Turkish guest workers in Europe remain attached to their home countries, a return home is more likely in the case of mental illness (Cochrane, 1983; Mandel, 1990). Another possible explanation of the low rates of mental illness among Muslims in Britain is the extended family where many generations live in the same household. The extended family provides both social support to its members as well as making the need for professional help less likely (Rack, 1982; Cochrane, 1983). A recent study has shown that British Pakistani children who live in an extended family are better adjusted than those who live in a nuclear family (Shah and Sonuga-Barke, 1995). However, the beneficial effects of the extended family were not supported with British Pakistani mothers; those who live in extended families reported feeling more depressed and anxious than those who live with nuclear families.

Social support in the Muslim community and its isolation from the indigenous population may protect individuals from the stresses associated with prejudice and discrimination (Al-Issa, 1997). Indeed, the prevalence of acute psychotic disorders among North Africans and Turkish immigrants in Europe, particularly during the first year (see Krahl, 1995), suggests the involvement of stressors associated with immigration in the new country. It was also found that previous contact with the West, which is expected to facilitate and increase the rate of assimilation of the immigrant into the new culture, tended to be associated with higher rates of hostility, paranoia, and depression among Saudi Muslim students in Canada (Al-Subaie and DiNicola, 1995). Isolation for Muslim communities may serve as a shelter against the experience of prejudice and discrimination.

Based on his data on mental illness among ethnic groups in Britain, Cochrane (1983) has argued for a negative relationship between assimilation and mental illness. These immigrants who isolate themselves from the host British community because of prejudice and their desire to remain separate are the least vulnerable to psychological problems. Pakistanis in Britain are the least assimilated group but tend to be the most protected from mental illness. In contrast, West Indians who desired integration with British society but were rejected, tended to have the highest risk of mental illness (see Table 11.1). The finding that the longer Pakistanis had lived in Britain, the higher their psychological disturbances, suggests that interaction with and experience in the host culture made them more vulnerable to mental illness (Cochrane, 1983). Pakistani women reveal the lowest rate of admission to hospitals and report fewer symptoms as compared with all groups. This may be related to lower rates of stressful life events (Cochrane, 1987; Mahmud, 1987). The housewife role of Muslim women may protect them from the stressors of the workplace.

North Africans

Studies of North Africans in France tend to be descriptive with no epidemiological data to indicate the rate of mental illness (Moussaoui and Ferry, 1985; Al-Issa and Tousignant, 1997). Psychosis tends to manifest itself predominantly in the form of acute *bouffée délirante*, paranoia, or acute schizophrenia (cf. chapter 4). It tends to be unstable at first and thus more difficult to label and integrate within Western nosology. The contents of symptoms are related to possession by the *jinn* (spirits) and the belief that the body is impure or being attacked or dismantled. These symptoms are often accompanied by delusions of persecution with or without hallucinations. Traditional themes of psychosis tend to be more predominant among first-generation immigrants than second or third generations who manifest the typical symptoms of psychosis. In general, fear of racism is more intensely expressed in the symptoms of North African patients than other ethnic groups (Chauvot, Pascalis, and Champanier, 1981).

Bouffée délirante is one of the most frequent psychotic reactions among immigrants from North Africa and black Africa (Johnson-Sabine, Mann, Jacoby, Wood, Peron-Magnan, Olie, and Deniker, 1983). It is characterized by sudden onset with vivid hallucinations, delusions, clouding of consciousness, and rapid mood swings. Among North Africans, the themes of delusions are related to religion (prophetic inspiration, divine revelation, messianic conviction, end of the world, and resurrection), sexuality, jealousy, poisoning, forced marriage, sexual abuse, and incest. For similar reactive psychotic reaction and schizophreniform symptoms among Pakistanis in Britain, see Rack (1990). One type of *bouffée délirante* specific to North African women is nuptial psychosis which happens after the wedding night as a result of stresses involved in arranged marriages and is usually experienced by the bride (Pfeiffer, 1982).

Somatic symptoms tend to dominate the manifestation of depression among North African patients. For example, "hypochondriacal" depression described by Chauvot et al. (1981) accounts for one-third of the psychiatric diagnoses of North Africans.

Marie-Cardine (1981) reported three groups of depressive patients among North Africans in France. *One group* is characterized by psychomotor inhibition: "my body is heavy, it cannot move anyone." This type of depression is dominated by physical symptoms which appear after a work accident and is quite similar to hypochondriacal depression described by Chauvot et al. (1981). The syndrome is pejoratively labeled as the *Mediterranean syndrome* by French psychiatrists. It tends to have a good prognosis. A *second group* of depressed patients express object loss: "my soul remains with my parents; I am like a dog that had lost its owner; my mind remains there, at home." The syndrome is seen among acculturated North Africans who have been living in France for a long period of time. This depression is usually precipitated by an accident at work or a current illness. The patients find it difficult to resume their work and end up in a psychiatric hospital. They stop eating, and become withdrawn and disoriented. These features are quite similar to those seen in autistic withdrawal or melancholic stupors. Whenever the patients are induced to communicate with the psychiatrist, they indicate that part of themselves remains in their home country. This clinical picture often resists medical treatment. Patients are sometimes reacting to real bereavement or to a negative life event in the family or may be simply grieving the loss of their culture.

Finally, the *third group* of North African depressed patients expresses affect associated with possession by the spirits, *jinn*, that are controlling their body, or by the devil, driving the spirit out of the body. The illness takes the form of *bouffées délirantes* with an acute and expressive onset. The clinical picture is related to possession and animistic beliefs which are widespread among disadvantaged lower social class North Africans in France. Contacts with a *marabout,* the North African native healer, tend to bring a relief of symptoms.

Chauvot et al. (1981) reported that suicidal behavior is rare among North Africans but is used as a means of communication with the environment by those who have been in the country for a long period and are relatively assimilated into French society. Attempted suicide is most prevalent among second-generation adolescent girls. Entrapment and confinement to the home are suggested as a factor underlying the high rate of attempted suicide among girls. In many cases, young North African girls come to France to live with their fathers, leaving their mothers in the home country. They are expected to do the housework as well as work outside the home. They are also exposed to conflicts between European values and the rigid, conservative values of their fathers. Another stressor associated with suicidal behavior among girls is simply to avoid a marriage arranged by the father. In contrast to girls, boys tend to react to stressors by showing academic failure, drug abuse, and delinquent behavior (Chauvot et al, 1981; Moussaoui and Sayeh, 1982). The patriarchal structure of the North African family, where the father or the oldest son holds absolute power in decision making, may contribute to the high rate of attempted suicide among acculturated North African adolescents in France as well as among Westernized youth in urban settings in their countries of origin (Al-Issa, 1990).

Traumatic neurosis, a diagnosis similar to posttraumatic stress disorder, was reported to have a high incidence in the migrant population. In a study of 95 clinical cases, of which 75 percent were of North African origin, the symptomatology was characterized by reenacting of the trauma, repetitive requests for medical attention, rumination, depressive affect, lack of interest in the social environment, and loss of sexual desire (Biznar, 1991). This disorder was also accompanied by gastrointestinal disturbances, anxiety reaction, and *délire de revendication* (a delusion with a sense of entitlement to claims). Most of these migrant patients were men (85%). The illness starts, in a majority of cases, 10 to 15 years after arrival in France. Most of these patients described by Biznar (1991) had suddenly stopped work and were either self-declared sick or given a diagnosis by a physician even though they had been functioning normally at work. Nearly half (46%) of their episodes were provoked by surgery and another 30 percent by work accidents. Many of the patients had very recently experienced a loss of a family member (a parent or a child) or had a newborn child. As many as 60 percent had lost a parent through death before the age of 10. Biznar (1991) attributed the cause of the traumatic state to delayed culture shock. North African immigrants, because of isolation from the dominant culture, may rely more on the family for social support and the definition of the self and thus are more vulnerable to the effects of a family loss. For these patients, the birth of a child is also an additional stressor because of the absence of the support of the extended family and the difficulty of transmitting their culture in a foreign environment.

Although anorexia nervosa is very rare in North Africa, a case of a North African girl was reported in France by Chazot, Lang, and Pellet (1989). Nora was hospitalized at age 19 with a history of anorexia nervosa since age 15. She comes from a relatively acculturated family that still keeps some of the Muslim traditions. The illness started during the fasting month of Ramadan in which Muslims abstain from taking food and drink from dawn to sunset. In Britain, Bhadrinath (1990) reported two 15-year-old Muslim girls with anorexia nervosa which got worse during Ramadan. Anorexia nervosa may be considered as an exaggeration of the Muslim rule of fasting in a prosperous environment where food is plentiful.

Somatization

Somatization, the expression of emotional distress in physical symptoms, is a frequent theme in the assessment of the mental health of Muslim immigrants (Rack, 1982; Gailly, 1985, 1997; Moussaoui and Ferry, 1985; Bal, 1987). A new field of guest worker medicine, *Gasterheiterkrankheit*, has emerged in Germany to deal with Turkish immigrants (Mandel, 1990). These immigrants themselves claim that they experience physical and emotional problems which they have never known before migration.

The physically oriented medieval Islamic humoral theory of temperament (*mizāj*) which emphasizes the four elements of air, earth, fire, and water (chapter 2, this volume) is still dominant in Muslim countries and among immigrants (Rack, 1982; Gailly, 1997). Muslim immigrants in Belgium and Germany go back to Turkey to restore their health with "good water" and "good air" (Mandel, 1990; Gailly, 1997). "Somatization is functional because it makes it possible, in the case of illness, to set the healing process in motion using physical tools such as bath, diets, and drugs, and the process explains the intensive and extensive use of medical examinations (to 'see' the cause of the disease)" (Gailly, 1997, p. 156). Thus somatization removes the problem from the interpersonal or psychological realm to natural causation. Muslim immigrants in Europe may believe that "open display of emotions in social interactions is undesirable. Somatic complaints also reduce the stigma of mental illness and legitimize entry into health care. In contrast to mental symptoms, which means stigmatized mental illness, physical pain is an opportunity to reintegrate the sick person into the social support group and to reaffirm the norms of solidarity and social control in [the Muslim community] (Al-Issa, 1995, p. 22).

The prevalence of somatic symptoms may be related to how Muslims perceive, interpret, and react to illness. There is less separation between psychiatric and physical problems among Muslim immigrants and therefore mental illness is presented in somatopsychic or psychosomatic form by patients (Fabrega, 1991; Al-Issa, 1995).

Among Pakistanis in Britain, as well as Muslims in general, the heart[1] is a metaphor for expressing emotions. Distress is

---

[1]Western patients may use metaphors by expressing anxiety as a "lump in the throat" or "butterflies in the tummy" and express depression as a "broken heart." This metaphor is used by Lynch (1977) in his book *The Broken Heart: The Medical Consequences of Loneliness*. His central theme is that the loss of loved ones through

described by patients as "my heart is sinking" or feeling "lonely, squeezed, and bored" (Aslam, 1979).

Illness may also be conceived as social dysfunction. The criterion for health is the ability to carry out one's social role or obligations. The following dialogue is familiar to British psychiatrists dealing with patients from Pakistan (Rack, 1982):

> Psychiatrist (English-speaking): "How is your wife getting on now?"
> Husband: "She is very well now doctor. She is fine. She is looking after the house. She is cooking the food, she is caring for the baby. Thank you, so much . . ."
> Psychiatrist: "Good. I am glad she is able to do those things: and is she feeling well herself?"
> (Brief conversation between husband and wife)
> Husband: "She is very well now, doctor, she is able to look after the family, she is cooking the food, I am able to go back to work now. . . ."
> Psychiatrist: "Yes, yes, but please ask her how does she feel in herself? Is she happy, is her mind clear? Is the *feeling* all right?"
> (A further lengthy conversation. Husband and wife both evidently perplexed, but wanting to answer the question helpfully.)
> Husband: "She is very happy now, doctor, because she is able to do the cooking, she is able to look after the family, she is able to care for the baby, she is able to clean the house. Thank you very much . . ." [p. 110].

The expression of emotions in a foreign language may be difficult for Muslim immigrants. Both in Canada and France, somatization in this group tended to be associated with knowledge of English and French respectively (Moussaoui and Ferry, 1985; Al-Subaie and DiNicola, 1995). Emotional distress could also be sorted out within the family or dealt with by using other sources (Rack, 1982).

Finally, in considering somatization among Muslim immigrants, attention should be given to *real* physical complaints. Pakistani and Turkish immigrants tend to be exposed to more

---

sudden separation or death and human loneliness significantly contribute to serious disease such as heart disease and sudden death.

infectious disease than the indigenous population (Bandaranyake, 1989; Gailly, 1997). For example, Pakistanis in Britain
tend to suffer more from tuberculosis and gastrointestinal infections than the British. Overcrowded living and bad housing
may be the main factor contributing to the poor physical health
of Muslim immigrants (Bandaranyake, 1989).

SUMMARY AND CONCLUSION

The description of Muslim immigrants to Western countries
gives a dismal picture of seclusion, isolation, and consistent
discrimination and prejudice. Their present plight is a reminder of the Qur'anic reference to the oppressed (*mustd'a-
fūn*) of the earth (Sura 4, 97) and their oppressors
(*mustakbïrūn*) (Sura 16:22–23) at the dawn of Islam in Mecca.
The Qur'an is referring to those Muslims who stayed behind
and could not join the prophet during his migration to Madinah where Islam had the full acceptance and support of the
host population, *Al-Ansār*. While the prophet was welcomed
by the Madinah population, current Muslim immigrants and
Muslim citizens of Western countries are among the oppressed
in a rejecting and alienating environment. The majority of
these immigrants belong to the lowest strata of European society: poor with a minimal level of education. Negative attitudes
toward Muslims make it more difficult for this large segment of
the population to integrate within the major European society.
Nevertheless, available epidemiological data suggest that the
mental health of Muslims in Europe is better or at least the
same as that of the indigenous population. The Muslim family
with its emphasis on close relationships and mutual respect
of its members may provide protection against mental illness.
Similarly, the Muslim community, with the mosque as a center
of religious and social activity, provides support to its members
in distress. Its cohesiveness and relative isolation from the indigenous population may also reduce its exposure to prejudice
and discrimination and protect it against mental illness. Unless
there is mutual respect and equality between the Muslim and

the European communities, conflicts will continue unresolved for a long time to come.

REFERENCES

Amar, M., & Milza, P. (1990), *L'immigration en France au XXc siècle* (Immigration in France in the twentieth century). Paris: Armand Collins.

Andreou, C. (1992), Inner and outer reality in children and adolescents. In: *Intercultural Therapy,* ed. J. Kareem & R. Littlewood. Oxford: Blackwell Scientific, pp. 146–154.

Aslam, M. (1979), *The Practice of Asian Medicine in the United Kingdom.* Doctoral thesis, Dept. of Pharmacy, University of Nottingham.

Backmann, R., & Aichoune, F. (1994), Violence urbaine: La cote d'alerte. *Le Nouvel Observateur,* 1568:4–8.

Bal, S. S. (1987), Psychological symptomatology and health beliefs of Asian patients. In: *Clinical Psychology: Research and Development,* ed. H. Dent. London: Croom Helm, pp. 101–110.

Bandaranayake, R. (1989), Ethnic differences in disease—An epidemiological perspective. In: *Health, Race and Ethnicity,* ed. T. Rathwell & D. Phillips. London: Croom Helm, pp. 80–99.

Batta, I. D., McCulloch, J. W., & Smith, N. J. (1965), A study of juvenile delinquency among Asians and half-Asians. *Brit. J. Criminol.,* 15:32–42.

Begag, A. (1990), *L'immigré et sa ville.* Lyon: Presses Universitaires de Lyon.

Berry, J. W., & Kalin, R. (1995), Multicultural and ethnic attitudes in Canada: An overview of the 1991 national survey. *Can. J. Behav. Sci.,* 27:301–320.

Bhadrinath, B. R. (1990), Anorexia nervosa in adolescents of Asian extraction. *Brit. J. Psychiatry,* 156:565–568.

Biznar, K. (1991), Les névroses traumatiques des migrants: Une quête compulsive de sens. Résultats d'un recherche systématique sur 95 cas cliniques (Traumatic neuroses of immigrants: A comprehensive survey. Results of systematic research on 95 clinical cases). *Psychologie Française,* 36:341–350.

Bouneb, K. D. (1985), Adaptation et identité culturelle des jeune Français Musulmans. *Cahiers d'Anthropologie et Biométrie Humaine,* 3:1–31.

Castles, S., Booth, H., & Wallace, T. (1984), *Here for Good. Western Europe's New Minorities.* London: Pluto Press.

Chauvot, B., Pascalis, G., & Champanier, J. P. (1981), Psychopathologie du migrant adulte et jeune dans la région de Reims (Psychopathology of adult and young migrants in the Reims region). *Psychologie Médicale*, 13:1801–1803.

Chazot, L., Lang, F., & Pellet, J. (1989), Réflexions sur un cas d'anorexie mentale: Nohra (Reflections on a case of anorexia nervosa: Nohra). *Psychologie Médicale*, 21:193–197.

Cochrane, R. (1979), Psychological and behavioral disturbance with West Indians, Indians, and Pakistanis in Britain. *Brit. J. Psychiatry*, 134:201–210.

────── (1983), *The Social Creation of Mental Illness*. New York: Longman.

────── (1987), The mental health of ethnic minorities. In: *Clinical Psychology: Research and Development*, ed. H. Dent. London: Croom Helm, pp. 87–92.

────── (1995), Mental health among minorities and immigration in Britain. In: *Culture and Mental Illness: An International Perspective*, ed. I. Al-Issa. Madison, CT: International Universities Press, pp. 347–360.

────── Bal, S. S. (1989), Mental health admission rates of immigrants to England: A comparison of 1971 and 1981. *Soc. Psychiatry & Psychiatric Epidemiol.*, 24:2–12.

────── Stopes-Roe, M. (1977), Psychological and social adjustment of Asian immigrants to Britain: A community survey. *Soc. Psychiatry*, 12:195–206.

Dunn, R. E. (1986), *The Adventures of Ibn Battuta, a Muslim Traveler of the Fourteenth Century*. Berkeley, CA: University of California Press.

Esmail, A. (1996), Islamic communities and mental health. In: *Psychiatry and Religion*, ed. D. Bhugra. London: Routledge, pp. 138–152.

Fabrega, H. (1991), Psychiatric stigma in non-Western societies. *Compreh. Psychiatry*, 32:534–551.

Gailly, A. (1985), Life recedes when exchange fails: Clinical anthropology among Turkish patients. *Internat. J. Psychol.*, 20:521–538.

────── (1997), Turkish immigrants in Belgium. In: *Ethnicity, Immigration and Psychopathology*, ed. I. Al-Issa & M. Tousignant. New York: Plenum, pp. 147–165.

Gellens, S. I. (1990), The search for knowledge in medieval Muslim societies: A comparative approach. In: *Muslim Travellers, Pilgrimage, Migration, and the Religious Imagination*, ed. D. F. Eickelman & J. Piscatori. Berkeley, CA: University of California Press, pp. 50–65.

Hubain, C. (1987), *La République Fédérale Allemande et ses immigrés.* Louvain-la-Neuve, France: Ciaco.

Al-Issa, I. (1990), Culture and mental illness in Algeria. *Internat. J. Soc. Psychiatry,* 36:230–240.

—— (1995), Culture and mental illness in an international perspective. In: *Culture and Mental Illness: An International Perspective,* ed. I. Al-Issa. Madison, CT: International Universities Press, pp. 3–49.

—— (1997), The psychology of prejudice and discrimination. In: *Ethnicity, Immigration and Psychopathology,* ed. I. Al-Issa & M. Tousignant. New York: Plenum, pp. 17–32.

—— Tousignant, M. (1997), The mental health of North Africans in France. In: *Ethnicity, Immigration and Psychopathology,* ed. I. Al-Issa & M. Tousignant. New York: Plenum, pp. 135–146.

Johnson-Sabine, E. C., Mann, A. H., Jacoby, R. J., Wood, K. H., Peron-Magnan, P., Olie, J. P., & Deniker, P. (1983), Bouffé délirante: An examination of its current status. *Psycholog. Med.,* 13:771–778.

Kagitcibasi, C. (1987), Alienation of the outsider; the plight of migrants. *Internat. Migration,* 25:195–210.

Kastoryano, R. (1986), Être en France: reflexions sur familles et communité. Paris: CIMI, L'Harmattan.

Krahl, W. (1995), Social and cultural factors in German psychiatry. In: *Culture and Mental Illness: An International Perspective,* ed. I. Al-Issa. Madison, CT: International Universities Press, pp. 249–268.

Lynch, J. J. (1977), *The Broken Heart: The Medical Consequences of Loneliness.* New York: Basic Books.

Mahmud, S. (1987), Life stress and symptoms: A comparative study of Pakistani and English women. In: *Clinical Psychology: Research and Development,* ed. H. Dent. London: Croom Helm, pp. 111–117.

Mandel, R. (1990), Shifting centres and emergent identities. Turkey and Germany in the lives of Turkish *Gastarbeiter.* In: *Muslim Travellers, Pilgrimage, Migration, and the Religious Imagination,* ed. D. F. Eickelman & J. Piscatori. Berkeley, CA: University of California Press, pp. 153–171.

Marie-Cardine, M. (1981), La relation médecin-malade entre psychiatre et maghrébin migrant. *Psychologie Médicale,* 13:1709–1713.

Masud, M. K. (1990), The obligation to migrate: The doctrine of *hijra* in Islamic law. In: *Muslim Travellers, Pilgrimage, Migration, and the Religious Imagination,* ed. D. F. Eickelman & J. Piscatori. Berkeley, CA: University of California Press, pp. 22–49.

El-Moudden, A. (1990), The ambivalence of *rihla:* Community integration and self-definition in Moroccan travel accounts,

1300–1800. In: *Muslim Travellers, Pilgrimage, Migration, and the Religious Imagination,* ed. D. F. Eickelman & J. Piscatori. Berkeley, CA: University of California Press, pp. 69–84.

Moussaoui, D., & Ferry, G. (1985), *Psychopathologie des migrants.* Paris: Presses Universitaires de France.

———— Sayeh, A. (1982), Les enfants de migrants ou l'impossible identité (Migrant children or the impossible identity). *Annales Médico-Psychologiques,* 140:588–592.

Pfeiffer, W. M. (1982), Culture-bound syndromes. In: *Culture and Psychopathology,* ed. I. Al-Issa. Baltimore, MD: University Park Press.

Rack, P. (1982), *Race Culture and Mental Disorder.* London: Tavistock.

———— (1990), Psychological and psychiatric disorders. In: *Health Care for Asians,* ed. B. R. McAvoy & L. J. Donalson. Oxford: Oxford University Press, pp. 290–303.

Richmond, A. H. (1994), *Global Apartheid. Refugees, Racism and the New World Order.* Toronto: Oxford University Press.

Saifulla Khan, V., Ed. (1979), *Minority Families in Britain: Support and Stress.* London: Macmillan.

Shah, Q., & Sonuga-Barke, E. (1995), Family structure and the mental health of Pakistani Muslim mothers and their children living in Britain. *Brit. J. Clin. Psychol.,* 34:79–81.

Solé, R. (1994), La France et l'Islam: Si proche et si loin. Le Monde: Sélection Hebdomadaire, October 1, p. 1.

Stein, S., Kerchouche, D., Pasquire, S., & Amine, N. (1995), Les leurs venues d'Alger. *L'Express,* 2312:22–24.

Al-Subaie, A., & DiNicola, V. F. (1995), Psycho-social adaptation of Saudi students and spouses in Canada. *Arab J. Psychiatry,* 6:186–199.

Tanaka-Matsumi, J., & Draguns, J. G. (1997), Culture and psychopathology. In: *Handbook of Cross-cultural Psychology,* Vol. 3, 2nd ed., ed. W. Berry, M. H. Segall, & C. Kagitçibasi. Boston: Allyn & Bacon, pp. 449–491.

Tinco, A. (1994, October 20), Une religion mal aimée, de fidèles mieux intégrés. *Le Monde, Selection Hebdomadaire,,* p. 1.

IV.

Treatment in an Islamic Context

12.

Psychotherapy in Islamic Society

Jawahir Al-Abdul-Jabbar, Ihsan Al-Issa

There are universal factors in all kinds of healing practices: faith in the therapist, active participation of the clients and their families, the authority figure and warm personality of the therapist, and the facilitation of emotional arousal as a prerequisite of changes in attitudes and behavior during therapy (Wittkower and Warnes, 1974). Other universal therapeutic factors that are emphasized in cross-cultural therapy are a shared worldview with patients, labeling of the disease and attribution of cause, the patient's expectations, and the important role of suggestion (Prince, 1984). However, many of the basic assumptions of psychotherapy techniques and principles employed by non-Western psychologists and psychiatrists reflect the sociocultural context of Western culture with the implication that these assumptions are universal and could be generalized to non-Western cultures. For example, the emphasis on the role of the healer in therapy may not be as important in many non-Western therapeutic practices (Prince, 1984) and treatment may not always involve the healer–patient dyad. As Prince (1984) stated:

---

[1]In this chapter, we use the term *Arab* or *Arabic* interchangeably with *Islam* or *Islamic*. The reason is that studies cited in this chapter were carried out mostly in Arab–Islamic countries. We think that for the purpose of our discussion the distinction is not a vital one since the Arab and the Islamic culture have much in common.

This point was striking because I had just returned from a visit to India, where I had observed a healing ceremony without a healer! In Lucknow, a large group of patients knelt at sundown before the ancient shrine of a deceased Islamic saint. Patients became violently possessed during a half-hour period. Most were required (on the basis of instructions issued by the possessing spirit to relatives of the patient who were in attendance) to present themselves at the shrine on thirty consecutive evenings to be healed. According to the local populace, the ceremony had been practiced from time immemorial and a good proportion of the supplicants recovered from their illnesses [Prince, 1980, p. 60].

Although psychotherapy across cultures has been extensively discussed (Frank, 1961; Kiev, 1964; Torrey, 1972; Prince, 1976, 1980, 1984; Sue and Sue, 1990; Aponte, Rivers, and Wohl, 1995), publications on psychotherapy in the Arab–Islamic world are rather limited and mainly deal with psychoanalytically oriented treatment (Al-Rakkawi, 1978; Zewan, 1986) with little attention to process or outcome research. In a strongly religious society, psychoanalysis was used in the treatment of Muslim patients, but issues related to its application to Islamic culture, its compatibility with Islamic doctrine, and the reaction of Arab patients to it was neglected (Al-Issa, 1992). This is particularly important, since the tenets of psychoanalysis are opposed to religion (see chapter 1, this volume). More recently, Dwairy and van Sickle (1996) discussed the application of "Western psychotherapy in traditional Arab societies," but no attention was given to Islamic doctrine.

This chapter attempts to address some issues pertinent to different principles and techniques of psychotherapy in Arab–Muslim culture. Since psychotherapy is not a single entity we will only review some major principles of psychotherapy with reference to some specific points which are relevant to Arab or Muslim clients. Cultural variables related to how clients perceive and react to the therapist may be vital for understanding the mode and the style of therapeutic interaction, which may in turn influence the therapeutic process. Some of these cultural variables that are of relevance to the psychotherapeutic process, such as the patriarchal Islamic culture, clients' intolerance of insight therapy, and the role of culture and religion, will also be discussed in this chapter.

THE PATRIARCHAL ISLAMIC CULTURE AND PSYCHOTHERAPY

The Arab or Islamic culture is strongly patriarchal, and the father tends to be the dominant figure in the family. This culture is also group oriented; the interests of society are considered to be far more important than those of the individual. Such a social context may affect the development of the concept of the self as an independent entity. The Western concept of autonomy as a state of individualization could not be achieved in this culture without alienation of the individual from society, making life adjustment even more difficult.

A patriarchal culture may affect the mode of psychotherapy in two ways. *First*, it dictates the type of interaction between the therapist and the client. "Parent–child" interaction would be the model followed as the therapist assumes the parent position, being directive, advisory, caring, and at times critical. Such interaction is incompatible with basic principles of Western psychotherapy where adult interaction is encouraged and an explorative–reflective technique is used. A therapist cannot assume an observant position; he has to use active manipulation of the cognitive processes and the clients' behavior. *Second*, a patriarchal culture would be expected to affect the outcome of psychotherapy where a therapist can only function within the norms of culture rather than considering individual needs. His only goal will be to work within the cultural framework and change behavior in order to be consistent with the client's cultural norms. A state of complete autonomy and individualization or independence is not desirable and is replaced by a type of "individualization" in which the position and the function of the individual in society must be acknowledged. Independence has to be replaced by a state of interdependence; that is, the patient has to understand that his independence is only accepted if it functions within the limitations of the family and society at large.

When the therapist is seen as a father figure, the client usually takes a passive position, seeing the therapist as omnipotent, intimidating, and highly respected. As a result clients tend to expect a miraculous cure rather than take an active role in the treatment. They take no responsibility for their behavior or any action to change it. In Western psychotherapy a client is expected to be responsible for his actions and emotions, as well as to take charge of his life and to be motivated to initiate a change. The following case demonstrates how an explorative and reflective type of therapy is not conducive for improvement and has to be replaced by an explanatory and directive method.

Nawal is a 28-year-old housewife with a ninth grade education. She came to the psychiatrist's office complaining of being constantly anxious, temperamental, and losing control with tantrum behavior. She described herself as being very irritable, and hesitant in making minor decisions. She felt constantly angry, crying without any apparent reason. Her tantrum outbursts, excitement, and periodic mood swings were diagnosed as manic–depressive illness by a psychiatrist. However, psychosis was excluded because she showed no thinking disorder and expressed her feelings appropriately. As psychotherapy progressed, the patient was able to relate her guilt at being torn between respect and gratitude to her husband on one hand, and her emotional attachment to another man with whom she had recently entered into an affair.

A classical format was first used with Nawal. The technique utilized was mostly exploratory and reflective, using open-ended questions, allowing the patient to examine her feelings and reflect upon them. The aim was to identify her inner intrapsychic conflicts and dynamics that led to her loss of control and depression. As the therapy progressed, it became apparent that her symptoms not only were not improving, but they actually had been worsening. At this stage, the therapist decided to use direct guidance to address her pressing problem. The therapist now considered the problem as an avoidance–approach conflict: she had to choose between keeping her despised husband or her lover. Although she was left to make the final choice, the therapist as a patriarch (i.e., representing a father) suggested the alternative that is compatible with societal demands (i.e., staying with her husband). The patient decided with the help of the therapist that having a stable and good social front with her husband was more valuable to her than pursuing her sensual needs. This decision was followed by the gradual disappearance of her symptoms!

CLIENT INTOLERANCE OF INSIGHT-ORIENTED PSYCHOTHERAPY

As in the case of Nawal, Arab clients are intolerant of exploratory and insight oriented therapy, in general being resistant and heavily defended against inner exploration of their psyche. Psychiatrists may use intravenous Amytal injections that might result in an "abreaction." There have been instances where exploration and expressions of insights have led to an extreme anxiety reaction rather than the expected positive therapeutic outcome. This may be illustrated by the case of Sarah.

Sarah is a 32-year-old female, twice divorced, with three children. She presented initially with classical symptoms of depression. She stated that for the last few years, she had been feeling sad, had no interest in doing anything, and found no pleasure in her environment. She had been treated with antidepressants by more than one psychiatrist, with only partial success.

Psychotherapy was started by an Arab psychiatrist who had recently come to the Middle East from Britain, eager to apply his Western wisdom. As the therapy started, it became apparent that the patient was reluctant to expose much of her inner feelings and thoughts. Furthermore, she did not give an adequate history about herself. The therapist decided to aid the therapeutic process by interviewing the patient under Amytal. The patient felt relaxed and was verbalizing her intense negative feelings. Much of these were anger and resentment toward her father. She had memories of him having affairs with other women. She finally broke out into a violent expression of anger as she was recalling some sexual material that she witnessed. At that point, the patient's outburst was beyond control. She had to be kept under sedation around the clock. Her father's visits to the hospital presented some difficulties, so they had to be limited. When the father was asked to stop his visits, he would not agree, and interpreted it as a personal attack against him. He tried to stop the therapy and blamed the psychiatrist for worsening his daughter's condition. The daughter herself started to vent her anger against the therapist because of the failure of the treatment. Since the expression of a negative feeling toward a father is a taboo in this patriarchal culture, it is possible that the procedure followed by the therapist was extremely stressful for the patient. The failure of insight psychotherapy may be in part the result of the lack of trust in a stranger (the therapist) who is not entitled to share the family problems. The attempt of therapy to foster individual expression seems to clash with the collective identity of the client. Thus, it is not surprising that negative material related to the client's family and social group revealed during the therapy session may be easily forgotten or ignored during consequent sessions.

To sum up, the following are some culturally relevant aspects of psychotherapy we observed with Arab–Muslim clients:

1. The therapist needs to be assertive and direct and might take an advisory role, addressing the emotional as well as the cognitive component of the client's conflict and personality.
2. The therapist needs to constantly reevaluate the needs of the clients, who are in the position of learners, teaching them problem-solving techniques, and taking into consideration social norms and values during therapy.
3. The therapy might take the form of consolation (Muwasat) of the patient. Unloading the burden of the client's problems by talking about them strengthens the client–therapist relationship, and relieves the client of some of the stresses of the problem.
4. The therapist is expected to express more of his own personal emotions than in a Western-oriented psychotherapy. This will increase learning and relearning through the security of the therapeutic experience. This is particularly true since most of the changes occur as a result of the nature of

the relationship rather than from the interpretive process and exploratory psychotherapy.

5. The learning experience during therapy is "teacher-based" rather than "student-based." It is assumed in Western therapy that the learning experience should be "student based" in which the client is expected to do most of the active work. This may not be true in this culture where some modification of the function of the therapists is required; they have to be active in manipulating the client's environment, behavior and thoughts, in order to achieve change.

6. The dependency versus independency dichotomy accepted in the West cannot be applied in a communal society. It should be replaced by dependency versus interdependency, where society should be taken into consideration, and the social responsibility of the individual has to be emphasized. Unlike Western psychotherapy which aims at achieving clients' independence, Arab–Islamic psychotherapy attempts to teach the client to be interdependent. The emphasis is not on the clients' individuality or their personal beliefs, but on the extent to which they conform to accepted norms. Nor is there any expectation that the clients' behavior must be consistent with their own personal beliefs. They are expected to express the common beliefs and behave in a socially acceptable fashion. While Western norms put the emphasis on individuality, Arab–Islamic norms stress group harmony. The objective is to achieve "conformity" rather than "self-realization."

7. The outcome of treatment is often assessed by the ability of the clients to carry out their social roles and meet their social obligations. The emotional states of the client are given less attention by the family than daily functioning (chapter 11, this volume).

SOME ISLAMIC PRINCIPLES IN PSYCHOTHERAPY

The role of religious values in psychotherapy has long been recognized by mental health professionals (Bergin, 1991; see chapter 1, this volume). In the Arab–Islamic culture, religion plays a significant role in everyday life. It involves every aspect of social interactions, daily activity, marital interchange, raising children, and legal legislation. It is, therefore, difficult to practice medicine and psychiatry, much less psychotherapy, without having the Islamic principles adequately considered and adapted in the client–therapist relationship. Culture sensitive psychotherapy requires understanding and adaptation of Islamic principles as the core of the therapeutic relationship. Although many Muslim clients accept a non-Muslim therapist, a Muslim therapist will be closer to the client reality (Wikler, 1989; McKee and Worby, 1990).

In this section, selected aspects of Islamic principles that could be used and integrated in the psychotherapy process will be identified and discussed. These principles are presented under the following headings: spiritual support and reassurance, and some practical applications of Islamic principles.

Spiritual Support and Reassurance

Islam, like other great religions, provides a source of spiritual satisfaction to believers. The Islamic religious interpretations of many aspects of life as well as religious rituals can help clients in achieving inner satisfaction and mental peace (Ruschoff, 1992). The following are examples of how spiritual support and religious ideas could be integrated into the therapy procedure.

1. Faith: Faith in and of itself provides great peace of mind to any individual regardless of their own personal religion. However, there are other aspects of Islamic faith that could provide additional emotional support to clients. These aspects could sometimes be identified to the patient during therapy (Daie, Witztum, Mark, and Rubinowitz, 1992). Faith in God is the basis of Islamic belief in fate. It states that human life and destiny have been "written," and that the will of God has to be carried out. The belief in fate occasionally gives the client a sense of acceptance, especially when it is realized that God might have his own reason for making decisions. Many decisions or life events may first appear harmful to the individual. However, the Qu'ran gives an optimistic view of adverse events:

Say: Nothing shall ever happen to us except what Allah has
ordained for us [Al-Taubah 51]. It may be that you dislike a
thing which is good for you and that you like a thing which is
bad for you. Allah knows but you do not know [Al-Baquarah,
216].

Belief in the day of judgment could be very reassuring
when things go sour, when clients feel that they have been
denied their rights, or their fair share in life. The reward might
come later in the afterlife. The idea of reward, *thawab,* for the
good deeds and living as good Muslims (cf., Bilu, Witztum,
and van der Hart, 1990) may occasionally be reassuring and
satisfying to Muslim clients.

2. *Prayer and Hope:* Prayer that asks God for relief from a
misfortune, and hopes for God's reward and forgiveness can
be satisfying on certain occasions. If the therapist feels that
clients are hesitant about praying for God's relief of their symptoms, they might deal with the clients' hesitation, encouraging
prayer. When clients are strongly religious but their symptoms
hinder them from religious practice, the therapist's support
and guidance might be helpful.

Group prayer may contribute to the sense of identity and
belongingness. Both group prayer and fasting have strong social components that give the faithful a sense of identification
with others as well as social support.

3. *Patience:* Islamic belief endorses patience.

O you who believe! Seek help in patience and As-Salat (the
prayers). Truly Allah is with As-Sabirin (the patient ones) [Al-
Baquarah, 153]. Who when afflicted with calamity, say: Truly!
To Allah we belong and truly, to Him we shall return [Al-Ba-
quarah, 156].

Patience does not only mean feeling the pain of a misfortune without protest or complaint, but also the acceptance of
God's decision. For example, in the case of bereavement, Islamic philosophy encourages acceptance of loss and thus accel-
erates the process of grieving and enhances emotional
adjustment (Al-Esawi, 1986; Al-Adawi, Burjorjee, and Al-Issa,
1997).

4. The Role of Responsibility: It is clearly stated in the scripture that human beings are responsible for their actions, and they will be rewarded for their good and evil deeds: "Say, shall I seek a lord other than Allah, while He is the lord of all things? No person earns any (sin) except against himself (only) and no bearer of burdens shall bear the burden of another" (Al-Anam, 164). However, Islam acknowledges human limitations, and a Qur'anic verse states that God will not ask from a human being more than he or she can do: "Allah burdens not a person beyond his scope. He gets reward for that (good) which he has earned, and he is punished for that (evil) which he has earned" (Al-Baquarah, 206). It is an important Islamic principle that under certain circumstances, human beings are relieved of responsibility and their limitations are acknowledged. Clients who are facing circumstances that are beyond their control or ability may be relieved from responsibility and guilt (Al-Esawi, 1986). To reduce clients' guilt, they are reminded that Islam is the religion of leniency, *Din Asamah.* Islamic teachings put much stress on the value of forgiveness. God is the most forgiving, the most merciful, and He would forgive any kind of wrongdoing regardless of how serious it might be, so long as He is believed in. "Say: O Ibadi (my slaves) who have transgressed against themselves (by committing evil deeds and sins)! Despite not of the Mercy of Allah, verily Allah forgives all sins. Truly, He is oft-forgiving, Most merciful" (Al-Zumar, 53).

Islam distinguishes between intention and action. There is no accountability for intention unless it is translated into action. Therefore, the concept of sin in the "heart" does not exist in Islam. In fact, the Prophet Mohammed has stated that if a person has evil intentions but does not act on them, he or she will be rewarded for restraining from action. Many Muslim clients are relieved from guilt by knowing this Islamic principle.

Some Practical Applications of Islamic Principles

Some Islamic principles and rituals associated with them could be applied in the therapy situation with some benefits. Consider for example compulsive washing and cleanliness associated with ablution. One Islamic solution to this problem is to allow the patient to replace physical cleanliness by spiritual cleanliness. In this case, patients suffering from excessive washing may be asked to do *tayamūm,* a ritual in which the person will tap his or her hand on clean sand as an act of spiritual cleanliness and then touch different parts of the body with the same hand as if using water. This activity could replace ablution and prepare the patient for prayer. Obsessive–compulsive disorder also can manifest itself as an excessive preoccupation with prayer. This could be treated by having patients stop praying alone and confine their prayer to the mosque in a group led by an *imam,* the Muslim priest. This will release them from the responsibility of making errors or repeating the prayer over and over again. It appears that doubts about having committed an error during prayer or omitting part of it is the main and possibly the only reason for the obsessive–compulsive preoccupation with the prayer.

Group prayer may also be perceived as an activity that could be used in the process of desensitization in treatment of social phobia. Going to the mosque to attend group prayer may be integrated in the behavior therapy procedure in the treatment of agoraphobia. The act of ablution five times a day before prayer could enhance the process of relaxation.

In the treatment of temper tantrums and behavioral outbursts, the Prophet Mohammed made many statements on how to manage anger. The emphasis was not on the feeling of anger as such, but on acting on that feeling. The believers were instructed by the prophet to change their position or activity (stand instead of sitting, or stop walking) in order to control outbursts of emotions.

DISCUSSION

Many problems associated with the application of Western psychotherapy to Muslim–Arab patients are also found in dealing with other ethnic groups in the West (Sue and Sue, 1990). Western therapy is *individual centered,* in a one-to-one relationship, and encourages clients to take responsibility for their own affairs. In many societies, the basic psychosocial unit is not the individual but the family, the group and the whole community; and the identity of individuals is defined within the context of the family and the group. Many important personal decisions are carried out by the family and the group. Therapy is not a confrontation with the culture or the family, but an attempt to solve the client's problem within the context of their culture. It is important that the therapist show respect for, and acceptance of, the client's culture. Insight, or understanding the causes of one's abnormal behavior may not be highly valued by many culturally different groups. Patients come to therapy seeking guidance and advice and expect the therapist to take a direct approach. A highly structured, short-term, goal-directed therapy that deals with the problem at hand has been recommended to ethnic groups including Arab–Muslim patients (Peoples and Dell, 1975; Atkinson, Maruyama, and Matsui, 1978; Dauphinais, Dauphinais, and Rowe, 1981; Ruiz and Ruiz, 1983; Kinzie, 1985; Atkinson, Morten, and Sue, 1989; Dwairy and van Sickle, 1996).

Problems posed by patients are social and interpersonal rather than psychological conflicts. *Self-disclosure* as characterized by openness and intimacy and the revelation of personal or social problems may not be acceptable for non-Western people, since such problems reflect not only on the individual but also on the whole family. In communal societies the individual is trained not to reveal personal matters to strangers. In an Arab–Palestinian society in Israel, it was found that issues related to sexuality and the family may be threatening to the patient and could produce discomfort and early termination of therapy (Dwairy and van Sickle, 1996). In the West, psychotherapy works best with individuals who are verbal and able to express their thoughts and feelings clearly. The word *alexithymia* (from the Greek: *a* = lack, *lexis* = word, *thymos* = emotion) is used to describe a disturbance characterized by inability of the psychotherapy clients to verbalize their emotions or to elaborate on their fantasies. Such clients are usually rejected as unsuitable candidates for psychotherapy. In an Arab-Islamic society verbalization is not highly valued and is considered as a manifestation of assertiveness. In the Arab–Islamic culture, as well as in other cultures, children are taught not to speak unless they are spoken to (Sue and Sue, 1990). Verbal communication usually flows from those of higher prestige and status (father, therapist) to those of lower prestige and status. While the expression of emotions is encouraged in Western psychotherapy, restraint of feelings may be highly valued in other cultures. Control of emotions and feelings may be considered as a sign of maturity rather than an indication of inhibition or lack of spontaneity. Although there are commonalities in psychotherapy among non-Western groups, Arab–Islamic society has its unique features which are reflected in psychotherapy. The veil, polygymy, and arranged marriage are some of the unique features of this society and will be discussed in the remaining part of this section.

Female patients who refuse to uncover their face may present a problem of communication to the psychotherapist. The observation of facial emotional expression will be missed during the therapy session. The veil is sometimes used by female psychiatrists. This can be an anxiety-arousing experience, particularly for Westernized patients. Veiled psychiatrists on the other hand may have a positive influence on more conservative patients and their families. These female psychiatrists are more accepted and trusted than Westernized female psychiatrists who have thrown away the veil. They are also favored by female clients who are not allowed by their husbands to see male psychiatrists.

Although polygymy, which is allowed in Islam, is limited to a small minority, it is seen in the clinic as a problem facing many Muslim women, as demonstrated in the following case:

Samia is a 36-year-old female schoolteacher, married with one child (a boy, 14 years old). She was brought to the psychiatric clinic for an urgent appointment. The condition was described by her husband as a "total emotional collapse." He stated that since his wife found out that he had been maintaining another wife secretly for the last year in a separate house, she had become progressively unable to contain her anger. She was not able to work, was crying constantly, screaming and yelling at him, expressing her hatred toward him. The husband thought her reaction was unreasonable because he divorced his second wife shortly after Samia found out about her. Samia at that point was utterly overwhelmed and had to be hospitalized. Her anger was not only against her husband's secret second wife, but the husband's use of her money to support that wife. Samia and Ali (the husband) had a traditional arranged marriage. After having their first boy, Ali had an illness that made him infertile. Male infertility is a source of shame and embarrassment, but it is the wife who declared publicly that she was the one who was infertile so that the husband would keep his masculine image. He used his wife's "infertility" as an excuse to have another wife. In this culture, a wife's infertility is an acceptable and understandable reason for having another wife.

After a rather intense crisis intervention, couple therapy was instituted in an attempt by the therapist to have Samia accept the status quo. Her own family, represented by her brothers (since her father was dead), was opposed to her demand for divorce. Her brothers thought that her refusal to live in a polygamous setting was unreasonable.

During the therapy, another crisis arose. Ali was in need of money and asked for all of Samia's salary. Samia refused. Ali threatened to use his authority as a husband to prevent her from working (the law and tradition allow the husband to prevent his wife from working). In individual therapy, a solution was reached that she would give him half of her salary. Ali accepted this solution. Samia continued to live miserably with Ali thereafter with no apparent solution.

With rapid change and Westernization, arranged marriage may also create serious adaptation problems for young educated Arab–Muslim men who are torn between modernity and tradition:

Kamal is a 31-year-old male physician in residency, married for three years with a 2-year-old daughter. He was in regular weekly therapy for about two-and-a-half years. He had to change therapists during that time due to relocation. He sought psychiatric help shortly after marriage. He felt tense, angry, frustrated, and depressed with sleep difficulties. He had just been married to his first cousin. Their marriage was arranged while they were teenagers by the family. He felt that his marriage was

a disaster; his wife was uneducated, and had difficulty understanding him. However, Kamal did not accept that his marriage
was the cause of his symptoms and seemed to accept the fact
that he could obtain satisfaction outside his marriage.

The story of his marriage started after graduation from
medical school. He thought that he was old enough to start
having children. Since his orphan cousin was living in the same
household he felt obliged to marry her.

After two months in therapy, Kamal realized that he had
made a grave mistake and wanted to divorce his wife. However,
he discovered that his wife was pregnant and she later gave
birth to a daughter. His life still continued to be miserable
with her. After almost three years of therapy, Kamal grew more
resentful of her but this did not help him to make any decision.
The sense of obligation toward keeping his wife was too strong,
particularly with a child at home. Toward the end of the therapy, Kamal realized that he could not leave his wife although
he was extremely unhappy with her.

CONCLUSION

In this chapter, it is shown that psychotherapy is different in
Arab–Islamic countries from the West in its objectives and underlying assumptions. This is not surprising since psychotherapeutic practices are the product of different social and cultural
realities. Theory and practice of psychotherapy in the West
cannot adequately explain or guide the practice of psychotherapy in the context of the different reality in Arab–Muslim cultures. Unfortunately, there seems to be no theoretical
framework which can especially address the Arab–Islamic sociocultural context. This puts the Arab–Islamic therapist with
Western training in a dilemma. There is, therefore, inconsistency and incongruity between the therapists' acquired Western orientation (through training) and actual practice. At the
outset of their practice, they find themselves giving the client
contradictory messages and are not always sure what direction
psychotherapy should take because neither the objectives nor

the techniques of therapy in the new cultural setting are clear to them. With practice, however, therapists usually find a compromise in adapting Western techniques to the realities of the culture. There is clearly a need for a theoretical framework to guide and direct psychotherapeutic endeavors to enable an Islamic psychotherapy to develop its full potential.

REFERENCES

Al-Adawi, S., Burjorjee, R., & Al-Issa, I. (1997), Mughaib: A culture-specific response to bereavement in Oman. *Internat. J. Soc. Psychiatry,* 43:144–151.

Aponte, J. F., Rivers, R. Y., & Wohl, J., Eds. (1995), *Psychological Intervention and Cultural Diversity.* Boston: Allyn & Bacon.

Atkinson, D. R., Maruyama, M., & Matsui, S. (1978), The effects of counselor race and counseling approach on Asian Americans' perceptions of counselor credibility and utility. *J. Counsel. Psychol.,* 25:76–83.

———— Morten, G., & Sue, D. W. (1989), *Counseling American Minorities: A Cross Cultural Perspective,* 3rd ed. Dubuque, IA: Wm. C. Brown.

Bergin, A. E. (1991), Values and religious issues in psychotherapy and mental health. *Amer. Psychologist,* 46:394–403.

Bilu, Y., Witztum, E., & van der Hart, O. (1990), Paradise-regained: "Miraculous healing" in an Israeli psychiatric clinic. *Cult., Med. & Psychiatry,* 14:105–127.

Daie, N., Witztum, E., Mark, M., & Rubinowitz, S. (1992), The belief in the transmigration of souls: Psychotherapy of Druze patient with severe anxiety reaction. *Brit. J. Med. Psychology,* 65:119–130.

Dauphinais, R., Dauphinais, L., & Rowe, W. (1981), Effects of race and communication style on Indian perceptions of counselor effectiveness. *Counselor Ed. & Supervision,* 21:72–80.

Dwairy, M., & Sickle, D. van (1996), Western psychotherapy in traditional Arabic society. *Clin. Psychol. Rev.,* 16:231–249.

Al-Esawi, A. (1986), *Al-Islam Wal Ilaj Al-Nafsi* (Islam and Psychotherapy). Alexandria, Egypt: Dar Alfikr.

Frank, J. D. (1961), *Persuasion and Healing.* Baltimore: Johns Hopkins University Press.

Al-Issa, I. (1992), La investigación psychológica en Argelia: Personalidad abnormal. *Boletin de psicologia,* 34:57–73.

Kiev, A., Ed. (1964), *Magic, Faith and Healing*. London: Free Press.

Kinzie, J. D. (1985), Overview of clinical issues in the treatment of Southeast Asian refugees. In: *Southeast Asian Mental Health Treatment, Prevention Services, Training and Research*, ed. T. C. Owan. Washington, DC: National Institute of Mental Health.

McKee, D., & Worby, M. (1990), Comparing a Christian physicians' support group with the Balint Group. *J. Fam. Prac.*, 30:65–68.

Peoples, V. Y., & Dell, D. M. (1975), Black and white student preferences for counselor roles. *J. Counsel. Psychology*, 22:529–534.

Prince, R. H. (1976), Psychotherapy as the manipulation of endogenous healing mechanism: A transcultural survey. *Transcult. Psychiatric Res. Rev.*, 13:155–233.

——— (1980), Variations in psychotherapeutic procedures. In: *Handbook of Cross-Cultural Psychology*, Vol. 6, ed. H. C. Triandis & J. G. Draguns. Boston: Allyn & Bacon.

——— (1984), Shamans and endorphins: Exogenous and endogenous factors in psychotherapy. In: *Mental Health: The Cross-Cultural Context*, ed. P. B. Pedersen, N. Sartorius, & A. J. Marsella. Beverly Hills, CA: Sage, pp. 59–77.

Al-Rakkawi, Y. (1978), *The Secret of the Game*. Cairo: Dal Al-Ghad.

Ruiz, P., & Ruiz, P. P. (1983), Treatment compliance among Hispanics. *J. Operational Psychiatry*, 14:112–114.

Ruschoff, S. L. (1992), The importance of Islam religious philosophy for psychiatric practice. *Psychiatric Prox.*, 19:39–42.

Sue, D. W., & Sue, D. (1990), *Counseling the Culturally Different*, 2nd ed. New York: Wiley.

Torrey, E. F. (1972), *The Mind Game*. New York: Emerson Hall.

Wikler, M. (1989), The religion of the therapists: Its meaning to Orthodox Jewish clients. *J. Clin. Psychiatry*, 11:131–146.

Wittkower, E. D., & Warnes, H. (1974), Cultural aspects of psychotherapy. *Amer. J. Psychother.*, 28:566–573.

Zewan, M. (1986), *Collected Papers in Psychoanalysis and Psychosomatics*. Beirut: Dar Al-Nahda (in Arabic).

13.

Sex and Sexual Dysfunction in an Arab–Islamic Society

Mona Al-Sawaf, Ihsan Al-Issa

Although sexuality is biologically determined, there are wide variations among peoples of the world in the restrictions placed on sexual behavior. Societies range from those that restrict sexual behavior and consider it an evil that should be avoided to those that encourage sexual experimentation and sexual exploration during early childhood (Ford and Beach, 1952). Islam preaches moderation and tolerance and stands between these two extremes. Taking both historical and sociocultural perspectives, Bullough (1976) considered Islam as a sex-positive religion in contrast to early Christianity which is depicted as a sex-negative religion. While castration and self-mutilation to avoid sex were reported among some early Christians, the enjoyment of sex within Islamic rules was characteristic of a good Muslim. However, there is little research on sexual behavior in the present Muslim countries. Similarly, in dealing with sexual problems and sexual dysfunction, the only available information comes from psychiatric clinics which are dominated by methods of treatment originating in the West (Masters and Johnson, 1970). In this chapter, we deal first with sexuality in traditional Islamic society. Second, we report clinical data on the treatment of sexual dysfunction in an outpatient clinic in Jedda,

Saudi Arabia. We also report a culture-specific sexual dysfunction characterized by a morbid fear of sex prevalent among
females in that country.

ISLAMIC SEXUAL ATTITUDES

For Muslims, sexual attitudes are based on the Qur'an and the
teachings of the Prophet Mohammed who followed the Arabic
tradition considering sex as a good rather than an evil aspect
of everyday life. The Qur'an encourages sexuality within the
framework of marriage: "marry such women as seem good to
you two, three, four; but if you fear you will not be equitable,
then only one, or what your right hands own; so it is likelier
you will not be partial" (Sura, 4, verse 3). This Sura from the
Qur'an indicates a basic difference between Islam and Christianity in attitudes toward sexuality. Such a difference between
the two religions is well expressed by Pickthall (1953). "For
Christianity, celibacy is the strictest religious ideal; even monogamy is a concession to human nature. For Mussulmans the ideal
is monogamy, the concession to human nature is polygamy"
(pp. 405–406). Although polygamy is allowed in Islam, it is
conditional on the equitable treatment of the wives. There is a
tacit endorsement of monogamy in the Qur'an. The Sura that
allowed polygamy (4, 3) also tells husbands that they will never
be able to treat their wives impartially, no matter how much
they try (4, 129). Another Qur'anic verse also discourages polygamy: "God has not provided two hearts in the body of any
man" (33, 4).

One reason for allowing polygamy among early Muslims
was to provide husbands for the many widows after heavy Muslim fatalities at the Ūhud battle. Phipps (1996) cites Al-Bukhari
which stated that the prophet said, "A woman is married for
four things: her wealth, her family status, her beauty, and her
religion" (p. 143). Thus the motive behind marriage is not
always entirely sexual. Phipps (1996) noted that "this saying
expresses some of the reasons why the prophet married: he was
probably influenced by Khadija's wealth, Umm-Habiba's family
status, Safiya's beauty, and Aisha's religion" (p. 143).

In contrast to Christianity, deep Muslim religiosity does not mean the inhibition of sexuality. Badri (1979) stated that the Qur'an refers to the joy of sex as a gift from Allah to mankind and that it will be the reward of the faithful in paradise. A nineteenth century author summarized the attitude of Muslims toward sexuality that reflects the teaching of the Qur'an and the Prophet Mohammed: "Coition is one of the causes of the preservation of health. Let him among you who is in a condition for having sufficient copulation marry: marriage gives moderation of the gaze and more obligatorily turns one away from incest and adultery" (Haleby, 1949, p. 10).

The joy of sex and the mutual happiness of marriage partners is alluded to in the Qur'an: "He created partners for you that you might comfort one another, and He ordained between you love and kindness" (30, 21). Attention is particularly given to the sexual satisfaction of the wife "Leave not your wife in suspense" (4, 129).

Sexual attitudes and behavior of Muslims are expressed in many sex manuals which describe love and sexual activity as a natural and a necessary part of life and the divine creation with no obsession or guilt feeling. Walton (1963) described these manuals as follows:

> Here we have affectionate consideration together with a highly developed "art of love," each based upon a reverence for religion, marriage, and family life. Sexual technique is encouraged as a natural means towards the happiness of the individual, the stability of the home, and, not least, the achievement of that union symbolic of the unity of the Divine. These, then, are the special and ideal characteristics of Oriental erotic treatises. That individuals and even groups, sometimes in quite considerable numbers, should fall short of the attainment of such ideals, is quite understandable. But at least the better way has clearly been delineated for them [p. 41].

One of the most popular of these manuals is *Kitáb Ruju'a al-Shaykh ila Sibāh (old man, young again)*. How the popular sex culture is shared widely by Muslims is indicated by our observation that this book is available in the semiliterate villages along the border between Iraq and Iran near the Persian Gulf as well as from the street sellers in the Arab Quarter near the Saint-Charles railway station in Marseilles, France. The author of the manual, Ahmad bin Sulayman, provides the reader with a list of seven other sex manuals that are popular in the Islamic world. Another well-known manual, translated into French and English is *Al Raud al atir wa nuzhat al Khatir (The Perfumed Garden)* written by Shaykh Umar ibn Muhammed Al-Nefzawi in the sixteenth century. The aim of this manual as well as others was to teach the public healthy sexual attitudes and practices as well as to promote a happy marital life.

In *The Perfumed Garden,* Nefzawi dealt with the physical aspects of sexuality, sexual techniques, and various coital positions. He also dealt with aphrodisiacs, stimulant foods, medicines, and the types of desirable men and women which are described according to physical appearance and temperament. The ideal of feminine beauty is a plump woman with oval cheeks, scarlet lips, firm breasts, rounded thighs, broad hips, a long neck, shining dark eyes, black hair or hair dyed with henna, and an erect posture.

The narratives, folktales, and poetry reported throughout *The Perfumed Garden* to illustrate the author's points give the reader a sense of the reality of sexuality in the everyday life of Muslim society. The contents and style of the stories is a reminder of the Arabian Nights. There is a recognition in the manual of gender differences in the sexual response. Much space is devoted to encouraging foreplay before intercourse. The emphasis is on increasing and prolonging of sexual pleasure and helping men and women avoid sexual satiation and monotony. Much attention is given to the delay of orgasm *(Imsāk)* to achieve mutual satisfaction with the partners. Many prescriptions reported in the manual to arouse women for intercourse are based on the ideas and practices of medieval Muslim physicians such as Avicenna (1966) and Al-Kindi (1966). Avicenna, for example, thought that women are colder and moister than men; it was necessary to arouse these women for intercourse. A good Muslim should indulge in some foreplay. Al-Kindi (1966) also reported many prescriptions for the increase of sexual arousal in women.

SEXUAL DYSFUNCTION IN SAUDI ARABIA

In Saudi Arabia as well as in many other Islamic countries, social and tribal pressures still govern many sexual behaviors and marriage. Marriage is still arranged for couples and only minimum attention is given to sex, affection, or the quality of the forthcoming marital relationship. Since male sexual potency and fertility are the cementing foundation of the marital relationship, marriages which are infertile can hardly ever survive for more than a few months. Thus, in their attempt to demonstrate dominance and sexual prowess, males may become overanxious about their sexual performance. In fact, the dominant theme of the young male's private conversation centers around sexual potency with misconceptions about male virility. This is not surprising in a culture where a popular character in the Arabian Nights manages to possess 40 women 30 times each in one night. Newly married young males are confronted with a formidable task in which their relentless effort to conform to these unreasonably high expectations of sexual performance could result in the development of severe anxiety.

In contrast, females are brought up to inhibit their sexual desires and fantasies, resulting in severe guilt and anxiety, particularly during early puberty. The emphasis on virginity in this culture may also result in anxiety and the avoidance of sex.

With this cultural background, we decided to study in detail the different types of sexual dysfunction and problems associated with their treatment in a clinic in an acute-care general hospital in Saudi Arabia.

TYPES OF SEXUAL DYSFUNCTION AND THEIR TREATMENT

The patients consisted of all cases at our clinic with sexual dysfunctions with no organic basis over a period of one year (July 1991 to June 1992). Because the main aim of the study was to identify the most common sexual dysfunctions seen in the clinic and their sociocultural implications, only Arab married couples were included (as cases of unmarried couples or cohabitants do not come to the attention of the general hospitals since they violate Islamic laws which considers such conditions as sinful and deserving of punishment). During this period, a total of 38 males were seen, including 25 with erectile dysfunction (66%) and 13 (34%) with ejaculation disorder accompanied by weak or partial erection. Thus, erectile dysfunction was almost universal among patients. Among the 38 males, 20 were governmental employees, 8 were self-employed, 6 were university students, and 4 were unemployed. Only five females were seen during the same period, two of them complained of vaginismus and the remaining three complained of dyspareunia. No female complained of other sexual disorders such as desire or orgasmic disorders. All the females were housewives. The majority of the male patients (33 patients; 87%) and all female patients were referred from the dermatology, venereology, or gynecology clinics after excluding organic causes, while five patients approached the clinic directly.

Erectile Dysfunction

There were a total of 25 married males with erectile dysfunction: 14 patients were Saudi, 5 Yemeni, 3 Sudanese, and 3 from other neighboring Arab countries. The duration of their marriages ranged from two weeks to 26 years. Nine patients were married for less than six months, with another six married for less than one year for a total of 15 patients (60%) being married for less than one year. Six of the remaining 10 patients were married for less than 5 years and only 4 patients were married for more than 7 years. Only 2 patients were married to more than one wife (in Islam it is quite acceptable for a man to have up to four wives at a time). Twelve patients were between 20 and 30 years, 10 patients between 31 and 40 years, and only 3 patients were between 54 and 68 years. Eighty-eight percent of the patients were younger than 40 years of age. Twenty-one patients had developed their erectile disorder suddenly after having one successful intercourse in the same night, but 18 patients suffered from a total disorder, and the remaining 3 had a situation disorder (with wife only). The duration of symptoms was relatively short (2 weeks to 5 months). Although an objective measurement of sexual anxiety was not carried out, self-report and clinical assessment showed that 23 patients (92%) were extremely anxious, agitated, and depressed, and 6 of them reported severe suicidal ideations generated by their intense fear of losing potency.

All the patients who were married for less than one year reported daily intercourse, very often more than twice a day throughout their entire marital life. Few of them admitted resorting to masturbation whenever their wives were menstruating. The six patients who were married for less than five years also maintained that they had daily intercourse but only occasionally exceeded once a day!

Because of the intensity of their reaction and the severity of their anxiety, patients were put on drug therapy for at least a few days. Diazepam (Valium 5 mg) was used with the first four patients but was found to be ineffective. Clozabam (Frisium 10 mg) was then substituted and proved to be superior to Valium, and was used for all the patients with erectile dysfunction. Clozabam was prescribed to be taken on a daily basis at least half an hour before going to bed with an emphasis on its function in enhancing performance and a deemphasis on its sedative quality. Drug therapy was combined with a modified Masters and Johnson (1970) technique in which patients were banned from intercourse for a minimum of 10 days but encouraged to engage in mutual, pleasurable sexual activities and masturbation when they felt like doing it. It was stressed that sexual activity other than intercourse is not religiously prohibited or sinful. During the first interview, a detailed interpretation of the vicious circle of performance anxiety and impotency was explained to the patient to show him the nature of his problem, and he was accordingly advised to avoid goal-oriented or self-testing sexual practices. The outcome of treatment was rather impressive: 21 patients (84%) were functioning normally within two to six weeks. Four of these patients actually resumed their sexual activity even before the end of the no intercourse time limit (10 days), 13 patients regained their normal function during the second or third week after encouragement from their therapist, and only 4 patients needed to continue treatment for up to six weeks before they had the first successful and satisfactory intercourse. Only 2 patients failed to improve and dropped out of the program.

Premature Ejaculation

There were 13 patients, 11 Saudis and 2 Yemeni. Seven of the patients were 41 to 50 years old, 4 between 51 and 62 years, and only 2 were younger than 40 years (29 years and 35 years). They were significantly older than the patients with erectile disorder and were married for longer durations (8–35 years). Four of them had more than one wife. Ten patients reported secondary disorder (for example, 4 of them after marrying the second wife) while the other 3 patients seemed to have a primary disorder. All patients complained of weak erections which in many instances seemed to be due to emotional problems rather than to a real physical weakness. Their sexual life continued to be active despite their difficulties: 6 patients maintained intercourse 2 to 3 times per week, 5 patients maintained daily intercourse, even though some of them were married for more than 10 years. The other 2 patients (married for 26 and 25 years) reported infrequent sexual activity.

The patients with premature ejaculation were treated with a combination of drugs and modified Masters and Johnson squeezing technique. The squeezing technique was found to be either ineffective or intolerable by most of the patients. Due to their high anxiety and failure of the squeeze technique, patients were advised to continue on thioridazine (Mellaril) in small doses (10–25 mg) every night. Seven patients improved remarkably via this therapy while the other 6 patients stopped coming to the clinic after a few consultations with no significant improvement. Generally, the outcome of treatment of premature ejaculation was poor.

Vaginismus and Dyspareunia

The two females with vaginismus were prescribed diazepam (Valium 5–10 mg) in one dose before intercourse after a detailed explanation of the joy of intercourse, giving them much reassurance. Both female patients did well and their respective marriages were consummated within a few days after treatment. Patients with dyspareunia were resistant to treatment and many needed joint counseling and drug therapy before they dropped out.

VIRGINITY, CULTURE-SPECIFIC SEX PHOBIA, AND HYMENECTOMY

In Saudi Arabia as well as in other countries in the Arabian peninsula, psychiatrists see virgin female clients with coitophobia (sex phobia) which usually starts on the wedding night as a result of an exaggerated cultural belief in the physical pain of penetration due to the rupture of the hymen (see chapter 5). We present two cases from Saudi Arabia of a nomadic woman and a schoolteacher with coitophobia. The first case is of a 21-year-old female from a nomadic and illiterate background who was referred from the infertility clinic. She had been married for three years (since the age of 18) to her cousin who was a 36-year-old soldier and father of three children from a previous marriage. The patient was interviewed alone as her husband refused to participate in the treatment. She expressed having a great fear of sexual intercourse. She felt shy and ill at ease during the foreplay. She refused to undress in front of her husband and always insisted on turning off the lights. When he tried to penetrate she became extremely fearful and stiff, cried, and refused to allow him to proceed any further. Her behavior initially was tolerated by the husband but later he became angry and suspicious that she might not be a virgin and she was acting out in a way to avoid being discovered. Furthermore, his family was pushing her to seek medical advice about not having children. Her severe anxiety and phobia of sex seemed to be the result of her belief that penetration and hymenal removal are very painful and could cause massive bleeding. This may explain her refusal of intercourse. The first step in the treatment was to give the patient thorough and detailed information about the anatomy of the vagina, as well as the sexual response cycle and physiological changes. Her husband was interviewed after a great deal of persuasion. He refused the use of vaginal dilators but agreed about the surgical removal of the hymen. The patient was given Ativan (lorazepam) 0.5 mg. which reduced her anxiety during the surgical procedure. She continued to attend the psychiatric clinic for about a month after surgery. After the operation, she was able to tolerate vaginal intercourse quite easily which resulted in a pregnancy.

A second case is of a 28-year-old Saudi female teacher, a university graduate who had been married for almost seven years with no children, and who was seen at the request of her husband (the husband himself had been admitted to the psychiatric inpatient unit in a delirious state after taking different kinds of medications for impotence given to him by a private psychiatrist). He stated that he had been married for seven years to his cousin who was eight years younger than he. Since the wedding night, he was unable to perform with her because of weak erection. His wife remained a virgin. Both the patient and her husband kept their sexual difficulties secret from everyone including their families. Yet, as the pressure from his family increased, urging him to get another wife, and blaming the present wife for not having children, he decided to seek medical help.

At the interview she expressed having a great fear of sexual intercourse because she believed that intercourse could be very painful. She suffered from vaginismus. However, because her husband suffered from erectile dysfunction, her vaginismus was not yet a problem. She was anxious and depressed, especially because of the criticism by her in-laws for not having children. In order to alleviate her depression and anxiety, she was put on amitriptyline 75 mg daily. During the third week of treatment, she was given information about the nature of sexual activity. She and her husband agreed about the surgical removal of her hymen which was done after a period of relaxation training. The husband also received treatment for his sexual dysfunction. After the operation, she became less anxious and depressed. The couple were able to perform quite successfully eight months after the start of treatment.

DISCUSSION

Cases reported in this chapter are not meant to demonstrate the effectiveness of drug therapy or the Masters and Johnson methods in the treatment of sexual dysfunction. Since no definite criterion for patient selection and no controls were used, conclusions about treatment outcome are unwarranted. However, these cases raise some cross-cultural issues in the development and treatment of sexual dysfunctions.

In contrast to the majority of Western reports (Hawton, 1991) which indicate that the number of males and females seeking help at sexual clinics is more or less similar, we found that females only rarely present with sexual dysfunction (5 females and 38 males in this sample). The other striking feature was the total absence of complaints among females related to orgasm, which are by far the most commonly encountered problems in Western countries (Cole, 1985; Hawton, 1991). The five female patients in this sample presented complaints related to physical performance (i.e., vaginismus or dyspareunia) which highlights the significance of performance over sexual satisfaction. This trend may be attributed to the tendency of females to seek help only when intercourse for the benefit of the male is interfered with. In Saudi Arabia, it is quite possible that women may not seek help for sexual dysfunction unless they are advised by the husband. Indeed, they are not considered as being sexually dysfunctional unless they present physical complaints which interfere with their passive role during the sexual act or impair their reproductive functions. Such remarkable differences in the ratio of females to males and the differential variation of their symptoms are difficult to attribute only to constitutional factors; rather, the restrictive upbringing and the pervasive tendency to continuously suppress sexual expression and satisfaction in females may be the major effective factor.

In Western countries, the sex revolution of the early 1970s (e.g., Masters and Johnson, 1970; Kaplan, 1974) made emotional and sexual satisfaction the primary objective of female sexuality. Thus female sex anxieties center mainly around sexual interest and orgasm which account for the high frequency of disorders in these areas. In contrast, in the present sample, all females presented disorders related to physical performance and avoidance of intercourse rather than sexual interest or orgasmic dysfunction.

In Saudi Arabia and other Muslim countries, sexual potency is highly valued and the dominant male seems to preserve his manhood by maintaining a highly active and potent sexual life. Any compromise, real or imagined, in the area of potency may generate intense fear and anxiety and initiate the vicious circle of performance anxiety—erectile dysfunction or premature ejaculation. Cole (1985) suggested that sex stress may interact with biological factors to result in either erectile dysfunction or ejaculatory problems. He pointed out that cultural differences in sexual dysfunction may indicate the effect of constitutional factors. Asians predominantly complain of ejaculatory problems, while West Indians frequently develop erectile dysfunction. Our data suggest that older age may be a factor in ejaculatory problems as compared with erectile dysfunction problems. Ejaculatory problems also seem to be more associated with having a second wife. Future study of other differential characteristics of the two groups of patients in the Saudi population is warranted.

Eighty-eight percent of the patients with erectile disorder sought help from a traditional healer compared to none among the premature ejaculators. This may be the result of the imputation of erectile dysfunction to supernatural causation which may act, at least temporarily, as an effective buffer system against a wife's protest against her husband's failing potency. Wives who believe strongly in bewitchment may only support their husbands if the problem is due to supernatural powers. The two females with vaginismus were still receiving some kind of local treatment when seen in the clinic. All patients who visited a traditional healer believed that the suddenness of the onset of their disorders, coupled with being relatively newly married, evoked their anxiety and fear of being bewitched or possessed by the *Jinni* (devil). Their symptoms were also imputed to the evil eye or sorcery. An ex-wife, co-wife, ex-fiancée, or an envious neighbor was usually believed to be responsible for these evil actions.

Because of the taboo on sexuality in the Saudi culture, complaints of sexual dysfunction are frequently discovered accidentally in the process of marital therapy. Sexual dysfunction as a marital problem is usually hidden and occasionally misrepresented as part of marital dysfunction. While marital dysfunction is usually referred to therapy through the female partner, sexual dysfunction is the main concern of the male. When a woman presents herself in therapy for a sexual problem in marriage, it often turns out to be a specific concern about, or fears of, losing the husband. Men are often reluctant to participate in sex therapy with the wife. They feel that it is inappropriate for her to know about their sexual problem or discuss it with a stranger in the clinic. Sex therapy with couples is almost impossible since the discussion of sexuality between husband and wife is taboo.

Even though female complaints are restricted to vaginismus and dyspareunia, clinical experience suggests that low sexual desire is probably one of the most frequent symptoms of these patients. When male low sexual desire is presented, it is usually secondary to depression or to other specific factors. However, in the female the cause is more difficult to identify. There are several factors that can produce this kind of disorder. In the Saudi culture, the female is brought up to behave in a conservative and socially acceptable manner which includes a modest dress code and an avoidance of behavior with sexual connotations. Girls are taught that enjoying sex is not what a good girl should do. This phenomenon is well illustrated by the continued practice of female circumcision in some Islamic countries (Egypt and Sudan) in order to decrease the pleasurable sensation of sex by cutting off the clitoris and parts of the labia minora. Psychological inhibition of sexual behavior will often continue into the marriage. A woman who has been inhibiting her sexual feelings from childhood will find it difficult to change suddenly after marriage. Arranged marriage may also interfere with the enjoyment of sexuality. Women are usually instructed by their mothers to accept passively the sexual advances of the husband, and they are not expected to express their own feelings but to accept sex as a duty to give sexual satisfaction to the male. Couples have little or no opportunity to interact with each other prior to their marriage, making the wedding night the first opportunity to meet. The treatment of low sexual desire is the most difficult with the highest failure rate. When this disorder is secondary to depression, prognosis is better and antidepressants are often used along with psychotherapy.

In a culture that gives much emphasis to masculinity, the pressure of performance is expected to be stressful for the male. Males are traditionally expected to consummate the marriage during the wedding night. Married couples have to perform with anxious family members outside their bedroom awaiting the proof of the bride's virginity, the blood-stained bedsheets or another piece of cloth. Needless to say, this ritual puts undue pressure on the male to perform, resulting in performance anxiety and "wedding night impotence" (Bazzoui and Al-Issa, 1966). Males with more than one wife are under pressure to prove that they can deal with the sexual demands of polygyny, especially when a new wife is of a much younger age. Females who are experiencing their first sexual encounter during the wedding night tend to develop vaginismus.

The basic principles of sex therapy as stated in the classical work of dual sex therapy and other kinds of treatment of sexual dysfunction, are basically not different in the treatment of Muslim patients. However, to accommodate this therapy to Arab–Muslim patients, certain specific modifications are needed; for example, in a traditional Muslim culture the sensate focus exercises or masturbation as described by Masters and Johnson (1970) would not be used in the same explicit manner as outlined by the originators of this method of therapy. Although dual therapy is strongly emphasized in the West,

Muslim patients find it difficult and socially embarrassing to have their wife or husband present in the doctor's office and have their most private and intimate problems discussed. The husband's pride often prevents him from disclosing his weaknesses in front of his wife. The male dysfunctional partner is quite often unwilling to have his wife interviewed, especially if she has to unveil. Sex therapy has to be carried out with only one partner. By the same token, because of the moral values of the culture, the use of sexual surrogates is strongly prohibited.

It is sometimes difficult if not impossible to conduct an explicit sexual interchange between a male therapist and a female patient or vice versa. When the dysfunctional partner is a female, then the choice of a female therapist would be the most appropriate. Sex segregation is the main factor putting gender barriers between patients and therapists. In a situation where there is a male–female therapist team, the presence of a male therapist is inhibitory, embarrassing, and confusing to a female patient. Husbands are also unwilling to have their wives' private affairs discussed in front of a male therapist.

Finally, since Islamic religion plays a major role in the lifestyle, attitudes, and moral values of patients, clarifying some Islamic principles that make sex less threatening is necessary. Failing to understand Islamic teaching results in strong prohibitions and inhibition of sexual urges. Reeducation of the patient about the permissiveness of Islam and its acceptance of human sexuality is necessary, Islamic principles are evident in many of the Prophet's sayings and in the Qur'an. For example, a 29-year-old male patient suffering from erectile dysfunction objected to our suggestion that his wife take a superior position during intercourse. The Qur'an is explicit about variations in sexual intercourse and the male patient was persuaded by recitation of the following sura: "Your women are a tillage for you; so come into your tillage as you wish" (Sura 2:223). With Islam as a sex-positive religion, religious sex education is warranted in Islamic society in order to change faulty attitudes toward sexuality.

SUMMARY

The chapter deals with attitudes toward sexuality in traditional Islamic society as well as with sexual dysfunction among males and females in Saudi Arabia. Islam is depicted as a sex-positive religion. Sexual behavior and sexual instructions are not only explicitly described in folktales and classics such as the Arabian Nights but also in manuals which circulate throughout the Muslim world.

Although Islam accepts sexuality as a natural and a healthy part of human life, patients from Saudi Arabia manifest negative attitudes toward sexuality quite similar to those of dysfunctional patients characterized by religious orthodoxy in North America (Masters and Johnson, 1970). Sexual dysfunction is a male problem with females seeking therapy only when the problem interferes with the sexual performance of the male (e.g., vaginismus and dyspareunia). Orgasmic dysfunction is the most prevalent disorder among females in the West but it is hardly seen in the clinics in Saudi Arabia. Young patients tend to suffer from erectile dysfunction while older patients with more than one wife tend to complain about premature ejaculation. Many principles of sex therapy outlined in sex manuals in the West, including the Masters and Johnson technique, have to be modified to suit a conservative society in Saudi Arabia. The emphasis of the Saudi culture on virginity seems to be associated with a culture-specific fear of sex that requires hymenectomy before sexual intercourse can take place.

REFERENCES

Avicenna. (1966), *Canon of Medicine,* tr. Mazhar H. Shah. Kharachi: Naveed Clinic.

Badri, M. B. (1979), *The Dilemma of Muslim Psychologists.* London: MWH.

Bazzoui, W., & Al-Issa, I. (1966), Psychiatry in Iraq. *Brit. J. Psychiatry,* 112:827–832.

Bullough, V. L. (1976), *Sexual Variance in Society and History.* Chicago: University of Chicago Press.

Cole, M. (1985), Sex therapy: A critical appraisal. *Brit. J. Psychiatry,* 147:337–351.

Ford, C. S., & Beach, F. A. (1952), *Patterns of Sexual Behavior.* New York: Ace Books.

Haleby, O. (1949), *The Sex Laws of Mohammed,* tr. A. F. Niemoeller. Girard, KS: Haldeman-Julius.

Hawton, K. (1991), *Sex Therapy: A Practical Guide.* Oxford: Oxford Medical Publications.

Kaplan, H. S. (1974), *The New Sex Therapy: Active Treatment of Sexual Dysfunctions.* New York: Brunner/Mazel.

Al-Kindi. (1966). *The Medical Formulatary of Arābādhīn,* tr. M. Lesy. Madison, WI: University of Wisconsin Press.

Masters, W. H., & Johnson, V. E. (1970), *Human Sexual Inadequacy.* Boston: Little Brown.

Nefzawi Shaykh (1963), *The Perfumed Garden,* tr. R. Burton. London: Neville Spearman.

Phipps, W. E. (1996), *Muhammed and Jesus: A Comparison of the Prophets and Their Teaching.* New York: Continuum (A Paragon House Book).

Pickthall, M. M. (1953), *The Meaning of the Glorious Koran.* New York: New American Library.

Walton, A. (1963), Introduction to *The Perfumed Garden,* by S. Nefzawi, tr. R. Burton. London: Neville Spearman.

V.

Epilogue

14.

Does the Muslim Religion Make a Difference in Psychopathology?

Ihsan Al-Issa

Research has clearly demonstrated that religiosity within a Judeo-Christian context is conducive to better mental health (see chapter 1) and it is tempting to generalize the findings to all other religions including Islam. Considering the overall evidence provided in the present volume, readers should be hesitant to reach either positive or negative conclusions about the relationship between Muslim religion and psychopathology. There has been a substantial amount of research carried out in Muslim countries on mental illness, but it has not directly dealt with religious observance. Although Islam originated in the Arabian Peninsula and is based on the Qur'an and the behavior and tradition of the Prophet, it has been adapted to multicultural environments in Asia, Africa, and other parts of the world. Thus, the investigation of the psychopathology of Muslims tends to be confounded by national or local factors and it is difficult to determine whether the results are related to Muslim doctrine or to other sociocultural factors reported by the investigators. Many beliefs and practices in Muslim countries go back to the pre-Islamic period and may have nothing to do with Islam. Overall, there is a paucity of information and

315

research which attempted to partial out the effects of confounding factors on the relationship between Muslim beliefs
and psychopathology.

However, speculation about the health benefits of Muslim
beliefs and rituals, particularly the preventive effects of the five
pillars of Islam, are abounding (the five pillars are the confession of the faith [shihada], the five daily prayers, almsgiving,
fasting during the lunar month of Ramadan, and the pilgrimage
to Mecca). Abou El Azayem and Hedayat-Diba (1994), for example, claim that prayer can be "preventive . . . against anxiety
and depression" (p. 45); almsgiving "promotes an emotional
attitude of generosity and gratitude that is believed to be preventive against depression, guilt feelings, and crime" (p. 46);
and "street crimes are practically nonexistent in Muslim countries" (p. 49). However, data in support of these claims are
lacking. Official statistics may underestimate the rates of mental illness in Muslim countries and the report of rates close to
zero of certain abnormalities (e.g., alcoholism in Saudi Arabia)
may only reflect lack of recognition of the problem rather than
being the result of the application of the Islamic law (Al-Yahya,
1991). Because of the use of native healers, many psychiatric
problems do not come to the attention of psychiatrists. There
is also some evidence that a substantial number of patients who
use modern psychiatric services in many Muslim countries are
young, educated persons in their second or third decades
whose psychiatric problems (emotional disturbance, schizophrenia, attempted suicide) are precipitated by intergenerational conflicts related to "family relationship, marriage, and
the emancipation of women" (chapters 5 and 9, this volume;
Osseiran, 1995).

The dependence of Muslim countries on foreign psychiatrists as consultants may create cultural misunderstanding and
misperception of Muslim behavior and customs. Many reports
by these psychiatrists are based on fiction rather than fact. For
example, Kline (1963) reported that 10 percent of Kuwaitis
are alcoholics, and 90 percent of the males had homosexual
relationships! More recently, another visitor to Saudi Arabia

(Dubovsky, 1983) described a frequently used Muslim invocation as an obstacle to the acceptance of health services and the treatment of psychiatric illnesses such as depression:

> Very difficult to manage is an almost universal attitude known as *in'shallah* (as God wills), a pervasive belief that good or bad outcomes, including whether one becomes ill, improves, or dies, are entirely in God's hands. As a result, patients may not obtain immunization, follow through with a medical regimen, or remain in the hospital, while they convey a passivity that mimics helplessness and makes achieving a therapeutic alliance in which the patient is actively involved in his or her own care extremely difficult [Dubrovsky, 1983, p. 1456].

Another foreign psychiatrist (El-Gaaly, 1984) in Saudi Arabia suggested that the word *in'shallah* is equivalent to the word *please* or *thank you* and it is not pervasive in Muslim society! In a therapeutic context, the term *in'shallah* (as God wills) indeed means that by the will of God, the patient will be cured, but it does not imply that this will happen without medication (this is evident in large governmental investment in modern medicine in Muslim countries). It is an Islamic medium of expressing optimism about the future and the expectation that individual effort is always combined with the help of God. This interpretation is more consistent with the Qur'anic verse that "Verily never will God change the condition of a people until they change it themselves (with their own souls)" (8, 11). Speculations such as the ones reported by Kline, Dubovsky, and Gaaly do not increase knowledge of how Islamic culture influences mental illness and its treatment.

I will first describe the collectivist communal context of psychopathology in the Muslim culture and compare it with the Western individualistic context. Second, I discuss Islamic psychiatry within the framework of the *new transcultural psychiatry* and compare it with current psychiatry in Islamic countries. Third, I present an overview of major psychopathology in Muslim countries covered in this volume (schizophrenia, depression, anxiety disorders, alcoholism and drug abuse, somatoform disorders, sexuality and sexual dysfunction). Finally, I deal with psychotherapy in an Islamic context.

THE SOCIAL CONTEXT OF PSYCHOPATHOLOGY IN ISLAMIC SOCIETIES

Collectivist vs. Individualistic Societies

Similar to many non-Western societies, Islamic society has a collectivist social structure which is different from the individualistic style of European–American society. Collectivist society emphasizes interdependence with others in the extended family, the tribe, and the community at large, rather than independence and self-assertion which characterize individualistic society. Within a collectivist context, people tend to view behavior as determined by what the person perceives to be the thoughts, feelings, and actions of others in a relationship. In contrast, the European–American culture conceives the person as an autonomous entity who behaves primarily as a result of internal attributes such as traits, abilities, motives, and values (Markus and Kitayama, 1991, 1994).

Individualistic and collectivist orientation may have some implications for the explanation of behavior. An individualistic society explains behavior in terms of personal attributes and disposition while a collectivist society utilizes explanations based on social roles, obligations, and situational constraints (Marcus, Kitayama, and Heiman, 1996). In the West, it has been well established that subjects tend to show what psychologists call *fundamental attribution error* or the tendency to explain behavior on the basis of internal predispositions and attributes. For most people of the world, however, such as the Arabs (Al-Zahrani and Kaplowitz, 1993), the Chinese, the Asian Indians, and Japanese (Miller, 1984; Markus and Kitayama, 1991, 1994), causality focuses on social relations and social context. It is the behavior itself and its relation to others rather than inner disposition that is predominantly emphasized by non-Western people (Markus et al., 1996).

The collectivist structure of Islamic society may influence both normal and abnormal behavior. The individual often strives to adjust to a relationship while repressing internal desires to facilitate interpersonal harmony and unity. Priority is given to in-group goals (family, co-workers, or country) even when these goals are in conflict with personal goals (Triandis, 1989). However, responsibility tends to be socially diffused and individuals in distress are given sympathy and kindness rather than being blamed for their behavior. Causal attribution and the allocation of responsibility in Muslim society may explain the rarity of guilt feelings among psychiatric patients. Similarly, a collectivist orientation may explain the involvement of the whole family in the treatment of a patient (chapter 5) and the modification of personal goals of psychotherapy in order to be compatible with family and community goals in Islamic settings (see chapter 12). In the following two sections, I discuss Islamic collectivist personality and the extended family and its relationship to the adaptation and reactions to symptoms of schizophrenic patients.

Some Aspects of Islamic and Collectivist Personality

For Muslims brought up in a traditional Islamic society, some of their basic personality characteristics may not be compatible with adaptation in Western social environments. Self-serving bias and self-focusing tendencies among Western people (Kagit-çibasi, 1997) are shunned by people from collectivist societies including Muslims. Instead modesty and humility are highly valued in these societies (Markus and Kitayama, 1991).

Islam has emphasized lowness, humility, and modesty, which are considered negatively in the West. The Qur'an instructed the prophet to tell the faithful that he is only a mortal like themselves (Phipps, 1996). Humility is also encouraged in words and action during prayer: "But say the words of humility and enter the gate in a posture of humility" (7, 161). Alternatively, there are many verses in the Qur'an against haughty behavior (*takabūr*):

Do not walk haughtily on earth . . . you can never rival the mountains in height [60, 10].
Do not treat people with scorn, nor strut about the earth. God does not love the arrogant and the boastful. Behave yourself

modestly and lower your voice—the harshest of all sounds is the braying of an ass [4, 35].
Do not eulogize me as the Christians eulogize the son of Mary. Just say 'God's servant and messenger' [65,4].

This humble and self-effacing demeanor of Muslims may appear to Westerners as a manifestation of weak and inadequate personality. Although studies have not been carried out with Muslim subjects, other non-Western subjects tended to score low on measures of self-esteem. For example, humble and self-effacing attributions of success were given by Chinese students (Bond, Leung, and Wan, 1982), while self-promotion was negatively perceived in Japan; self-enhancing peers among school children were considered less competent than modest peers (Markus and Kitayama, 1991). Among these groups as well as Muslims it may be more appropriate to use group self-esteem measures which would reveal in-group bias rather than self-serving biases. Furthermore, although people from collectivist societies are low on self-esteem, they may be high on self-respect *(Izet Annafs)*, a facet of personality that has been neglected by Western researchers even though it is highly valued by Muslims.

The Extended Family, Expressed Emotion, and Schizophrenia

The extended family system is not unique to Islamic society. It is prevalent in almost all non-Western societies. However, the Qur'an has repeatedly urged the faithful to be kind to their parents and show gratitude to them, particularly in their old age (17, 23; 29, 8; 31, 14; 46, 15). As the following two Suras reveal, kindness to parents and gratitude to them come next to the worship of God or gratitude to Him respectively.

Thy Lord hath decreed that you worship none but Him, and that ye be kind to parents. Whether one or both of them attain old age in thy life, say not to them a word of contempt, nor repel them but address them in terms of honour [17, 23].

Show gratitude to Me and to thy parents: To Me is (thy final)
Goal [31, 14].

In the West, studies of the relationship between psychopathology and the family are carried out in the context of the nuclear
family, where the family unit consists of parents and children.
In the traditional Islamic family, three generations or more
may live in the same household and thus findings from the
nuclear family may not be generalized to Islamic society.

One area of research that has been active in the West is
the relationship between expressed emotion (EE) by family
members and the disturbed behavior or the relapse and the
rehospitalization of schizophrenic patients (Leff and Vaughn,
1985). However, the major components of EE such as criticism,
hostility, overinvolvement, and warmth may not have the same
effect on the patient in the extended family. Indeed data suggest that patients in extended families with high EE may have
a better outcome! Mexican-American households, for example,
are characterized by a high level of verbal and nonverbal emotional interchange, and lack of contact with key relatives is
considered as culturally atypical (i.e., indifference, withdrawal
of attention) and tends to be an emotionally disturbing experience to the patient (Karno, Jenkins, De La Selva, Santana, Telles, Lopez, and Mintz, 1987). Karno et al. (1987) pointed out
that unlike the nuclear family, contact with high EE relatives
in the extended family occurs within the context of contact with
low EE relatives as well which has a buffering effect on stress.

The meaning of EE may be different in the nuclear family
from the extended family. In the West, *criticism* is almost always
associated with *hostility* while in the Asian Indian context, it is
associated with warmth. Indeed, there are less critical comments among Asian Indian relatives who show hostility toward
the patients as compared with Western families (Wig, Menon,
Bedi, Ghosh, Kuipers, Leff, Korten, Day, Sartorius, Ernberg,
and Jablensky, 1987). Furthermore, overt criticism and critical
comments seem to be part of normal interactions in Islamic
countries such as Saudi Arabia and Egypt respectively and
should have no adverse effects (Al-Subaie, 1989; Okasha, El-
Akbawi, Snyder, Wilson, Youssef, and El-Dawla, 1994). *Overinvolvement,* on the other hand, may be characterized by extreme

self-sacrifice, overprotectiveness, and overconcern in the context of the extended family in a Muslim culture (El-Islam, 1979). These characteristics found by El-Islam in Qatar are very rare in members of the nuclear family in both the United Kingdom and the United States (Vaughn, Snyder, Jones, Freeman, and Falloon, 1984). In Islamic or Latin American contexts, members of the extended family depend on a family network more than others for social support (Karno et al., 1987; Al-Issa and Ismail, 1994). Thus, the use of overinvolvement in measuring EE raises the question of the boundaries between normal concern and "negative" overinvolvement of relatives (El-Islam, 1989).

The degree to which the culture assigns responsibility and considers patients accountable for their symptoms may be related to EE, such as the frequency of critical comments and in turn to the relapse of patients. In the West schizophrenic patients are considered more responsible for their passive symptoms (social withdrawal, apathy, and inertia) rather than their active symptoms such as hallucinations and delusions (Leff and Vaughn, 1985). Belief in fate among Muslims *(Qada' wal Kadar)* reduces the tendency to blame patients for their symptoms. In both Muslim and traditional Latin-American cultures (El-Islam, 1982; Jenkins, Karno, De La Selva, and Santana, 1986) there is more tolerance of negative symptoms: the patient sleeps whenever he or she wants; sleeping until early afternoon is considered beneficial to the patient. A follow-up study of male schizophrenics by El-Islam (1979) found that those patients living with the extended family in Qatar, a Muslim country, tended to have less chronic negative symptoms.

Overall, the evidence seems to suggest that the meaning of the concept of EE and its influence on the level of disturbance in schizophrenia may be different in the extended family from the nuclear family in the West.

ISLAMIC PSYCHIATRY OR PSYCHIATRY IN THE ISLAMIC WORLD?

The training of Muslim psychiatrists and clinical psychologists is based on the Western biomedical concepts of disease. Thus, psychiatric and psychological research in Muslim countries has been predominantly conceived and construed on the basis of the universality of the biomedical disease model. Transcultural psychiatry itself began with an etic approach to disease entities (schizophrenia, depression, and so on) including their epidemiology, symptoms, and prognosis in different cultural settings (e.g., Wittkower and Rin, 1965; Murphy, 1982a). Since the 1980s, however, we have been witnessing a *new transcultural psychiatry* which advocates an emic approach to the study of different societies starting with the native illness lexicons and local idioms of distress as the basis of the investigation of mental illness (Kleinman, 1978; Littlewood, 1990). In the context of the *new transcultural psychiatry*, a distinction has been made between *disease* which deals with biological malfunctioning, and *illness* which is relevant to personal, interpersonal, and cultural reaction to the disease. Thus, rather than starting with preconceived ideas about psychological disturbance in a certain culture, the investigator attempts to collect information from the patients themselves, the native healers, and other informants from the culture. This investigative approach has been traditionally followed by anthropologists but it has been rarely practiced in psychiatry and psychology. It is therefore not surprising that almost all the research reported in the present volume is etically oriented following traditional transcultural psychiatry. However, I will give two examples of an emic approach in the investigation of mental illness of Muslims in Britain (Aslam, 1979) and Iran (Good, 1977), to be contrasted with a traditional biomedical approach in Qatar in the Arabian Peninsula (El-Islam, 1975).

Aslam (1979) studied the practice of *ūnani-tibb* (literally means Greek medicine) in the Pakistani community in Britain. He was present with many *hakims* (native healers who practice *ūnani-tibb*) during their interviews with patients while making diagnoses and prescribing treatment. The *ūnani-tibb* is based on medieval Islamic Galenism and humoral theories of Greek medicine (see chapter 2). The services of the *hakim* seem to be widely used by Pakistanis in Britain. In a questionnaire survey, 232 out of 250 respondents stated that they had consulted *hakims* in the past in India and Pakistan and 202 out of 250 were still consulting *hakims* in Britain. Local knowledge and cultural understanding are the major assets of the local *hakims*. Although the *hakims* see physically and mentally ill patients, they deal predominantly with psychiatric and psychosomatic problems. The *hakim* attempts to restore the body balance in terms of hot and cold humors. Aslam classified hot and cold conditions (e.g., skin rashes or toothache are hot, while paralysis or rheumatism are cold) and the related hot foods (e.g., meat, fish, carrots, eggplant, peppers, etc.) and cold foods (e.g., cabbage, cucumbers, spinach, citrus fruit, watermelon, rice, cheese, yogurt, vinegar, etc.). If one has a hot condition, one should not eat hot foods. Heat and coldness seem to be unrelated to the temperature or the spiciness of the food. The basic principle is symmetry in every aspect of life and the *hakim* helps patients to conserve or restore their symmetry. Aslam found that the *hakims* are more successful with emotional and psychosomatic problems than psychosis. In addition to the *hakims*, the *mulla*, a Muslim cleric, also plays a role in treating illness but he does not use medication. Instead, the *mulla* uses religious procedures such as verses from the Qur'an for *tavees* (or amulets). Along with the help of the *hakim* and *mulla*, patients use the British health service, particularly when native treatment fails in such illnesses as schizophrenia.

Good (1977) also found three systems of medicine in his study of the population of Maragheh, an agricultural Turkish town in the northwest of Iran: the Galenic–Islamic medicine practiced by traditional physicians, the cosmopolitan medicine practiced by Western-trained physicians, and the sacred medicine practiced by the *mullas* or Muslim clerics. He found that popular medicine tended to integrate these three systems into a distinctive system of health care. However, instead of studying the traditional healer as Aslam did, Good started with the patients themselves. He found that those men and women who felt distress in this small town of Maragheh frequently complained that their heart was pounding or beating irregularly and that they were sick *(marīz)*. Good started his study by asking the following questions: "What does it mean to have heart distress, *narahatiye galb,* in Maragheh? Can we gloss this illness complex simply as mild anxiety or depression with tachycardia if we are to understand *heart distress?* Why are seemingly diverse anxieties—contraception, pregnancy, old age, interpersonal problems, money worries—all associated with one illness?'' (pp. 27–28). For the local physician in Maragheh, these people (mainly women but also the elderly and lower class individuals) were neurotic and were usually given a tonic or tranquilizers. However, Good did not consider *heart distress* as a disease entity, but as an expression of distress which conveyed meanings relevant to the subjective world of the complainants and consisting of ''a network of symbols, situations, motives, feelings and stresses which are rooted in the structural setting in which the people of Maragheh live'' (p. 48). The world of meanings of the inhabitants of Maragheh which is rooted in a historical–religious background seems to be quite different from a Western technological society in which the word *neurotic* is meaningful and part of the subjective world of patients. The complaints of these women seemed to be more similar to those of the eleventh century Islamic mystic Al-Ghazali (cited by Good, 1977, p. 25) than to Western neurotic women:

> The impediment in my speech produced grief in my heart, and at the same time my power to digest and assimilate food and drink was impaired; I could hardly swallow or digest a single mouthful of food. My powers became so weakened that the doctors gave up all hope of successful treatment. ''This trouble arises from the heart,'' they said, ''and from there it has spread through the constitution; the only method of treatment is that the anxiety which has come over the heart should be allayed.''

In contrast to Aslam and Good, El-Islam (1975) started his study with the Western concept of neurosis as follows: ''The object of the present investigation is to demonstrate the social correlates of a chronic neurotic syndrome dominated by somatic symptomatology. . . . The syndrome is mainly encountered in Qatari women who fail to satisfy the criteria of social success as women'' (p. 26).

The somatic medium of expressing distress of these Qatari women (e.g., ailments of the heart and stomach) were quite similar to those women in Maragheh described by Good. Both groups were also experiencing stressors associated mainly with family problems. However, El-Islam divided these women into those with mild symptoms which he called "neurotic women presenting orthodox neurotic syndrome" (p. 26) and those with the more severe somatic symptoms called "culture-bound neurotic women." Similar to women in Maragheh, Qatari women may be expressing the same social *"heart distress"* with different degrees of severity. However, Good chose to study the Maragheh women as an insider while El-Islam imposed a Western diagnostic system on the subjects of his study.

The above illustrations lead to the proposal that psychiatric research in the Islamic culture may be guided by two kinds of psychiatry (cf. Al-Issa, 1996). One kind may be called *psychiatry in the Islamic world* which is etically oriented and is guided by Western diagnostic systems (e.g., Anglo-Saxon, French, and international). Psychiatric research following this orientation can be carried out anywhere in the world, as has been demonstrated by the World Health Organization research project on schizophrenia (WHO, 1973). In contrast, *Islamic psychiatry* deals with research which emphasizes Muslim religion and deals with problems and issues specifically related to abnormal behavior in an Islamic context. Islamic psychiatry shares scientific concepts and techniques with psychiatry in general, but it also has its unique features. Its historical Islamic context is different from that in the West which has influenced the development of psychiatry not only in Muslim countries but all over the world. In Islamic psychiatry, research is emically oriented without preconceived ideas about the patients and their illness. The initial point for the research is the patient, the native healer, and the society at large with a theoretical orientation based on the Qur'an, the prophet tradition and behavior. A starting point may deal with the Islamic definition of normality and abnormality where behavior is conceived by the *Shari'ah* (Islamic law) on a continuum ranging from obligatory behavior *(fard* or *wajib)* at the normal end to prohibited behavior *(haram)* at the abnormal end, with recommended *(mandub)*, permissible *(mubah)*, and reprehensible *(makrūh)* behavior in between. Unfortunately, no one has yet investigated how this Islamic definition of behavior applies to and influences Islamic conceptualization of mental illness and its symptoms.

Islamic psychiatry may also deal with behavior, beliefs, questions, issues, and problems which are specific to Islamic society, even though they may not be related to the basic Islamic doctrine. Consider, for example, the study by Al-Adawi and Al-Issa (1997), which started with the observation that during the process of bereavement in many Muslim countries there is extreme preoccupation and close attachment to the deceased for a long period of time such as praying for the deceased, a belief in reunion in heaven, naming a child after the deceased, and using the wishes of the dead as a guidance for action. It was found, however, that there is an exaggerated form of attachment to the dead in Oman called *Mu Ghayib* in response to a sudden untimely death. In this Muslim culture, *Mu Ghayib* is a response to bereavement which involves a prolonged denial of death even after elaborate burial and mourning rituals. These traditional Omanis believe in the return of the deceased: after burial, the deceased will leave the grave, live in a cave, and roam the fields and streets and later return to the family when the spell placed on them by the sorcerer is broken. For Western professionals, this extreme denial of death seems to border on psychotic delusion (Kastenbaum, 1986). However, *Mu Ghayib* is a culturally sanctioned response which helps the Omani community to deal with the psychological consequences of sudden loss. Instead of emotional damage (Worden, 1991), depression (Bowlby, 1980; Kissane and Block, 1994) and physical illness (Engel, 1961) expected from the denial of the reality of death, it was found that "Mu Ghayib had brought hope, reduced stress of sudden death and facilitated a long but easy transition through bereavement" (Al-Adawi and Al-Issa, 1997).

In sum, there is a similarity between the *new transcultural psychiatry* discussed earlier and the approach of Islamic psychiatry to mental illness. Both approaches advocate the study of mental illness within the culture, recognizing cultural diversity within human biological unity.

MENTAL ILLNESS IN MUSLIM COUNTRIES

Muslims have no immunity against madness. They are also aware of different types of madness as indicated by the popular saying *Al-Junūn Fūnūn* (madness is of many kinds). *Al-Junūn* (madness) was known in pre-Islamic Arabia, and the Prophet Mohammed himself was accused of madness by his tribe. This would indicate that in pre-Islamic society, the label *majnūn* (mad) was used to stigmatize its Muslim opponents.

The total rates or the relative frequency of different kinds of mental illness in Islamic societies reported in this volume should be considered with caution. Almost all statistics are based on hospital admission and outpatient clinic records. These services are limited to large cities and are beyond the reach of large segments of the population. Patients who see only native healers are also not counted in the statistics. This makes it difficult to compare Islamic countries with others to assess cross-cultural rates of psychopathology.

However, when Muslims are a minority group or immigrants in another country (see chapter 10) they could be compared with the majority population. For example, Muslims in Britain, Belgium, and Germany (see chapter 11; Cochrane, 1995) show a significantly lower rate of mental illness than the indigenous population. These findings are consistent with extensive studies carried out by Kok and Tsoi (1995) comparing Muslim Malays with the Chinese and Indians in Singapore on suicide and alcoholism. The suicide rate of the Chinese was 12.7 per 100,000, the Indians 13.2 per 100,000, and the Malays 2.8 per 100,000. Among patients who were hospitalized for alcoholism, the rate of the Malays was 3 percent compared with 39 percent for the Indians, and 61 percent for the Chinese (the racial breakdown for Singapore is Indians 6 percent, Chinese 77 percent, and Malays 15 percent [Kok and Tsoi, 1995]). These differences between Muslims in the diaspora and non-Muslims are so large that it is difficult to attribute them to confounding factors such as alternative treatment. In this section I deal with major psychopathology reported in this volume (schizophrenia, depression, anxiety disorders, alcoholism and drug abuse, somatoform disorder, and sexuality and its dysfunctions). In particular, I discuss the transcultural implication of research carried out in Muslim countries on mental illness.

Schizophrenia

Although there is strong evidence that the rates of schizophrenia are different across cultures (Murphy, 1982a,b; Al-Issa, 1995), there are only few community studies of the rates of schizophrenia in the traditional Islamic societies. Muslim countries represent cultures in transition from nomadic or agricultural communities to urban industrialized societies; yet there is little research on cultural change or rates of schizophrenia in these countries. Algerian psychiatrists observed that schizophrenia used to be rare in the traditional society with only reactive psychosis, but this picture has changed after independence (see chapter 4). Observations by the author in Abul-Khassib, a small traditional Muslim town in the south of Iraq, indicated that before the advent of Western schooling there used to be eccentric wise fools (see chapter 2) who functioned well as entertainers, poets, and religious healers, but there was not a single case of schizophrenia. However, when the following generation attended modern schools and pursued professional training (e.g., teaching profession) severe forms of schizophrenia appeared. Some of these schizophrenics were close relatives to the wise fools, who were the last traditional generation in the town before the advent of modern schooling. Are Western education and style of living more stressful or more conducive to different types of stressors which made this new generation of relatives of the wise fools more vulnerable to the development of the illness? Was this Islamic communal society more tolerant of deviance than a system of education which emphasized individual achievement? It is unfortunate that, with almost universal education in Muslim countries, these questions will remain unanswered.

However, the rates of prevalence of schizophrenia of 0.80% in Iran (chapter 6, this volume) and 0.57% in Tunisia

(Hachemi, Srairi, Khiari, Zouari, and Douki, 1996) are not significantly different from Western countries. Yet, problems in the reliability and validity of the diagnosis of schizophrenia in Muslim countries still remain. The high prevalence of visual hallucinations with culture-specific contents (*jinn,* insects, and historical figures) as well as the low rate of Schneider's First Rank Hallucinations in some Muslim countries (Zarrouk, 1975; Al-Jadiry, 1996) may raise questions about the WHO findings related to the universality of the criterion for the diagnosis of schizophrenia (Carpenter and Strauss, 1974).

Although there is no objective research demonstrating the relationship between Muslim religion and rates of schizophrenia and vulnerability to the illness, Muslim religion may influence the form and content of symptoms of schizophrenia. An early study by Murphy, Wittkower, Fried, and Ellenberger (1963) found that religious delusions and delusions of destruction were rated very frequent or common in 60 percent and 34 percent of their Muslim samples respectively. The corresponding percentages were 91 percent for religious delusions and 56 percent for delusions of destruction in the Catholic samples. Samples belonging to oriental religions such as Hinduism and Buddhism as well as Judaism were lower than those from Islamic countries.

Regarding the religious content of symptoms such as hallucinations, Malay patients attribute voices to God, demons, or spirits (see chapter 7, this volume). Thus Malay patients cannot be persuaded that their voices are imaginary and should be ignored since they are coming from God. Grandiose delusions of Malays also have religious content: having power given by God or being a descendent of God or the Prophet.

Ammar, Altia, Douki, Tabone, and Hamouda (1980) described what they called "mystic psychosis" in 12 men and three women with a traditional Islamic background from rural Tunisia. These rural men and women were caught in a rapidly changing urban environment in which Western technology brought about many stresses without the promised material paradise. In order to assert their existence, they assumed the identity and powers of saints, the Prophet, and God.

Oztürk (1964) reported that if the patients in Turkey, a Muslim country, have hallucinations and delusions, particularly if these symptoms are religious and mystical, they are not considered insane. On the contrary, they are regarded with reverence and awe because of the belief in their natural capacity to communicate with the supernatural world. As the Turkish expression indicates, the dividing line between sanity and insanity is often blurred: "Some said he was deli (insane) some said he was veli (saint)" (Oztürk, 1964, p. 349).

Al-Subaie and Al Hamad (see chapter 9) describe a type of psychosis in Saudi Arabia called *wishrah* with symptoms which remind the reader of thinking disorders in Western schizophrenia (incoherent and irrelevant speech). Indigenous theories and treatment of *wishrah* need further investigation and require collaboration between psychiatrists and native healers.

Depression

In the study of depression Muslim psychiatrists and psychologists have the same preoccupations and face similar problems as other researchers in transcultural psychiatry (Al-Issa, 1995). Major topics discussed in the present volume are the rates of depression and the prominence of somatization, lack of depressive mood, and guilt in its symptomatology, and the low rate of suicide in Muslim countries. There is, however, little research reporting negative relationship between the degree of Islamic faith and depression (chapter 6, this volume).

The use of alternative native treatment, the unavailability of psychiatric treatment for the majority of the population in Muslim countries, and difficulty of differentiating between depression as a normal state or as an illness may explain the absence of reliable data on the rates of depression. However, contrary to expectation (Brown and Harris, 1978, 1982), Okasha (unpublished data) found that rates of depression are higher among rural (19.7%) than urban (11.4%) populations! Social support and integration, particularly within the framework of the extended family and the mosque, are expected to be higher in the rural environment and thus have beneficial effects on depression on rural populations. Whether the data reported from Egypt reflect a true, reliable incidence or are due to methodological factors is not clear.

The higher prevalence of depression among women than men has been established internationally with only few exceptions (Weissman and Klerman, 1977; Al-Issa, 1982). There are, however, very few reliable studies on gender differences in depression in Muslim countries. Similar to findings in other countries, depression is between 2.48 to 3.53 times higher in women than men in Iran (see chapter 6). Osseiran (1995) cited a study in Bahrein reporting a male/female ratio of 1:2.4. She also reported that females receive electroconvulsive therapy three times more than males and such gender difference in treatment was attributed to the severity of female depressive condition. Clinical observation in Algeria and Saudi Arabia (see chapters 4 and 9) suggests that depression and affective disorders are highest among middle-aged housewives with many children. The menopause and the inability to have more children may expose these women to the possible stresses of divorce or the marriage of their husbands to a second wife. Using the Beck Depression Inventory with a small number of students in Kuwait (Al-Issa and Ismail, 1994) and outpatients in Saudi Arabia (West and Al-Kaisi, 1982), females obtained higher scores than males (mean scores of 15 for males and 22.11 for females in Kuwait, and 19.71 for males and 31.44 for females in Saudi Arabia).

A major theme in the description of symptoms of depression is the tendency of patients to somatize depressive mood and express their feelings in body language. However, when the symptoms of depressed patients were compared with three other studies, one in India and two in Britain, the stereotype about the inability of Muslim patients to express emotions is not supported (Gawad, 1995). One hundred percent of both Egyptian and Indian patients showed depressed mood as compared with only 60 and 63 percent of two British groups respectively! Ninety-nine percent of Egyptians and 80 percent of Indians also manifested anxiety as compared with 61 and 48 percent of the British. In another study by El-Islam, Moussa,

Malasi, Suleiman, and Mirza (1988), the rank ordering of the symptoms of depression in Kuwait indicated that sadness, joylessness, and anxiety/tension were manifested by 98, 95, and 88 percent of the patients respectively. It appears that although somatization is manifested by patients in Islamic culture, this does not seem to exclude affect as a medium of expressing distress by the same patients. It also appears that anthropological observations are incompatible with psychiatric observations of lack of mood expression in Muslim culture. Wikan (1988) stated that:

> Egyptians live in a world where to express one's feelings of unhappiness and anger is deemed necessary for health and also to attain one's social dues. . . . To express anger and bitterness, like suffering and grief, is regarded as essential. . . . Small children are encouraged to give vent to their feelings by screaming, shouting, crying, quarreling and above all, by talking. It is a model for suffering consciously inculcated that also receives authority from the behaviour of adults they observe [p. 458].

It is quite possible that psychiatrists deal with a selected group rather than the Egyptians Wikan met during her anthropological studies in Cairo. Alternatively, these patients may express their feelings and share their emotions with relatives and friends, but when they meet psychiatrists they only express physical symptoms in order to obtain physical treatment for their illness and avoid the stigma of mental illness.[1]

---

[1]Leff (1973, 1988) has popularized the idea that in some cultures, people are unable to express emotional distress because of deficiency in their language and therefore report somatic symptoms. Although Leff's ideas are rejected by almost all researchers in transcultural psychiatry (see review in Al-Issa, 1995), a similar theme has been developed by Muslim psychiatrists relating the Arabic language to emotional expression and somatization (El-Islam, 1982; Okasha, Bishry, Khalil, Darwish, Seif Al-Dawla, and Shohdy, 1994). El-Islam (1982, p. 12) stated that:

> Since the Arab language tends to be overempathetic and hyperbolic (Prothro, 1955) it is expected that individuals will exaggerate in their verbal communications, otherwise they will not be taken by other Arabs to mean what they say (the Arab language has been held to express emotivity at the expense of rationality [Shouby, 1951]). Therefore it should not be surprising that patients and their relatives exaggerate their verbal reports of distress.

This statement is based on the Shouby (1951) study in which the theory of linguistic relativity and the methodology used to support that theory have been criticized and

Guilt feeling is another symptom which is reported to be low in frequency in Muslim patients. In their classic study of symptoms of depression across cultures, Murphy, Wittkower, and Chance (1970) found that while guilt was frequently reported by psychiatrists in Catholic and other Christian countries, it was reported infrequently in Muslim countries (also in Hindu and Buddhist countries). More important is that within Muslim countries, where the society is religiously active and devout (one would think of the present Iran, Malaysia, and Saudi Arabia as examples), the reports of guilt as "usual" were nil. There were other early reports of lack of guilt feeling in depressive patients in Muslim countries (e.g., Bazzoui and Al-Issa, 1966; Bazzoui, 1970). However, more recent reports reveal a different picture. For example, El-Islam et al. (1988; see also chapter 5) found that the majority of their patients expressed guilt feelings. El-Islam (chapter 5) also reported that the contents of these delusions were religious, such as guilt about negligence in religious duties or fear of punishment for past

---

rejected by psychologists (e.g., Prothro, 1955; Slobin, 1979; R. Brown, 1986). However, the same ideas about the "emotivity" of the Arabic language and the tendency for exaggeration by patients is also used more recently by Okasha et al. (1994) to explain symptoms of panic disorder. Okasha et al. (1994, p. 822) stated that:

> The way patients described their panic attacks in our sample is a reflection of the emotivity in verbal communication in Arabic (Shouby, 1951; Prothro, 1955) and the cultural pattern of Arab patients' expression of their complaints. Arab patients do not usually complain of depressive, anxiety or panic symptoms directly. They tend to somatize their symptoms and exaggerate in their verbal communication, otherwise they will not be understood by other Arabic speakers to mean what they say.

These assumptions about the Arabic language are merely based on speculation with no empirical support. Indeed, common observation suggests the opposite of these assumptions since the Arabic language was the language of science and medicine throughout the medieval era. During that era, scientists from different linguistic backgrounds used Arabic in their communication. To give one example, La Wall (1927) in his history of pharmacy (a basic science that is hardly liable to exaggeration), was incredulous about the productivity of Jabbir ibn Hayyan and stated that "If Geber did exist, then he is entitled to be considered as the father of chemistry" (p. 94). Considering the historical evidence, it is clear that a statement such as "Arabs are forced to overassert and overexaggerate in almost all types of communication" (Shouby, 1951, p. 300) because of their language is not supported by any scientific evidence. Muslim scholars now use English not because of a deficiency in their languages (e.g., Arabic, Farsi, Turkish, and Urdu) but because English is the international language for scientific communication.

misdemeanors. Similarly, Gawad (1995) found that 23 percent of depressive patients in Egypt experienced guilt, and the figure from the WHO study in Tehran was 32 percent (see chapter 6).

One question is whether the report of guilt feeling is related to religious denominations. Murphy (1982a) suggested that religion by itself is not a primary factor in the report of guilt feeling. He pointed out that in some Catholic countries there are no reports of guilt with depression, while this symptom is found in non-Christian countries such as India (see Al-Issa, 1995, pp. 18–19 for further discussion). The historical fluctuation of the symptom of guilt in Western patients (i.e., its appearance in patients only in the seventeenth century and its present decline in the West) seem to support the influence of other sociocultural factors than religion (Murphy, 1978; see chapter 1).

In dealing with guilt and religion, it is necessary to distinguish between sin which is related to the actual breaking of religious rules, and irrational guilt which is associated with depression (see chapter 1; Nayani and Bhugra, 1996). There is a need for the study of the semantics of sin and guilt and how they are expressed in different languages in Muslim countries (Arabic, Farsi, and Urdu) in order to make a distinction between the feelings of sin on the one hand and guilt on the other in Muslim countries.

In contrast to the absence of guilt feeling, it is reported that depressive patients in Islamic countries such as Algeria and Iraq tend to show paranoid tendencies, including delusion of persecution (see chapter 4; Bazzoui and Al-Issa, 1966). It was suggested that delusions in depressive patients may reflect a sociocultural phenomenon rather than a manifestation of the illness. Bazzoui and Al-Issa (1966) pointed out that "the recent influx of oil revenues has been one of the main factors leading to a harsh struggle for power or even for survival among different religious, ethnic, and political groups in Iraq. Internal intrigues, both on the public and the personal level may render misleading Western criteria for assessing delusions of persecution and ideas of reference" (p. 828). The presence of delusions of persecution is not only limited to depression but also found in other mental illnesses in Algeria (see chapter 4) suggesting that they are pervasive phenomena.

There is a general agreement that the rate of suicide is very low in Muslim countries, but when suicide is not acceptable in a culture, this may result in its underreporting. As McCarthy and Walsh (1975) found in Dublin, the actual rate of suicide is between two and four times higher than the official figures. However, suicidal ideations and attempted suicide are relatively high in Muslim countries. The profile of the suicide attempter reported by many authors (e.g., chapters 4, 5, 6, and 9) is of a single young woman experiencing an intergenerational conflict. Family problems and mental illness seem to be the leading causes of suicide among female and males respectively (see chapter 6).

There is little research on the relationship between suicide and attempted suicide on the one hand and religiosity on the other in Islamic countries. Caruso and Moussaoui (1992) found that Muslim subjects who attempted suicide practice Islamic religious duties (e.g., prayer and fasting) less than controls. However, 70 percent of the suicide attempters were practicing Muslims when they attempted suicide, a finding which weakens the relationship between religious practice and attempted suicide among Muslims. Furthermore the researchers did not partial out the effect of social and occupational integration which was also found to be significantly related to attempted suicide. As it is pointed out by Al-Issa (see chapter 1), the practice of religion may not be a viable index of religious feeling or belief and the differentiation between extrinsic and intrinsic religiousness is necessary in this type of research (see chapter 1).

Little attention has been given to the concept of death and dying in Islamic society and its effects on suicide or suicidal ideations. In describing patients in Saudi Arabia, Dubovsky (1983) stated that: "If asked directly if they are having thoughts of killing themselves, most depressed patients reply that they are good Muslims and would never entertain such thoughts. If, however, potentially suicidal patients are asked if they wish that God would let them die, they usually will reply in the affirmative" (p. 1457). The expression "God may let me (let you) die" is used often by certain Arab–Muslim communities to express helplessness, anger, or annoyance but has nothing to do with a real wish for dying. The verbalization of the patients about death seems to have been taken out of its social context by Dubovsky. Preoccupation with death may have nothing to do with suicide. Murphy (1982a) reported that in Montreal, Canada, when patients are asked whether they think about their (own) death, more French Canadians responded in the affirmative than English Canadians. However, it was found that thinking about death by English Canadian patients was related to suicidal thoughts; but for the French Canadians, it was an indication of religious orthodoxy; the priest regularly urged parishioners to think about death. It is evident that a study of the religious meaning of the concept of death is necessary before relating its verbalization to suicidal thoughts among Muslim patients.

Anxiety Disorders

The rate of anxiety in some Muslim countries seems to be similar to the rates reported in the West. For example, Okasha (unpublished data) reported that anxiety disorders were estimated at between 2 and 4 percent in the general population. However, anxiety states were found in 38 percent of a sample of university students! The prevalence of generalized anxiety was 5.12 percent in an Iranian study but other anxiety disorders were less than 1 percent. Women also had double the rates of anxiety than men (see chapter 6). Other reports from Egypt, Saudi Arabia, and Turkey indicated higher scores of test anxiety among university students than students in Europe and the United States (Al-Issa and Oudji, 1998). Similarly, social phobia is one of the most prevalent anxiety disorders in Saudi Arabia in the clinical population, affecting single young males with high educational and occupational levels (see chapter 9). Although these data clearly show a high level of anxiety among the educated population seen in the clinic, the relationship between religiousness and the anxiety level of subjects has been rarely investigated (see chapter 6).

Other types of anxiety disorders are also observed in Muslim countries. El-Islam (see chapter 5) reported death phobia with religious contents: fear of judgment and torture after death by angels in the grave and fear of hell after resurrection. Panic disorder with or without agoraphobia seems to be relatively high among anxiety disorder patients (see chapter 10). Muslim housewives rarely suffer from agoraphobia in Qatar, in contrast to their counterparts in the West, because they are often accompanied by males or other females when they are outside the home. Obsessions related to cleanliness with religious connotations *(waswās)* are reported in Muslim countries (see chapters 1, 5, and 6). Azhar and Varma (see chapter 7) reported religious ruminations such as doubts about the unity of God or belief in the Prophet. However, obsessions related to dirt and washing compulsions seem very rare, an observation different from the often-reported *waswās* in Indonesia (Pfeiffer, 1982) and in other Muslim countries (Bazzoui and Al-Issa, 1966; see chapters 6 and 11,). Blasphemy is an obsessive symptom usually found among Western religious Christians (e.g., priests) rather than Muslims.

Alcoholism and Drug Abuse

Alcohol is prohibited in Islam and thus drinking alcohol itself with no physical or psychiatric problems is regarded as abnormal (see chapter 5). Drinking and alcoholism seem to be a serious problem in some Muslim–Arab countries. Data published by the World Health Organization (cited by Murphy, 1982a) show that Egypt is the only Muslim country listed with a relatively high rate of death from cirrhosis. As compared with 53 Christian countries, Egypt ranked higher than 38 countries on mortality from cirrhosis of the liver. However, strict Muslim rules which limit the availability of alcohol may influence the nature of drinking and alcoholism, such as the ability to abstain, the rarity of both chronic alcoholism and cirrhosis of the liver (see review by Al-Issa, 1995). Apart from some severe cases of chronic alcoholism and cirrhosis which come to the attention of physicians, statistics about alcohol abuse are unreliable in Muslim countries because of the stigma associated with drinking and its prohibition in Islam that makes it difficult to admit to drinking.

One finding of transcultural interest is the prevalence of psychiatric disorders among Algerian alcoholics, raising the question whether or not drinking and alcoholism are secondary to these disorders (see chapter 4). It is possible that with acculturation in Muslim countries there may be two groups of alcoholics with different social and religious backgrounds. One group is brought up in the traditional family where the Muslim religion is strictly practiced and where the individual is strongly influenced by the Qur'anic prohibition and the Prophet's tradition (the curse of God is not only on the drinker, but also on the brewer, the seller, the buyer, and even the carrier of alcohol). In this religious setting, drinking and alcoholism may be secondary to mental illness (i.e., positively related to mental illness) rather than associated with the degree of religiousness. In another group who are Westernized (e.g., educated or live in Christian neighborhoods, or where religious norms are relaxed), drinking and alcoholism may be more associated with lack of adherence to the Muslim religion rather than to mental illness. These hypotheses relating Muslim beliefs and alcohol may not apply to other drugs which, unlike alcohol, are not mentioned specifically in the Qur'an.

The relationship between alcohol abuse and psychological disturbance is supported in a recent study by Chinnian, Taylor, Al-Subaie, Sugumar, and Al-Jumaih (1994) in Saudi Arabia. Alcohol abusers were significantly higher than normals and heroin abusers on anxiety, neuroticism, and psychoticism. However, drug abusers were not significantly different from normals, supporting the hypothesis that since drugs are only implicitly forbidden in the Qur'an, their abuse may not be as significantly related to psychological disturbance as alcohol in this highly religious society. Unfortunately, Chinnian et al. (1994) did not assess the level of religiousness of their subjects as compared with normal controls.

Studies of subjects in the Judeo-Christian context reviewed by Al-Issa (see chapter 1) strongly suggest that religiousness is protective against drinking and drug abuse. However, there is no research on the interaction between religiousness, mental illness, and Westernization on the one hand and drinking patterns and drug abuse in Muslim countries on the other.

Somatoform Disorders

Although Charcot and Freud treated a large number of hysterical patients, these cases have been declining in Western industrialized countries (Al-Issa, 1995) and are seen more often among rural populations (Folks, Ford, and Regan, 1984). However, dramatic forms of conversion hysteria (aphonia, paralysis, and fainting) are still seen in outpatient clinics in Saudi Arabia (see chapter 9) even though they are declining in Egypt in urban outpatient clinics (Okasha, unpublished data). The decline in conversion disorder in many parts of the world may be the result of medical and psychological sophistication where dramatic physical symptoms that do not make good sense are not tolerated and have become less fashionable than other symptoms such as vague physical complaints and anxiety.

Epidemic hysteria used to be frequent in medieval Europe but it is very rare now. However, it appears to be prevalent in Malaysia (see chapter 7) and tends to afflict young females in residential schools and hostels or female factory workers. Its occurrence is associated with the belief that the spirits find it easier to disturb females since they have weaker "soul substance" than males. Overall, dramatic symptoms of somatoform disorders are changing in many countries as a result of historical and sociocultural factors that have not been adequately investigated.

Sexuality and Sexual Dysfunction

Islam is depicted as a more sex-positive religion than Christianity (Bullough, 1976). Al-Sawaf and Al-Issa (see chapter 13) provide a contrast between positive medieval sexual attitudes in the Islamic society and present-day sexual problems of Saudi

Arabian patients. In treating sexual dysfunction, psychiatrists in Muslim countries tend to slightly adapt Western techniques of sex therapy rather than explore indigenous techniques used in traditional sexual manuals (see chapter 13). However, performance anxiety suggested by Western therapists (Masters and Johnson, 1970) seems to play a major part in sexual dysfunction regardless of cultural differences, even though its source may be different. Polygamy may be a source of performance anxiety for some Saudi males, but the same problem may arise as a result of negative attitudes toward sexuality and religious orthodoxy reported by Masters and Johnson (1970) in North American patients. While rape and early aversive sexual experience may condition Western females against heterosexual relationships (Al-Issa, 1980), the emphasis on virginity before marriage and the culturally constructed physical pain of penetration on the wedding night seem to play a major role in sexual dysfunction among women in the Arabian peninsula (chapters 5 and 13).

Cultural emphasis on virginity of women until marriage in Muslim societies has different consequences for young women living in Muslim countries as compared with those in Europe. Sexual anxiety related to anticipated pain as a result of the rupture of the hymen during the wedding night leads these women to the surgeon requesting hymenectomy (see chapter 13). In European countries such as the Netherlands, Muslim women ask for the reconstruction of the hymen (Bekker and Rademakers, 1997). These women are the victims of a conflict between an Islamic home environment which prescribes virginity and the outside European society (school, workplace) which permits premarital sexual relationships. Since loss of virginity tends to have serious consequences, it is not surprising that it is a source of depression, despair, and suicide, and that a surgical reconstruction of the hymen or even a virginity certificate from the physician is necessary.

Homosexuality is not considered as a psychiatric abnormality in most Muslim countries and therefore homosexuals rarely come to the attention of psychiatrists (see chapter 4; Bazzoui and Al-Issa, 1966). It is a sociocultural or legal and religious issue rather than psychiatric illness (see chapter 9).

There are many passages in the Qur'an that condemn homosexuality (7, 80, 81; 16, 165–168; 12, 77–78; 14, 28–29): "And
Lot! (Remember) when he said unto his folk (inhabitants of
Sodom) 'Will ye commit abomination *(fahisha)* such as no crea-
tures ever did before you' " (7, 80). Thus, homosexuality is not
approved in Muslim societies. However, it is the homosexual
behavior of the Muslim rather than his or her personhood or
identity that is condemned by God or by law. In the West the
whole identity of the person is stigmatized (Ross, 1987).

Homosexuality is reported less frequently among the Arab
Bedouins than among city dwellers (Thesiger, 1959; Burckhardt, 1831). This is consistent with the finding by Endleman
(1986) that homosexuality is very rare in tribal societies as compared with Western society. There are, however, no reliable
statistics of the rates of homosexuality in Muslim countries and
it is certain that such behavior would be underreported by Muslim populations. Speculation about these rates is rather premature (Kline, 1963).

PSYCHOTHERAPY IN AN ISLAMIC CONTEXT

Western psychotherapy is based primarily on psychoanalytic
concepts which are incompatible with basic Islamic doctrine.
While Islam through the Qur'an emphasized reason *(aql)* and
the good nature of a Muslim, psychoanalytic theory conceived
human beings as irrational and bad. It is, therefore, not surprising that it is difficult to apply Western psychotherapy to Muslim
patients without modification, even when dealing with middle-
class Westernized and educated Muslims (chapter 12, this
volume).

Azhar and Varma (chapter 7) found that psychoanalysis is
not accepted by Muslim patients in Malaysia and therapists had
to develop cognitive therapy based on Muslim beliefs to deal
with their patients. The purpose of the Islamic therapy was not
to make the patient more logical or rational, as suggested by
the proponents of cognitive therapy in the West, or to deal
with intrapsychic conflicts as suggested by psychoanalysis, but

to change the value system and ideals of the patients to conform with Muslim religion. Tehrani (1996) also used Islamic religious ideals and values in group therapy in the treatment and rehabilitation of criminals in Iranian prisons.

Group therapy in its Western form raises many problems in the treatment situation (chapter 10). However Al-Radi and Al-Mahdi (1989) employed an Islamic group therapy with patients of different diagnoses but a large number (47%) were suffering from social phobia. The sessions were conducted in the mosque starting with washing the face, head, and extremities (Muslim ablution ritual), followed by a prayer: "My God, I beg you a peaceful mind, I believe in your presence, I am contented by my fate and satisfied by your giving" (Al-Radi and Al-Mahdi, 1989, p. 274). The solidarity and cohesion of the Muslim community are emphasized by reciting religious phrases such as "Hold fast together by the rope of Allah (God) and not be divisible among yourselves" or "Believers are like a building, strengthening and supporting each other." The therapists reported that 30 percent of the clients experienced symptom relief and another 17.6 percent showed improvement.

Meditation as practiced in *Zikr* (the remembrance or repetition of the divine unity, *La Ilaha Illa Elah)* described by travelers to the Middle East (cited by Prince, 1980) is a potential method of relaxation. *Zikr* is mentioned in the Qur'an as having a calming effect on the believers:

> Those who believe, their hearts being at rest in God's remembrance—in God's remembrance are at rest the hearts of those who believe and do righteous deeds; theirs is blessedness and a fair resort [13:28].

The Muslim daily five prayers are themselves an excellent medium for meditation and relaxation. The prayer and concentration required from Muslims during the recitation of the Qur'an is an ideal distraction from daily hassles and anxieties (see chapter 9). The effects of the recitation of the Qur'an on postoperative pain is a good example of religious therapy in an Islamic context (see chapter 6). It should be noted that prayer including Qur'anic recitation *(Zikr)* are suitable for Muslim patients to carry out by themselves since the patient–healer dyad may not be essential in Islamic psychotherapy. Unlike Christianity there is no clergy in Islam that mediates between God and the individual. The person himself is expected to pray to God and ask for his mercy and compassion.

Native healers are popular in all Muslim countries reported in this volume and all types of healing are allowed in Muslim religion, except when it is against Muslim beliefs or when the healer appeals to supernatural forces other than God, such as the devil (see chapters 2 and 9). In Muslim countries, a high percentage of patients tend to see the native healer before contacting a psychiatrist. Muslim patients, like others all over the world, tend to seek almost any type of therapy when they are in distress, and it is not surprising that they contact psychiatrists when native healing fails. In addition to understanding the circumstances of patients, the native healers are ready to devote more time with the patient and try to provide them with rational advice without destroying their faith in the therapy. For example, if the client asks for an amulet against mice which are infesting his or her home, the native healer will not disappoint the client, but will advise him or her to hang the amulet on the neck of a cat or else it will not work (Hes, 1964). An ingenious way of combining spiritual therapy with drug therapy is when soaking sacred writing in water for the patient to drink (a popular native treatment in Muslim countries) (see chapter 9), the ink used may consist of active ingredients (Hes, 1964). It is, however, unfortunate that in Muslim countries there is little cooperation between psychiatrists and psychologists, on the one hand, and native religious healers on the other (see chapters 4, 5, 7, and 9). The first step in such cooperation is the evaluation of the physical and psychological treatment provided by native healers in the context of a comprehensive health care system.

When Western psychotherapy is attempted in an Islamic context (chapter 12) the therapeutic relationship, the reactions of patients, and the procedure used are no different from those reported in the therapy of ethnic groups such as Chinese and Hispanics in North America (Sue and Sue, 1990). The therapeutic situation tends to involve the extended family with such characteristics as (1) the emphasis on emotional restraint rather than verbal–emotional expressiveness; (2) patterns of verbal communication tend to flow from persons with higher status (therapist) to lower status (patient); (3) self-disclosure and revelation of personal and social problems to strangers is not acceptable; (4) there is little distinction between mental and physical functioning; (5) the therapy is action oriented emphasizing practical problems rather than insight; (6) and finally the aim is to find immediate solutions and use concrete, tangible forms of treatment (advice, confession, consolation, and medication) (Sue and Sue, 1990). It is, therefore, important that in the application of psychotherapy in Muslim countries, a distinction should be made between factors which characterize non-Western cultures and those that are specific to Muslim culture.

SUMMARY

Little research has attempted to relate Muslim religion to psychopathology. In contrast, there is much speculation about both the positive and negative effects of Islam on mental health. Muslims live in collectivist societies which may create problems of conceptual equivalence to psychiatrists and psychologists trained in the West. Concepts and behavior in Muslim societies are defined in terms of social role and interdependence rather than being divorced from the social milieu. In these societies the extended family provides both emotional and material support to the sick, and isolation of patients is almost unknown. Concepts such as "expressed emotion" used by Western researchers do not have the same meaning when used in Islamic societies.

A differentiation is made between Islamic psychiatry and psychiatry in the Islamic world. While research and practice of psychiatry in the Islamic world is based on the Western medical model and could be carried out in non-Muslim settings, Islamic psychiatry deals with issues specific to Muslim patients. Studies of Muslims in Britain, Iran, and Oman are cited as examples of Islamic psychiatry.

As a result of methodological problems, it is difficult to compare mental illness among Muslim countries or these countries with the West. Evidence from more reliable studies in the West shows that Muslims in the diaspora tend to have lower rates of mental illness than the native population. One neglected area of research is the relationship between recent social change and the rates and symptoms of mental illness in Muslim countries, such as Saudi Arabia (Al-Issa, 1995, for a review; chapter 9). While severe types of schizophrenia (e.g., catatonic schizophrenia) are almost nonexistent in the West, they are still prevalent in Muslim countries. Muslim religion seems to affect both the form and content of hallucinations and delusions in schizophrenia. Schizophrenic symptoms with religious contents are tolerated by the population, such as in Turkey. Both psychometric and clinical data suggest higher rates of depression in women than men. There is consistent evidence that depressive patients tend to somatize, but they tend to express depressive mood as well. There is no evidence that the expression of specific depressive symptoms is related to the nature of the Arabic language. Although early studies reported low rates of guilt feelings among Muslim patients, this finding has not been recently supported in some Muslim countries. No research has been reported on the concept of sin in Muslim religion and its relationship to guilt feelings. In some Muslim countries such as Algeria and Iraq, depressive patients tend to express delusions of persecution rather than guilt feelings.

There is a consensus among authors that suicide is rare in Islamic countries; but no reliable data have been reported about its rates. Rates of anxiety appear to be high in some Muslim countries and the Islamic culture tends to affect both the form and content of anxiety disorders (e.g., obsessive–compulsive disorder). Alcoholism is not a problem in traditional Islamic society but with social change it has become of much concern. No research has been carried out on the pattern of alcoholism and its comorbidity with other mental illnesses. Islam is described as a sex-positive religion, but sex anxiety and sexual dysfunctions tend to be influenced by specific cultural factors among Muslims. Homosexuality is reported in Muslim societies but its rates are subject to speculation. Hysteria in its dramatic form as well as epidemic hysteria which are rare in the West are still prevalent in some Muslim countries.

Psychodynamic therapy based on psychoanalytic theory or on an individualistic concept of the person is not suitable for Muslim patients. The aims of therapy in an Islamic context are not independence and self-actualization, but interdependence and adjustment to the demands of society. Many attempts have been made to apply Muslim principles and practices in psychotherapy. Group therapy, within a religious context, is also found useful. There seems to be very little cooperation between psychiatrists and native healers in Muslim countries.

REFERENCES

Abou El Azayem, G., & Hedayat-Diba, Z. (1994), The psychological aspects of Islam: Basic principles of Islam and their psychological corollary. *Internat. J. Psychol. Religion,* 4:41–50.

Al-Adawi, S., & Al-Issa, I. (1997), *Mu Ghayib: A Culture-Specific Response to Bereavement in Oman.* Typescript.

Ammar, S., Altia, S., Douki, S., Tabone, B., & Hamouda, C. (1980), A propos de la recrudescence des délires mystiques en Tunisie au course de la présente décennie. *L'Information Psychiatrique,* 56:711–715.

Aslam, M. (1979), *The Practice of Asian Medicine in the United Kingdom,* Doctoral thesis, Department of Pharmacy, University of Nottingham.

Bazzoui, W. (1970), Affective disorders in Iraq. *Brit. J. Psychiatry,* 117:195–203.

———— Al-Issa, I. (1966), Psychiatry in Iraq. *Brit. J. Psychiatry,* 112:827–832.

Bekker, M. H. J., & Rademakers, J. (1997), Study examines Islamic virginity issues. *Psychol. Internat.,* 8:1–8.

Bond, M. H., Leung, K., & Wan, K. C. (1982), How does cultural collectivism operate? The impact of task and maintenance contributions on reward distribution. *J. Cross-Cultural Psychol.,* 13:186–200.

Bowlby, J. (1980), *Attachment and Loss: Vol. 3.* Harmondsworth, Middlesex: Penguin Books.

Brown, G. W., & Harris, T. O. (1978), *Social Origins of Depression: A Study of Psychiatric Disorders in Women.* London: Tavistock.

——— ——— (1982), Social class and affective disorder. In: *Culture and Psychopathology,* ed. I. Al-Issa. Baltimore: University Park Press, pp. 125–155.

Brown, R. (1986), *Social Psychology,* 2nd ed. New York: Free Press.

Bullough, V. L. (1976), *Sexual Variance in Society and History.* Chicago: University of Chicago Press.

Burckhardt, J. L. (1931), *Travels in Arabia.* London: Frank Cass, 1968.

Carpenter, W. T., & Strauss, J. S. (1974), Cross-cultural evaluation of Schneider's first-rank symptoms of schizophrenia: A report from the International Pilot Study of Schizophrenia. *Amer. J. Psychiatry,* 131:682–687.

Caruso, M., & Moussaoui, D. (1992), Tentative de suicide, pratique religieuse et insertion sociale. *Rev. Maghrébine de Psychiatrie,* 2:29–32.

Chinnian, R. R., Taylor, L. R., Al-Subaie, A., Sugumar, A., & Al-Jumaih, H. (1994), A controlled study of personality pattern in alcohol and heroin abusers. *J. Psychoactive Drugs,* 26:85–88.

Cochrane, R. (1995), Mental health among minorities and immigrants in Britain. In: *Culture and Mental Illness: An International Perspective,* ed. I. Al-Issa. Madison, CT: International Universities Press, pp. 347–360.

Dubovsky, S. L. (1983), Psychiatry in Saudi Arabia. *Amer. J. Psychiatry,* 140:1455–1459.

Endleman, R. (1986), Homosexuality in tribal societies. *Transcult. Psychiatric Res. Rev.,* 23:187–218.

Engel, G. L. (1961), Is grief a disease? A challenge for medical research. *Psychosom. Med.,* 23:18–22.

Folks, D. G., Ford, C. V., & Regan, W. M. (1984), Conversion symptoms in a general hospital. *Psychosomatics,* 25:285–295.

El-Gaaly, A. A. (1984), Letter to the editor. *Amer. J. Psychiatry,* 141:1019.

Gawad, M. S. A. (1995), Transcultural psychiatry in Egypt. In: *Culture and Mental Illness: An International Perspective,* ed. I. Al-Issa. Madison, CT: International Universities Press, pp. 53–63.

Good, B. (1977), The heart of what's the matter: The semantics of illness in Iran. *Cult., Med. & Psychiatry,* 1:25–58.

Hachemi, Z., Srairi, L., Khiari, G., Zouari, B., & Douki, S. (1996, November), *Etude épidemiologique des troubles psychotiques et depressif en milieu urbain tunisien.* Paper presented at 7th Pan-Arab Congress of Psychiatry, Kaslik, Lebanon.

Hes, J. P. (1964), The changing social role of the Yemenite Mori. In: *Magic, Faith, and Healing. Studies in Primitive Psychiatry Today,* ed. A. Kiev. New York: Free Press, pp. 364–383.

El-Islam, M. F. (1975), Culture-bound neurosis in Qatari women. *Soc. Psychiatry,* 10:25–27.

——— (1979), A better outlook for schizophrenics living in extended families. *Brit. J. Psychiatry,* 135:343–347.

——— (1982), Arabic cultural psychiatry. *Transcult. Psychiatric Res. Rev.,* 19:5–24.

——— (1989), Collaboration with families for the rehabilitation of schizophrenic patients and the concept of expressed emotion. *Acta Psychiatri. Scand.,* 65:112–119.

——— Moussa, M. A. A., Malasi, T. H., Suleiman, M. A., & Mirza, I. A. (1988), Assessment of depression in Kuwait by principal component analysis. *J. Affect. Disord.,* 14:109–114.

Al-Issa, I. (1980), *The Psychopathology of Women.* Englewood Cliffs, NJ: Prentice-Hall.

——— (1982), Gender and psychopathology in perspective. In: *Gender and Psychopathology,* ed. I. Al-Issa. New York: Academic Press, pp. 3–29.

——— (1995), Culture and mental illness in an international perspective. In: *Culture and Mental Illness: An International Perspective,* ed. I. Al-Issa. Madison, CT: International Universities Press, pp. 3–49.

——— (1996), *Arab psychology or psychology in the Arab world.* Paper presented at the 26th International Congress of Psychology, Montreal, Canada.

——— Ismail, S. J. (1994), Social support and depression of male and female students in Kuwait: Preliminary findings. *Anxiety, Stress & Coping,* 7:253–262.

——— Oudji, S. (1998), Culture and anxiety. In: *Cultural Clinical Psychology,* ed. D. Evans & S. S. Kazarian. New York: Oxford University Press, pp. 127–151.

Al-Jadiry, A. (1996, November), *Hallucinations in chronic schizophrenia.* Paper presented at the VII Pan-Arab Congress of Psychiatry. Kaslik, Lebanon.

Jenkins, J. H., Karno, M., De La Selva, A., & Santana, F. (1986), Expressed emotion in cross-cultural context: Familial responses to schizophrenic illness among Mexican Americans. In: *Treatment of Schizophrenia: Family Assessment and Intervention,* ed. M. J. Goldstein, I. Hand, & K. Hahlweg. Berlin: Springer-Verlag, pp. 35–49.

Kagitçibasi, C. (1997), Individualism and collectivism. In: *Handbook of Cross-Cultural Psychology*, Vol. 3, 2nd ed., ed. J. W. Berry, M. H. Segall, & C. Kagitçibasi. Boston: Allyn and Bacon, pp. 1–49.

Karno, M., Jenkins, J. H., De La Selva, A., Santana, F., Telles, C., Lopez, S., & Mintz, J. (1987), Expressed emotion and schizophrenic outcome among Mexican-American families. *J. Nerv. & Ment. Disord.*, 175:143–151.

Kastenbaum, R. J. (1986), *Death, Society and Human Experience*, 3rd ed. Columbus, OH: Charles E. Merrill.

Kissane, D. W., & Block, S. (1994), Family grief. *Brit. J. Psychiatry*, 164:728–740.

Kleinman, A. (1978), Concepts and models for the comparison of medical systems as cultural systems. *Soc. Sci. & Med.*, 12:85–93.

Kline, N. S. (1963), Psychiatry in Kuwait. *Brit. J. Psychiatry*, 109:766–774.

Kok, L. P., & Tsoi, W. F. (1995), Culture and mental illness in Singapore: A sociocultural perspective. In: *Culture and Mental Illness: An International Perspective*, ed. I. Al-Issa. Madison, CT: International Universities Press.

La Wall, C. H. (1927), *The Curious Lore of Drugs and Medicines (Four Thousand Years of Pharmacy)*. Garden City, NY: Garden City.

Leff, J. (1973), Culture and the differentiations of emotional states. *Brit. J. Psychiat.*, 123:299–306.

———— (1988), *Psychiatry around the Globe*. London: Gaskell.

————Vaughn, C. (1985), *Expressed Emotion in Families; Its Significance for Mental Illness*. New York: Guilford Press.

Littlewood, R. (1990), From categories to context: A decade of the "New Cross-Cultural Psychiatry." *Brit. J. Psychiatry*, 156:308–327.

Markus, H. R., & Kitayama, S. (1991), Culture and the self: Implications for cognitions, emotions, and motivation. *Psycholog. Rev.*, 98:224–253.

———— ———— (1994), A collective fear of the collective: Implications for selves and theories of selves. *Personal. & Soc. Psychol. Bull.*, 20:568–579.

———— ————Heiman, R. J. (1996), Culture and "basic" psychological principles. In: *Social Psychology Handbook of Basic Principles*, ed. T. H. Higgins & A. W. Kruglanski. New York: Guilford Press, pp. 857–913.

Masters, W. H., & Johnson, V. E. (1970), *Human Sexual Inadequacy*. Boston: Little Brown.

McCarthy, P. D., & Walsh, D. (1975), Suicide in Dublin I: The underreporting of suicide and the consequences for national statistics. *Brit. J. Psychiatry*, 126:301–308.

Miller, J. G. (1984), Culture and the development of everyday social explanation. *J. Personal. & Soc. Psychol.,* 46:961–978.

Murphy, H. B. M. (1978). The advent of guilt feelings as a commmon depressive symptom: A historical comparison on two continents. *Psychiatry,* 41:229–242.

———— (1982a), *Comparative Psychiatry.* New York: Springer Verlag.

———— (1982b), Culture and schizophrenia. In: *Culture and Psychopathology,* ed. I. Al-Issa. Baltimore: University Park Press, pp. 221–249.

———— Wittkower, E. D., & Chance, N. W. (1970), The symptoms of depression—a cross-cultural survey. In: *Cross-Cultural Studies of Behavior,* ed. I. Al-Issa & W. Dennis. New York: Holt, Rinehart & Winston, pp. 479–493.

———— ———— Fried, J., & Ellenberger, H. (1963), A cross-cultural survey of schizophrenic symptomatology. *Internat. J. Soc. Psychiatry,* 9:237–249.

Nayani, T., & Bhugra, D. (1996), Guild, religion and ritual. In: *Psychiatry and Religion,* ed. D. Bhugra. London: Routledge, pp. 198–213.

Okasha, A., El-Akabawi, A. S., Snyder, K. S., Wilson, A. K., Youssef, I., & El-Dawla, A. S. (1994), Expressed emotion, perceived criticism, and relapse in depression: A replication in an Egyptian community. *Amer. J. Psychiatry,* 151:1001–1005.

———— Bishry, Z., Khalil, A. H., Darwish, T. A., Seif Al-Dawla, A., & Shohdy, A. (1994), Panic disorder: An overlapping or independent entity. *Brit. J. Psychiatry,* 164:818–825.

Osseiran, N. (1995), *Review of psychological and psychiatric research in Bahrein.* Paper presented at the IV European Congress of Psychology, Athens.

Oztürk, O. M. (1964), Folk treatment of mental illness in Turkey. In: *Magic, Faith and Healing,* ed. A. Kiev. New York: Free Press, pp. 343–363.

Pfeiffer, W. M. (1982), Culture-bound syndrome. In: *Culture and Psychopathology,* ed. I. Al-Issa. Baltimore: University Park Press, pp. 201–218.

Phipps, W. E. (1996), *Muhammad and Jesus: A Comparison of the Prophets and Their Teachings.* New York: Continuum.

Prince, R. H. (1980), Variations in psychotherapeutic procedures. In: *Handbook of Cross-Cultural Psychology,* Vol. 6, ed. H. C. Triandis & J. G. Draguns. Boston: Allyn & Bacon.

Prothro, E. T. (1955), Arab-American differences in the judgement of written messages. *J. Soc. Psychology,* 42:3–11.

Rack, P. (1982), *Culture, Race and Mental Disorder.* London: Tavistock.

Al-Radi, M. A., & Al-Mahdi, A. (1989), Group therapy: An Islamic approach. Mimeographed, 7 pages. Abstracted by R. Prince, *Transcult. Psychiatric Res. Rev.,* 26:273–276.

Ross, M. W. (1987), A theory of normal homosexuality. In: *Male and Female Homosexuality: Psychological Approaches,* ed. L. Diamant. Washington: Hemisphere, pp. 237–259.

Shouby, E. (1951), The influence of the Arabic language on the psychology of the Arabs. *Middle East J.,* 5:284–302.

Slobin, D. I. (1979), *Psycholinguistics,* 2nd ed. Glenville, IL: Scott Foresman.

Al-Subaie, A. (1989), Psychiatry in Saudi Arabia: Cultural perspectives. *Transcult. Psychiatric Res. Rev.,* 26:245–262.

Sue, D. W., & Sue, D. (1990), *Counseling the Culturally Different.* New York: Wiley.

Tehrani, S. M. M. J. (1996), Iran launches model prison project. *Psychol. Internat.,* 7:1, 3.

Thesiger, W. (1959), *Arabian Sands.* New York: Dutton.

Triandis, H. C. (1989), The self and social behavior in differing cultural contexts. *Psycholog. Rev.,* 93:506–520.

Vaughn, C., Snyder, K. S., Jones, S., Freeman, W. B., & Falloon, I. R. H. (1984), Family factors in schizophrenic relapse: A California replication of the British research on expressed emotion. *Arch. Gen. Psychiatry,* 41:1169–1177.

Weissman, M. M., & Klerman, G. L. (1977), Sex differences and the epidemiology of depression. *Arch. Gen. Psychiatry,* 34:98–111.

West, J. S., & Al-Kaisi, H. H. (1982), Depression scale for Arabs. *Proceedings of the Seventh Saudi Medical Meeting.* Dammam, Saudi Arabia: College of Medicine and Medical Sciences, King Faisal University, pp. 119–128.

Wig, N. N., Menon, D. K., Bedi, H., Ghosh, A., Kuipers, L., Leff, J., Korten, A., Day, R., Sartorius, N., Ernberg, G., & Jablensky, A. (1987), Expressed emotion and schizophrenia in North India. 1. Cross-cultural transfer of ratings of relatives' expressed emotion. *Brit. J. Psychiatry,* 151:156–173.

Wikan, U. (1988), Bereavement and loss in two Muslim communities: Egypt and Bali compared. *Social Science and Medicine,* 27:451–460.

Wittkower, E., & Rin, H. (1965), Transcultural psychiatry. *Arch. Gen. Psychiatry,* 13:387–394.

Worden, J. W. (1991), *Grief, Counseling and Grief Therapy.* New York: Springer.

World Health Organization (1973), *Report of the International Pilot Study of Schizophrenia,* Vol. 1. Geneva, Switzerland: WHO.

Al-Yahya, F. S. (1991), Saudi Arabia: Acknowledging problems in a transitional culture. In: *Mental Health Services in the Global Village,* ed. L. Appleby & R. Nraya. London: Gaskell.

Al-Zahrani, S. S. A., & Kaplowitz, S. A. (1993), Attributional biases in individualistic and collective cultures: A comparison of Americans with Saudis. *Soc. Psychol. Quart.,* 56:223–233.

Zarrouk, E. T. A. (1975), The frequency of visual hallucinations in schizophrenic patients in Saudi Arabia. *Brit. J. Psychiatry,* 127:553–555.

Name Index

Subject Index